Books by VICTOR WOLFGANG VON HAGEN

Exploration
    Off with Their Heads
    Ecuador the Unknown
    Jungle in the Clouds
    South America Called Them
Ethnology
    The Tsátchela Indians of Western Ecuador
    The Ethnology of the Jicaques of Honduras
    The Aztec and Maya Papermakers
        (*limited to 220 copies*)
Introductions and Prefaces
    Herman Melville: Encantadas
        (*Grabhorn Press; limited to 550 copies*)
    Maeterlinck: Life of the White Ant
For Children
    Quetzal Quest
    Treasure of Tortoise Islands
    Miskito Boy
    South American Zoo
Textbooks
    Riches of Central America
    Riches of South America

SOUTH AMERICA CALLED THEM

Charles Robert Darwin (1809–82) as a young man four years after the return of the *Beagle*. Drawn by George Richmond in 1839.

South America CALLED THEM

EXPLORATIONS *of the Great Naturalists*
La Condamine
Humboldt
Darwin
Spruce

VICTOR WOLFGANG VON HAGEN

1945 ALFRED A KNOPF *NEW YORK*

To CHRISTINE VON HAGEN, who walked with me through the tangled paths of the Amazon jungles, who crossed over the heaven-high Andes, and who thirsted with me on the thrice-cursed isles of the Galápagos, and who, throughout all these eventful years, gave me inspiration and companionship — this volume of heroic, tenacious lives is affectionately dedicated.

"Multum adhuc restat operis, multumque restabit; nec ullo nato post mille sæcula præcludetur occasio adhuc adjiciendi. . . ."

SENECA

"Much remains to be done, much still will remain . . . nor shall any man born after the revolution of a thousand ages be denied the opportunity to contribute something. . . ."

ACKNOWLEDGMENTS

No BOOK is wholly an author's, least of all a biography whose canvas is as large as that of *South America Called Them*. From the encouragement of my wife, Christine, and from the stimulation of Mr. Philip Ainsworth Means, the book has taken shape. Dr. A. C. Smith and Dr. Paul C. Standley, both eminent botanists, aided me in the botanical sections. From Professor E. T. Bell, of the California Institute of Technology, a long letter (itself almost a manuscript) helped me in unraveling the intricacies of the early concepts about the shape and size of the earth-orb. From Dr. Robert Cushman Murphy, famed Curator of Oceanic Birds at the American Museum of Natural History, came assistance in presenting the early history of the discovery of the Humboldt Current. Finally, the whole book, filled with errors of fact and misspellings, was carefully corrected by Miss Carol Woodward of the New York Botanical Garden, to whom I owe a lasting expression of gratitude. My publishers, through their editors, J. R. de la Torre Bueno, Jr., and Clinton Simpson, helped form the book while I marched with my regiment under the Texas sun; and in the chapters on Charles Darwin the aid of Geoffrey West's book *Charles Darwin,* which he so kindly allowed me to use, was invaluable. Thanks are also due to Messrs. Dodd, Mead & Co. for the use of material contained in Felix Riesenberg's *Cape Horn.* These are the only specific acknowledgments; but from numerous anonymous librarians have come much aid and much patience. To one and all who made this book more complete, the author's profound gratitude.

CONTENTS

[vii]

Contents

ILLUSTRATIONS

[ix]

Illustrations

FOREWORD

THIS IS THE STORY *of man's conquest of the earth-mansions of South America.*

It is the story of men, all inspired by the spirit of creative curiosity and directed enthusiasm, who scrambled over the rock-hard Cordilleras; who fought through the voiceless regions of the South American jungles, reeking under the equatorial sun; who trekked across the colorless anemic llanos to push back the frontiers of the unknown.

There are neither conquistadores nor pirates, fierce-eyed and blood-stained, in this conquest, no steel-clad knights, no fire-spouting harquebusiers. The most offensive weapons of these men of conquest are vasculums, sextants, and pincers, for its heroes are the naturalists, the scientists who opened South America.

Yet it is not with all the South American naturalist-explorers that this book concerns itself, for such a work would have to be encyclopedic. Most of the naturalists do appear, yet only for a short time. Alfred Wallace is here, as well as his bug-searching companion, Bates. The badly-used Félix de Azara makes a brief appearance; we see Boussingault patiently working with his thermometer, M. d'Orbigny collecting birds; we catch a glimpse of the ill-fated expedition of Count Castlenau descending the Amazon, and of the indefatigable Richard Schomburgk and his brother Robert. They are here, but only in passing. They were not ground-breakers, they were not leaders, they did not initiate or represent epochs in South America's history.

Instead, this book concerns itself with four men: Charles-Marie de La Condamine, Alexander von Humboldt, Charles Darwin, and Richard Spruce — four scientific explorers who represent four time-periods, four geographical regions, and four distinct sciences. All are men of vivid personality whose interests leaped over and beyond the narrow confines of one selected subject. They are, in sum, the greatest of the explorer-naturalists who also represented the Zeitgeist of their time.

Still it is not alone with the minutiæ of their discoveries that this book deals, nor with an exhaustive list of their achievements in exploration. This will be the story of young men — for all were young when they went to South America. It will not be the biographies of savants, bemedaled and bewhiskered, and wrapped in the chiton of immortals' dignity, who stare out at us from the pages of textbooks; instead it will be an account of their early strivings, the life story of their ideas, of how they came to be, and in what manner and under what circumstances they developed.

More than mere biographies, theirs will be also the history of their times, for man's fate is inextricably bound up with the historical space through which he travels. So South America marches with them and becomes the crucible in which their explorations are cast.

And now it is time to begin, for South America is calling.

Santa Monica, California

[xii]

SOUTH AMERICA CALLED THEM

PART I

❖◈❖◈❖◈❖◈❖◈❖◈❖◈❖◈❖◈❖◈❖◈❖◈❖

CHAPTER I

"Joyfull Newes out of the Newe Founde Worlde"

"Venient annis
"Sæcula seris, quibus Oceanus
"Vincula rerum laxet el ingens
"Pateat tellus Typhisque novos
"Ultima Thula. . . ."

SENECA: *Medea*

L IKE AN utterly new world, the continent of South America
burst into men's consciousness in 1498. Christopher Columbus,
Admiral of the Ocean Sea, had skirted the South American mainland, his caravels had been wafted along the island-spangled coast
where the Río Orinoco debouched its jungle-spawned alluvium
into the sea, and made the landfall of the isle of Trinidad.

The discovery of a new land mass was received by all strata of
European society with the greatest joy: the walls of the unknown
had at last been breached; the treasure houses of a new Orient
had been discovered, a new Orient even more fabulous than Asia.
The spirit of Europe was renascent. Everyone, rich and poor,
great and small, felt the upsurge. They had broken the last of
the medieval chains; they had sailed past the Rock of Gibraltar,
beyond the confines of the Continent. Shattered was the ancient
symbol of the Pillars of Hercules. Gone was its motto: *Nec plus
ultra* — Go no farther.

Oppressed by want and starvation, all Europe had been haunted
by the dream of the horn of plenty and the fruits of an earthly
paradise. The food on which it fed was unspeakably insipid, dull,
monotonous. Europe's stomach had led the revolt. Man wanted
something beyond the mere huddle and vacuity of society. Desires for spices, silks, damasks were the restless prelude to the vast
efforts and initiatives of the explorers. And now this search for
the "Spiceries" had brought about the discovery of a *mundus
novus* — a new world.

The presses of Europe worked overtime. Broadsides flooded the

[3]

hamlets, the villages, and the walled cities. Everywhere was proclaimed the *"Joyfull Newes Out of the Newe Founde Worlde"* *
. . . *"the rare and singular vertues of divers Herbs, Trees, Plantes, Oyles & Stones"* . . . of barbaric princes who walked streets paved with gold, of delectable foods, of spices and strange fruits, the proclamations shouted.

There had never been such mass hysteria since the Crusades. Whole populations swept down to the seaports to find a place upon vessels bound for the New World. Unemployed, cutpurses, debt-ridden noblemen, wastrels, with a preponderance of honest men, besieged the hiring offices. Every month, every week, every day saw the departure of new expeditions to the *mundus novus*.

Europe settled back breathlessly, waiting for the flood-gates to be opened and for the riches and all the "Goode Things" to pour in from the "Newe Worlde." Then the blow fell.

There had been a skulking rumor of it for some time. But only when broadsides were plastered over the rain-stained, weather-worn announcements of the "Joyfull Newes" could be read what had happened.

The *mundus novus* was closed. Sealed. There had been a convention at Tordesillas between Portugal and Spain. With the Pope's blessing, a line had been drawn, running north and south 370 leagues west of Cape Verde. All newly discovered lands east of the line (that is, much of Brazil, all of Africa, and the Spiceries) were to belong to Portugal—*exclusively*. The rest was to go to Spain. Pope Alexander had given to the Spanish and Portuguese *de jure* possession of all the "Newfounde Lands of the Worlde."

The people of Europe were aghast at this turn of events. They had a single spokesman, King François of France. He raged, he threatened, he screamed. He, the King of France, wanted "to see the clause in Adam's will which entitled the Kings of Castile and Portugal to divide the earth between them." But it availed nothing. Spain and Portugal were given most of the world by priority of discovery. The sons of Iberia, confirmed in their new worlds, began to assert their monopoly. The curtain that had been lifted from this wonderful *terra incognita* called America slowly dropped once more, not to rise again, so far as the common man of Europe was concerned, until the year 1735.

The Spanish conquistadores, meanwhile, plunged into the lands which had been specially reserved for them. Gold-lust and soul-lust, typically European motives, sent the clanking legions of

* An actual title of a book, *Joyfull Newes out of the Newe Founde Worlde*, by Nicolas Monardes, one of the celebrated Spanish physicians of his time. Translated into English in 1577 by John Frampton.

Spain into the heights and depths of the New World. Animated by a crusading spirit compounded equally of piety and perfidy, they sent expeditions in every direction. The effective occupation of Mexico in 1520 by Hernán Cortés and the conquest of the Aztec realm were a clarion call to all adventurous spirits. Expeditions sped southward into Guatemala and Central America. Expeditions set off northward. Cabeza de Vaca began his great trek across North America, from Florida to the Gulf of California. While Coronado was pressing northward to California, to the color-spangled ravines of the Grand Canyon, and while Hernando de Soto floated down the waters of the Mississippi, other Spanish condottieri, led by Francisco Pizarro, "passed the line of Atacames" and panted up the sides of the Andes to lay siege to the golden kingdoms of the Inca. Gonzalo de Quesada climbed from the Caribbean to the Colombian Andes; Nicolas Federmann, the little *Gauleiter* of the Welsers, came up from Venezuela; Sebastián de Belalcázar, the conqueror of Quito, clanked down the Andes to Colombia. There they all made junction knee-deep in the blood of the vanquished Chibchan peoples.

Other expeditions struck off to new lands. Captain Almagro battered his way south from Peru across the deserts, over the Andes, through opposing Indians, to the 37th degree south latitude. Mendoza and Valdivia followed him and explored the regions of the tip of Chile, spilling over into the icy purgatory of Tierra del Fuego, which had been breached by the fate-bound galleons of Magellan.

By 1540 the town of Asunción had been settled. The Río de la Plata had been explored. Buenos Aires had been erected as a city. Patagonia was overrun. And now the Amazon. Francisco Pizarro, secure in his conquest of the Incas, "had received the tidings that beyond the city of Quito there was a wide region where cinnamon grew." The lure of spices again. He commanded his brother Gonzalo and his lieutenant, Francisco de Orellana, to search out this cinnamon land. And so they did. With five hundred Spaniards, four thousand Indians, herds of llamas and pigs, Pizarro and Orellana went down the Andes into the jungle. A bark resembling cinnamon was found in trifling quantities, but where would this plunging river lead them? They built a brigantine on the banks of the Napo, and Orellana sailed in it from there down the entire length of the great river, which he named the Amazon. The discovery of the Río Amazonas threw open still another unknown land, and within a decade the jungle-bound rivers of the Amazon basin swarmed with the vessels of the most dangerous human fauna that had ever roamed its dank earth.

Naturally, all these far-flung explorations paid handsome dividends — to Spain. The conquest of the native civilizations of the Americas yielded a flow of silver and gold so vast that it created a capitalistic Europe. Cochineal and brazilwood for dyes came to Spain. So did some of the foodstuffs that had been so highly extolled. But so far as the rest of Europe was concerned, the herbs, the fruits, the dyes, the medicinal plants might as well have been non-existent. All of the "joyfull newes" which the European had been led to expect never arrived. The European knew as little of the South American continent as he did of the moon. Of adventure, of conquest, of the star-dust of the imaginations of the conquistadores — yes. Of meaty facts of the New World, practically nothing. And for good reason. Information was suppressed. Whenever a Spaniard compiled a manuscript on the natural wonders of America, the report was concealed. A book to be published had to pass the rigid censorship of the King, the Holy Office of the Inquisition, the Council of the Indies, and the Casa de Contratación. Excellent reports were written, for the Spaniard was a superb observer, but the world never saw or read them. One by one the classic reports were buried in the archives. The official policy of exclusivism had crystallized. All foreigners were excluded from America; * Europe must be kept in ignorance of the wealth, potential or actual, that lay in Spain's colonies. The veils of Isis, which Columbus had lifted, had fallen back again and to most of the world it was as if America had never been discovered at all.

Then South America was rediscovered. The pirates had been biting at the edges of this continental citadel for centuries. They hacked at the Spanish convoys; they sank ships; they stormed the bastions of Puerto Bello and Cartagena. Periodically they interrupted the majestic flow of riches from the far-flung interior points of South America to Spain. They pillaged, killed, and burned. What they could not carry off they destroyed. Whole cities were razed to the ground. Yet they did not break the hold of the unknown. The gold-motive was still too strong.

No, it was not the freebooters, with all their fury of shot, shell, and cutlass, who opened the continent. This was reserved for men of a different breed. The continent that would not yield to steel-clad knights and fire-spouting harquebusiers was opened by nothing more terrifying than vasculums, sextants, and pincers.

For it was the explorer-naturalists who opened South America. It was these knowledge-thirsting men who, because they were

---

* Soldiers of diverse nationalities, however, were permitted to serve in Spain's armies. Taking part in the conquest were Italians, Irishmen, Germans, and Greeks.

The American paradise as pictured by sixteenth-century German explorers. Dragons, sea-serpents, and cannibals were common in conceptions of South America until the eighteenth century.

The American scene as pictured by a sixteenth-century German artist. In front of the belching volcanoes are the animals of the New World. Although drawn in improper perspective, some of the animals — coatis, iguanas, marmosets — are surprisingly accurate.

deemed "harmless," were permitted entry where others were not. It was they who methodically and systematically pushed aside the frontiers of South America and dug it from its oblivion. With an enthusiasm that bridged every barrier they climbed the Andes, they swept down dark mysterious rivers, they trekked across the deserts, and struggled through the Laocoön entanglements of its firefly-spangled jungles. They dispelled legends, they uncovered facts. They rediscovered rubber, studied quinine and the coca leaf. They measured the earth's surface, they crawled into the jungle and collected plants, they studied the animals, they measured the tides, and they established meteorology. The natural phenomena that made America America were investigated, codified, and put into literature — a literature that freed the continent completely from the fantasies which had flourished for three hundred years.

Yet it is not among the dark rivers of America that the story of the explorer-naturalists begins, nor among the roots of jungle trees crusted with black earth, but in the silken chambers of the Académie des Sciences in Paris.

The argument began with Isaac Newton, or rather it began over the theories of Newton, who held that the earth was a globe flattened at its poles. He proved, theoretically, that the shape of the planet determined the length of the day; that the earth, flattened at its poles, was pushed out at its middle; that the pull of the moon and sun on the equatorial bulge of the earth caused the planet to wobble like a top. This brought a roar from the Cassinians, who were to France what Newton was to England. They had evolved a different theory of the earth. They said: "Man infests a globe which lengthens in the direction of the polar diameter. The world is a prolate spheroid, lengthened at the poles, pulled in at the equator, much as a pot-bellied man might pull in his girth by taking a few notches in his belt."

Soon the scientific world was divided between the Newtonians, the earth-flatteners, and the Cassinians, the contentious earth-elongators. It did not help the tempers of the controversialists when Voltaire returned from England and entered the lists a convinced Newtonian. He and his aristocratic mistress, Émilie de Châtelet, translated Newton's *Principia* into French and gathered about them a group of young enthusiasts. The gauntlet had been thrown down. Newton had crowded into a field which the Académie des Sciences believed essentially its own.

Toward the end of the seventeenth century the Académie des Sciences spent much of its time in trying to ascertain the length of a degree of latitude. There had been constant complaints of seagoing captains that the charts were not accurate. The Navy, and Jacques Cassini, Astronomer Royal, as cartographers were responsible for them. But before correct charts could be made, the length of a degree had to be known. Jean Picard, Academician, measured by triangulation the meridian of an arc of a degree between Corbeil and Amiens and found it to be 69.1 miles. But his measure could only be definitive if the earth-planet was spherical. A general map was in the making using his measurements just about the time that the Dutchman, Christian Huygens, arrived in Paris with his patented pendulum clock; this brought up the phenomenon of the force of gravitation.

Now, the astronomer Cassini had evolved the theory that the earth was an elongated prolate spheroid. Physical proof being needed, he sent young Jean Richer to Cayenne, French Guiana, with one of Huygens's pendulum clocks. There in the midst of flourishing slave trade and piratical wars Richer set up the pendulum and — behold! the pendulum clock beat slower there. This discovery was instantly seized upon by Isaac Newton. It was an additional proof that his concept of the shape of the planet was the correct one. The earth-planet bulged at the equator; that explained M. Jean Richer's results. In order to keep time, the pendulum of the clock set in Paris in latitude 49° had to be shortened at the equator. The explanation of this, as we now know, is that the bulging of the earth in the region of the equator decreases the pull of gravity.

Jean Richer had unwittingly helped Newton. Back in Paris, Jacques Cassini believed himself betrayed by his colleague, for he had stoutly maintained that the earth is flattened at the equator and that the polar radius was greater than the equator's. He denounced poor Jean Richer as *"un hypocrite, traître,"* and for good measure *"un caffer et un papelard."* So in this atmosphere of tension the shape-of-the-earth controversy raged. It was now no longer a mere abstruse problem in physics. Reputations were staked upon the outcome. Careers depended upon which side one took. Patriotism was involved, and the prestige of nations and kings. Had this been just another polemic, it would have meant little to the world; but it went beyond that, for these curious ingredients — Newton's abstract speculations, the swinging of a pendulum, and the arguments of the earth-flatteners and the earth-elongators — formed the opening wedge into South America.

If one must look for the beginning of the modern history of South America, let him seize upon December 1734, for on that date the arguments ceased in the Académie des Sciences. A resolution had been passed. It was to bring momentous results. . . .

CHAPTER II
Les Grands Aplatisseurs

THE GAVEL POUNDED insistently on the polished oak desk. "Gentlemen! Gentlemen! Quiet."

Under the metronomic beat of the gavel, the buzzing of voices within the hall of the Académie des Sciences gradually died away. Sunlight, breaking into multicolored shafts, fell from the tall, slightly arched windows of the King's library, which served for the meeting-rooms of the Académie.

The sixty-odd gentlemen — courtiers, mathematicians, soldiers, and priests — who formed the body of the Académie, crossed their silken calves, arranged their periwigs, and settled back in their chairs.

The argument, *Dieu merci,* was over. For months the Royal Library had been rocked by the controversy. It had begun at first in the empyrean of objective science, then had shifted earthward into the laps of the savants. Learning was torn from its Olympian heights and the Academicians heard scholar denounce scholar in harangues in which Rabelaisian epithets were in preponderance.

The gentleman who had been pounding the gavel now rose from behind his desk. His head was almost buried in a Louis Quatorze wig, which all but covered a face weather-worn like crumbling brick in which were set, like two jewels, the blue eyes of a child. Having created the silence which he desired, M. Bernard Le Bovier de Fontenelle, Secrétaire perpétuel of the Académie des Sciences, faced its members and, pausing for dramatic effect, dipped his bejeweled fingers into an enamel box and with a flourish of his elegantly laced cuffs filled his nostrils with snuff. Already in his seventy-seventh year, the celebrated author of the *Pluralité des mondes* was a man of rare erudition. He balanced it, as a sort of equipoise, with a dry and ready wit. He had guided the Académie through the stormy sessions created by the Newtonians and the Cassinians, skillfully and adroitly forming a resolution out of it. Prudent, cold in temperament, M. de Fontenelle passed his whole life-span (which involved an entire century) in discussions without ever stumbling into disputes. This was a sort of triumph for him. His blue eyes danced as he flipped away sundry grains of snuff — then, in a colorless, dry voice, he proclaimed the King's pleasure:

". . . Thus, gentlemen, the Académie, with the gracious consent of our sovereign, King Louis XV of France — may God preserve him — and with the generous permission of King Philip of Spain, sends out two expeditions to ascertain the true shape of the earth. One expedition goes to Lapland and the other to the equator. The Académie participates in a problem that has exercised the mind of man since the earliest times. . . ."

M. de Fontenelle, rapping his snuffbox at the close of each particularly pointed phrase, finished his discourse and then, turning his head in the direction of a fine-looking man, he said:

"From M. Maupertuis, who leads the expedition to Lapland, we have already heard; now, gentlemen, we shall hear from one of the gentlemen who will go on the other expedition — to the equator."

There was a stir among the Academicians. All eyes turned upon the tall, slim, almost boyish figure of Charles-Marie de La Condamine. At first glance Charles-Marie de La Condamine would have been dismissed as a typical aristocrat of Louis XV's court. Yet he was more than that. He was an ensemble of all the forces of that strange age in which religion, debauchery, intellect, fashion, and brutality seethed and bubbled together in such an extraordinary potpourri. As a mathematician and a most able geodesist (a relatively new branch of applied science which determined by observation and measurement the shape and size of the earth) he had been admitted to the Académie at the age of twenty-nine. All this would have been little, however, had he not been possessed of a restlessness and an enthusiasm unbounded — *"d'une curiosité ardente,"* as Voltaire described it.

Voltaire had known La Condamine ever since he was a young man. They had first met at a dinner in honor of the Comptroller of Finance, who had proposed a lottery to pay off some notes issued by the municipality. La Condamine explained to Voltaire, with a brilliant sweep of figures, that the Comptroller had not printed enough lottery tickets. If anyone should purchase all, he might easily make a million francs. Voltaire denounced the lottery. His contentions challenged, he bought all the tickets — and made, thanks to La Condamine, five hundred thousand francs.

Yet he was drawn to Charles-Marie by more than this singular bit of fortune. He liked the young man's enthusiasms, his insatiable curiosity. Voltaire used all his extraparliamentary tricks, got La Condamine into the equatorial expedition, and saw him emerge as one of its leaders.

Now La Condamine's moment had arrived. He swept the Académie with his eyes and then said, simply and easily:

"Gentlemen, all is in readiness. Our instruments have been sent to the port at La Rochelle, from which point it is our intention to embark. As the Académie is aware, our official party will consist of ten members: M. Pierre Bouguer, astronomer; M. Louis Godin, mathematician, and his cousin, Jean Godin des Odonais; also members of the party will be Captain Verguin of the Royal Navy; M. de Morainville, draftsman; Joseph de Jussieu, botanist; Dr. Jean Senièrgues, physician; M. Hugot, watchmaker and technician; M. Mabillon; and the young M. Couplet, nephew of the member of the Académie. We will proceed from La Rochelle in May of this year, 1735. After visiting the isle of Santo Domingo in the Caribbean Sea, we will proceed in the convoy of His Catholic Majesty's ships to the port of entry, Cartagena. Here we will be met by two officers of the Spanish Navy, Captain Jorge Juan y Santacilla and Captain Antonio de Ulloa, who are assigned to our party. From thence we shall make our way by the best means at hand to the province of Quito in the Viceroyalty of Peru. There we shall begin our work."

But why must they go off to Peru, the ends of the earth, to measure the arc? Well might the Academicians shake their powdered periwigs. It was an expense the Académie could ill afford. Yet a glance at the map gave the reason: the Audiencia de Quito in South America was the only accessible spot on the equator, as it encircled the globe, where such an expedition might work. Equatorial Africa was still unexplored and unsettled; Borneo was unopened; the lower Amazon was a mass of bottomless quagmires and hostile Indians. Only in the Audiencia de Quito might the natural philosophers complete their projects: the measurement of an arc of the meridian at the equator, and the experiments on the force of gravity at the equator.

There was much controversy among cartographers on the length of the degree, and the expedition hoped also to be able to lay down a universal measure of it. The Frenchman Picard, in 1670, had measured a degree and found it to be 69.1 miles. The Englishman Snell, had computed 66.91 miles, and his countrymen had further persisted in their views by publishing a *Seaman's Practice* which adopted 60 miles to a degree, or one nautical mile for each minute of latitude. So there was much to be done.

Charles-Marie was the son of the *Receveur général des Finances du Bour Bonnis*. Born in the year 1701, when King Louis XIV was at the zenith of his power, he arrived in troubled times. In his youth he was surrounded by the poets and soldiers of France. Generals and marshals frequently visited his home; at eight he was fully acquainted with the gilded ennui of Boileau and Corneille and with the sparkling delicate gaiety of the natural philosophers. But his youth was cast in the crucibles of war, and uniforms dominated the times. When he was only three years old, his dark eyes had seen soldiers marching off to the War of the Spanish Succession. The throne of Spain was vacant. Louis XIV sought to confer it upon his grandson, Philip, Duc d'Anjou. By all legal rights the Duke of Anjou, grandson of both the monarchs of Spain and France, should have possessed it peacefully. But when Louis shouted: "Henceforth the Pyrenees no longer exist," his purpose was made clear. The delicate balance of power was upset. England raised a Grand Coalition against Louis's candidate, and Charles-Marie could remember little else in his boyhood than the rumbling of caissons and the braying of the voices of the recruiting officers. When Marlborough overwhelmed the French at Blenheim, the family of La Condamine was bereft of several of its members fallen in battle. Through all his early years, when impressions can be indelible, war scourged Europe.

The winter of 1708 was cold and bitter, the Seine froze over. There was famine. Charles-Marie remembered the frozen bodies along the Pont Neuf. Riots multiplied and spread. Even King Louis was forced to turn his silver and gold plate over to the mint and to put the royal jewels in pawn. Yet within a decade, by the time young Charles-Marie was ready to enter the College of Louis le Grand, Louis XIV had died, and France, chameleon-like, had passed from destitution to prosperity and from prosperity to speculation. John Law of Edinburgh had come upon the scene. He convinced the Regent of France of the feasibility of his wildcat financial schemes; the "Mississippi Bubble" was being blown. Shares of stock were sold on the basis of the returns of unfound mines in Louisiana which were supposed to rival those of Potosí in Peru and Taxco in Mexico.

France went through five years of delirium. John Law promised twelve per cent interest on investments, and modest incomes became colossal fortunes. Servants who had been one night mousepoor emerged the next with money enough to buy fabulous estates. When at last the bubble broke, millions were ruined; destitution of the great and small was countrywide; but the La Condamines emerged with a fortune. By this time young Charles-Marie had passed from college into the Army.

The political repercussions of the "Mississippi Bubble" continued for years. The ruined nobility blamed the machinations of the Regent for their plight and so sought by intrigue to revoke his regency with the aid of the Duke of Anjou, who was now safely ensconced on the throne of Spain as Philip V. The scatterbrains of the great houses of France were involved in the conspiracy; papers implicating many were found upon one Abbé Portocarrero when he sought to cross the Pyrenees into Spain. France broke at once with Philip V, and war was declared.

In the midst of the festivals that welcomed Peter the Great of Russia to France, the French battalions marched to the Spanish border. Charles-Marie, aged eighteen, took his place as a junior officer under Marshal Berwick, the natural son of James II. He took part in the siege of Rosas and under fire showed great daring and intrepidity. But more happened there than cannonades. It was at this siege that Charles-Marie's view of life abruptly changed. They had captured a Spanish soldier lately returned from the colonies. Under the sound of the cannon the young Spaniard told Charles-Marie of the vast mountain chain called the Andes that stretched along the entire Pacific coast, of the swirling rivers, of the palaces of the Incas. It fired La Condamine's imagination. Henceforth his interest became scientific. Mathematics, and its geometrical offspring geodesy, became his main pursuit. With a garrison for his university, he plunged into the study of science with an all-devouring curiosity, with all the ardor of a soul that never relinquished a subject until it was exhausted. Thus Charles-Marie, like Descartes and Maupertuis before him, became a soldier-scholar.

At the age of twenty-nine he was elected to the Académie des Sciences. At once he left on an expedition with the squadron of Duguay-Trouin to the Barbary Coast, where he passed an adventurous two years. Ashore he displayed his genius for organization, at sea his ability to determine the ship's position through astronomy, which the seamen thought little short of miraculous.

On his return to Paris his restless, eager curiosity plunged him instantly into the controversy that engaged all intellectual Paris: the fight between the contentious earth-elongators, the Cassinians, and the earth-flatteners, the Newtonians.

There was little doubt on which side La Condamine stood. He was well aware that the Cassinians wished to refute the theories of Newton; their reputation demanded it. Here was his chance. When the resolution was finally passed to send an expedition to South America, Charles-Marie began to use his connections at court, and Voltaire his vitriolic pen. From this union of activity La Condamine emerged one of the leaders of the expedition to the equator. True, he gave 100,000 livres from his own purse toward the expenses of the expedition; true, he was forced to take along the young boy Couplet. But Couplet was the nephew of the Treasurer of the Académie, and Charles-Marie merely used a device not uncommon in modern expeditions: he took along a young member of the family that held the purse-strings.

But these were unimportant details. Here, at last, he was on the floor of the Académie des Sciences; the expedition was a fact, and he a part of it.

Charles-Marie, addressing the Academicians, continued:

"The gentlemen may well wonder why the King of Spain has permitted an official body to enter his colonies. In this we have been singularly honored. . . ."

As indeed they were. The King of Spain had made them the first exception in two hundred and fifty years — and, incredibly enough, just at a time when Spain was suffering repeated attacks both in her own realm and in her colonies. Why did Philip V permit the Academicians access to the innermost secrets of his Empire? The answer is contained in the War of the Spanish Succession.

The King of Spain was the grandson of Louis XIV. During Philip's lifetime, when the war was buffeting him about, he had written: "I will use all my efforts to maintain myself upon the throne on which God has placed me and on which you, after Him, have set me." Now he was paying back an old debt. He had heard and sulked over the entreaties of the French emissaries, Comte de Maurepas and Cardinal de Fleury. At last he had yielded, over the violent protests of the Council of the Indies. But in order to be sure the Frenchmen did not dig too deeply into Spain's colonial secrets, two loyal naval officers were attached to the expedition, and secret instructions were sent to all places they might visit. Local officials were to give all aid, but they were to be careful not to permit the Academicians to *"poner los ojos en la Tierra"*; in short, they were not to be allowed too much of an "eyeful."

Had Philip V had the slightest conception of what he was initiating, he would have listened more carefully to his Council. For these Frenchmen were about to pry off the veils with which America purposely had been shrouded since its discovery.

When these men set sail, who could have foreseen what they would find and what they would set off? On that gray day of May 16, 1735, when Charles-Marie de La Condamine left with the astronomers and chain-bearers, the botanists and mathematicians, aboard the French man-of-war at La Rochelle, a new epoch in human progress had begun. In the history of the Americas 1735 is a date that might be set beside the year 1492. Two great scientific events, unrelated to each other, had occurred. Linnæus had published his *Systema Naturæ*, a work which opened the green world of botany; and an expedition of the Académie des Sciences set out to open South America.

"Nec sit terris Ultima Thule!"

Charles-Marie de La Condamine (1701–74), leader of the first scientific expedition to South America. From a portrait done in Paris after his return from America.

The people and costumes of South America in the eighteenth century. Left to right: a Spanish creole, an *india palla* (the highest Indian caste), an Indian *barbero* (barber), a *mestiza*, and *indios rústicos* in their native dress.

CHAPTER III
The Door to America is Opened

THE PLACE was South America; the time, November 1735; the door, Cartagena de las Indias.

With nothing more than passports signed by the Bourbon Kings, these natural philosophers had breached the thick lichen-covered walls of the cyclopean fortress that guarded the entrepôt to the Americas.

They sailed through La Boca Chica, they made their way into the bay and were all but overcome by the ardent hues of flowers, the odor of vanilla, the luscious smells of generative earth about the great harbor. They were delighted and astonished at all that met their eyes.

They watched the peons, dressed in tight white trousers, short white jackets, with dark-brown straw headgear, stagger down the *malecón* with *"las cosas de España"* — hides from Córdoba, wine from La Mancha, arrobas of oil from Jaén, and from the workshops of all Europe glass, guns, and madras cloth. Palm trees lined the surf-kissed beaches; balsams and acacias, now in full bloom, wafted their perfumes across the enlivened streets. At the edge of the city they walked through groves of cacao trees, "the most valuable treasure that nature could have bestowed on America," which produced the chocolate which only the very wealthy of Paris might have. They ate of the papaya, the guayaba, the cherimoya; they filled themselves to the bursting-point with the soft delectable fruit of the sapote, they went into rhapsodies over the pineapple, "which, when ripened and peeled, is so full of juice that it entirely dissolves in the mouth."

Cartagena, they were not long in discovering, was the hub, the main commercial highway between Spain and its Pacific kingdoms. All vessels bound to the New World had first to call at Cartagena. It shared with Puerto Bello, in Panama, and Vera Cruz, in Mexico, the distinction of being the only gateways to the Americas. Convoys from Spain first touched at Cartagena in South America, and there jettisoned the cargo destined for that part which is now Colombia and which was then the Viceroyalty of Santa Fé. The choice of Cartagena had been made not so much for its geographical location, since it was most difficult to bring any amount of goods over the Andes, thence oceanward on the sluggish Río Magdalena to the Caribbean, but for its very inaccessible position, which made it the more impregnable.

The Frenchmen strolled through the city and found it and its suburbs "well laid out." The streets were straight, broad, uniform, and well paved. The houses "were built of stone, a few of brick, but almost all consist chiefly of only one story above the ground floor; the apartments therein well contrived." The buildings had that secretive solidity of Seville, with massive doors studded with iron nails, and grated windows. Many were dominated by massive armorial bearings which proclaimed the owner a *Hidalgo,* a contraction of *Hijo de Algo* — Son of Somebody. These phalanxes of brick and stone would suddenly end in plazas, green and shady, forming a series of oases among the piles of low brown houses.

The largest of these plazas was surrounded by the standard-bearers of empire — the Cathedral, the Cabildo, the Army Barracks, and the Tribunal de la Fé, the House of the Inquisition. The architecture, solid, severe and practical, was established by the laws of the Indies, as were the city's institutions. These laws prescribed, with incredible minutiæ, the forms to be observed in founding a town. In the British colonies the town grew up to meet the needs of the inhabitants; in the Spanish colonies the population of the country grew to meet the needs of the towns. So Cartagena had its Governor who, although appointed by the King, was subservient to the Viceroy; it had its Cabildo, which administered local affairs; a garrison with a commander who answered to the Governor, and a House of Inquisition which answered to no one.

For the Frenchmen, recently arrived from Paris, where one's actions were unhindered and where freedom of speech, if sufficiently clothed with urban niceties, permitted one to say almost anything, to find in this land a functioning Holy Inquisition was a rude jolt. It was positively medieval.

Established in 1569 by a decree of Philip II, the Tribunal was composed of three inquisitors, two secretaries, and a number of familiars who administered the hangings, burnings, and jailings that stemmed from their decisions. The wits of Cartagena said that the Tribunal consisted of *"Un Santo Cristo, dos candeleros y tres maderos"* — one crucifix, two candlesticks, and three blockheads — but it was not wise for a foreigner to echo these sentiments, for the Tribunal was a powerful body, far beyond any temporal authority. It controlled the whole of the intellectual lives of the inhabitants. It maintained rigid supervision over everything, including the introduction, publication, and sale of all forms of literature. Every bookseller was required to furnish lists of all the books he offered for sale and was forced to destroy all that the Inquisition condemned; such was its power. The people of the "Pearl of the Indies" had long learned to steer clear of the Tribunal and ceaselessly reminded themselves of it by saying: *"De Rey y Inquisición — chitón"* ("Of the King and the Inquisition — not a word").

But it was the people of Cartagena that were most surprising to the Frenchmen. They found the variety of bloods, and the skin-colors that stemmed from it, utterly bewildering. There were three main divisions of people — the European, the Indian, and the African — and these fell into color-divisions which ran together like paint on a palette. The offspring of white and Indian were *mestizos,* with a skin-color of *café au lait;* the miscegenation of Negro and Indian produced *sambos,* and these, mixed with others, became *sambalvos, barcinos* or *barcenas,* and mayhap *coyotes.* There were classes the Cartageños referred to as *"tente en el ayre,"* those "suspended in the air," who knew not whether they were dark or white; there were the *salta atrás* — the *"back jumpers"* — who began as "almost white," but who had retrogressed toward the black.

In Cartagena the Academicians met with the captains of the Armada Real who were to be their colleagues in the measurement of an arc of the meridian. There was Don Jorge Juan y Santacilla, mathematician, Commander of the Order Aliaga and of Malta. With him, his junior and the King's spokesman, was Don Antonio de Ulloa, young — only twenty — remarkably astute, an able mathematician and one-day Governor of Louisiana. They were charged with two duties: to assist in every way possible the completion of the scientific program of the Frenchmen, and to allow them to go no farther in their investigations of his realm. They were also charged by the King to make out a report on the "state of the colonial empire," which they did under the title of *Noticias secretas de América.* The most astute and penetrating report ever made of a colonial empire, with specific recommendations for reforms, the *Noticias secretas* were never acted upon and never published — until the English got hold of a copy and printed it seventy-five years after it was written.

The two Spaniards welcomed the Frenchmen with a warmth and a sincerity that seemed to blow away the clouds of any possible suspicion. Ulloa was full of humor. He laughed at the foibles of the colonists. He made light of serious matters, and with an ease of command he was able to bridge the great difficulties which they all faced in this still raw, unopened world.

Three days after landing in Cartagena, M. de Ricour, captain of the French frigate that had brought them, reminded them that, should they be disposed to accept his offer, he would carry them to

Puerto Bello, at the neck of the Isthmus, the second port of call of the Spanish convoys.

Now, there were only two ways of getting to their destination in the Audiencia de Quito. One was to take a vessel from Cartagena to the mouth of the sluggish Magdalena River, transfer the equipment to flat-bottomed bungos, and be poled four hundred miles upstream, after which they would have to transfer to mules and ascend the Andes to Santa Fé de Bogotá. Here they would face another five hundred miles of tortuous mule-pack along the Andes to Quito.

Don Antonio de Ulloa explained this fully to the Academicians before an enormous map that hung in the Governor's office. M. Hugot, the watchmaker, in whose charge were the expedition's telescopes, pendulums, watches, and octants, the most valuable part of the equipment, gave voice to his opinion "that such a voyage would unseat the correctness of the instruments." For this, as well as other reasons, they decided to take the alternative route. They would first go to Puerto Bello, 230 miles due west of Cartagena on the Isthmus of Panama. From Puerto Bello they could either take the overland route, a hard day's ride — a *"jornada"* in muleteer's parlance — to the way-station of Venta de Cruces, or go another fifty miles southwest of Puerto Bello to the Río Chagres, which, being navigable by canoes, would take them to the same town of Venta de Cruces. This would mean only a short mule trip of six hours to the other side of the Isthmus, Panama City, which was the depot of the Plate Fleet arriving from Peru, and the place from which they would embark for the Ecuadorian coast.

The expedition called, en masse, upon the Governor and thanked him for the courtesies of the city. Then they turned their faces west with the helmsman toward Puerto Bello.

". . . Porto Bello," ran an old piratical report, "is a City on the north side of the isthmus of America, to which port the Old Spain Ships bring their Loedings which is carried by Land Carrage to Panama and is Distributed Southward to the Coast of Peru. . . ."

As such, Puerto Bello was the most important port of the whole Spanish Main, the point where the convoyed fleet system arrived to disgorge its cargo from Europe and take on, in turn, the treasure of conquest. It was the "focus of foreign envy." It had been plundered by the most famous pirates of the Spanish Main: Hawkins had tested it, Drake had dug into it — his body lay sealed in a lead casket somewhere in the still, pellucid Bay of Puerto Bello — and, of late, Henry Morgan had seized it and razed it. As a boy La Condamine had thrilled to the tales of Esquemeling and the buccaneers of America, he had followed the rape of Puerto Bello by Morgan and his "Boyes" with all the ardor of a romantic boy to whom bloodletting and rapine seem normal, because they are enveloped in a romantic nimbus. Now he was walking down the single cobblestoned street of this same fabulous city.

The convoy had moved on from Cartagena and now filled the harbor. The city itself was overflowing with *guardas marinas,* soldiers and militia, ever on the alert for attack. The markets were filled with merchants from Bogotá, Quito, Popayán, Panama, and Guatemala who had piled in with their mule-packs, carrying cacao, *quinaquina* or Jesuit's bark, vicuña wool, *canelo* or stick cinnamon, and bales upon bales of ipecac, sarsaparilla, and vanilla.

To La Condamine it was like the fairs of the Levant which he had seen years ago. Goods changed hands, gold and silver and emeralds were thrown about with a carelessness that made his head swim. Millions of maravedis were involved in the sales. Business was concluded as quickly as figures could tumble from mouths. No sooner were the goods disposed of than the brokers closed their chests, put them on their mules, and disappeared.

Anyone who emerged alive from Puerto Bello considered himself especially blessed by the Trinity. Whoever came there made his will first and arranged his affairs and had prayers said for the repose of his soul, for this was the pest-hole of America. Epidemics and fevers scourged the port, slaves from Africa brought their infections, hosts of malaria-carrying mosquitoes plagued the inhabitants without cease, seamen died by the hundreds. For a priest or soldier to be sent to Puerto Bello was like being sent to a living death. Spanish ships seldom departed without burying half or at least a third of their crew. Puerto Bello had become the graveyard of the Spaniard. Still, the fight for trade made it persist.

"We were happy to quit it," wrote Don Antonio de Ulloa. "It had always been our fixed design to stay no longer than absolutely necessary in any place . . . our ardor to enter upon our work, together with a desire of quitting this dangerous climate, induced us to make the utmost dispatch. We sent advice from Puerto Bello to Don Dionysio Martínez de la Vega, President of Panama, of our arrival, the motives of our voyage . . . together with His Majesty's orders relating to the assistance to be given us by all his officers, adding our requests that would he be pleased to send one or two vessels used on the Río Chagres to bring us to Panama. . . ."

Much to La Condamine's surprise the President of Panama sent the dugouts with dispatch. They were waiting for them when they arrived from Puerto Bello. Beating off the myriads of flies, mosquitoes, and gnats that stung and sucked their well-fed Parisian flesh, and hypnotized by the steady beat of the paddlers, they settled back in the canoes, laden to the gunwales.

The jungle overlapped the river, sealing them in as effectively as if they were passing down some narrow winding street of Paris. The air was still, except for an occasional piercing lyrical "ding-dong" of the bell-bird. Trees were so thickly massed that they seemed like a front of polished emerald, a congestion of still leaves. Individual sprays and palm fronds projecting from the green mass bent in charming parabolas with flamboyant abandon. To La Condamine it seemed that their trunks stood like regiments of soldiers, stiff and straight with their pallidly buttressed roots awash in the black jungle loam. Higher up, the forest seemed to be knit by climbing lianas that stretched from tree to tree, like the warp of a magical carpet.

For two days the canoes went up the river, which grew more narrow with each passing hour until finally they were completely enclosed by two vividly green walls of quiet jungle. Alligators lay on the surface of the water; with a furious swish of their tails and a clap like thunder, they would disappear as soon as the bungos hove into sight. Flocks of white egrets paced the dugouts on silent wings, and large blue-headed kingfishers flew ahead of them.

The Río Chagres cut into the heart of that mistily defined region discovered by Columbus on his fourth voyage and included in the ephemeral captaincy of Castilla el Oro — Golden Castile. By 1736 it was embodied in the three provinces — Panama, Darién, and Veraguas — that formed the Kingdom of Tierra Firma. Most of Tierra Firma was covered with forests, deep, penetrating, and majestic; on the Pacific slope these were less dense, and somewhat drier. The line of the central cordillera, a continuation of the South American Andes, was fairly well defined east of the valley hollowed out by the Chagres until, arching south, it broke into a mass of tangled crests and ridges, holding high plateaus between the ranges.

The Río Chagres (now included in the Panama Canal) was the scene of the first efforts of the Spaniards to "cut" the Isthmus. After having discovered the continent, the next obsession of the Spaniards was to find a strait to the Southern Seas. In 1529 a report went to Charles V: "We have not found the passage — we must cut it." Royal engineers surveyed the Río Chagres. Within fifty years after America's discovery they poled up the river until they bumped into a tangled mass of broken hills and mountains. They looked at their pumps, their engines, and their hand-shovels; they looked at the jagged verdure-splashed mountains, and gave up their project. The Spaniards had "thought out" the Canal, but their ideas were centuries in advance of their technology. So they constructed the only thing they could, a road between Puerto Bello and the city of Panama. The path of empire, the most valuable asset of Spanish commerce, it became the artery most sought after by all other nations.

Venta de Cruces was the base of a V of communication. It was one day's ride from Panama City and the most important of the stopping-places on the trans-isthmian route maintained by the authorities of Tierra Firma. The end of the Cruces Trail stood 130 feet above sea-level where the air was "more benign," and so it was used for a hospital station as well as a depot with customs and warehouses. In dry weather mule trains went across on the cobblestone path between Panama and Puerto Bello; in the eight to nine months of wet weather, when the Río Chagres was high, cargo went by boat from Venta de Cruces down the river past Fort San Lorenzo to the Caribbean, thence eastward to Puerto Bello.

The town stood within a large cleared area, tastefully planted with orange trees and the sweet guayabas. A small, well-constructed town, it consisted in the main of warehouses and customs arenas, built of stone, roofed with tile, and guarded by a fort such as the one at the entrance to the Río Chagres. The Alcalde of the town acted with the customary politeness of the country. He quickly urged the Indians about him to unload the bungos and make ready the mules to take the "earth-measurers" on their six-hour journey to the city of Panama on the edge of the Pacific.

In the late afternoon of the same day a soft breeze sprang up, a fresh, invigorating, salt-filled air; and the expeditionists, covered with the filth of the mule journey, weary from the last days in the dugouts, felt the first luscious touch of the Pacific. They caught sight of the hills of Ancón, then the ramparts of the fort that guarded the city of Panama, and then behind it the deep blue of the South Sea. No wind crowded its peacefulness. There it lay, blue and indolent, without mist or movement. The Atlantic, the Pacific, the jungle, the plain surrounded them, like a fugue of four themes.

On the savanna was the central theme — Panama, a testimony, if not to man's greatness, at least to his tenacity, for the city had been destroyed successively by earthquake, pillage, and fire. But now it stood whole again and alive with all the hurried activity of harvester-ants gathering in the newly arrived *"cosas de España."* Bells of the cathedral were ringing the Angelus when the Academicians clattered into Panama, followed by the riff-raff of the city, the dogs, and curious-eyed Indians, as if they were a traveling circus of mountebanks.

There was much to do. "First," as Antonio de Ulloa wrote, "we made it our first business to wait upon the President, Don Martínez de la Vega, a mark of respect due, not only to his dignity, but also for the many civilities he had shown us. The worthy gentleman received us all . . . in the most cordial and endearing manner. He also recommended to all the King's officers, and other persons of distinction in the city, not to be wanting in any good office or mark of esteem: a behavior which showed at once the weight of the royal orders."

And yet all the weight of royal orders was not enough to expedite the sailing to the province of Quito. There were some "indispensable preparations" to be made which plowed deeply into the reservoir of their time. Time, the Academicians soon learned, was not measured in the Americas. To be sure, people of exalted stations sported watches, but none ever referred to them. Full of bluster and pisco rum, the master of their vessel called upon them in their apartments overlooking the main plaza. He assured them that his ship, the *San Cristóbal*, would sail "soon," but when pressed for a sailing date, he waved away a definite time by smiling vague assurance: it would be "soon, Caballeros, soon."

Antonio de Ulloa avowed that "soon" was nothing more than a figure of speech and that they could, with perfect safety, unpack their instruments and put their stay in Panama to profit. None of the Academicians needed to be told that. Joseph de Jussieu, armed with the traditional botanist's satchel, was already scouring the hills for fruiting and flowering plants for his collection, ably assisted by Jean Senièrgues, the physician to the expeditionists, and Morainville, the draftsman. Charles-Marie de La Condamine and the others departed with Godin, Bouguer, and Captain Verguin of the French Navy to chart the Bay of Panama. For they had been asked by the celebrated French cartographer d'Anville to supply corrections for his new map of South America.

"Get me angles, gentlemen, and triangulations, correct meridionals, for I am merciless to legends." With this dictum in mind, they swarmed over the Isthmian jungle-side.

The site of Panama City had been discovered by Tello de Guzmán as early as 1515 and had taken its name from the Isthmus. The whole area was so called by the Indians because of the presence there of a tall, smooth-barked, sterculian tree named "panamá." Its settlement followed by only two years Vasco Nuñez de Balboa's discovery of the great South Sea. It took but a moment for the geographically-minded Spaniard to see the advantage of a settlement on the Bay of Panama, to control the entrance to the Isthmus. By 1521 Carlos V had constituted it a city, with all its proper privileges. For more than a century it was the gateway to the gold and silver mines of Peru and Bolivia, as well as to the Philippines and the Spice Islands of the far Pacific. The pirates struck at it again and again. In 1670, after overpowering the Fortress of San Lorenzo on the Río Chagres and razing Venta de Cruces, Henry Morgan advanced to Panama, seized the city, plundered it at his leisure, and surrendered it only on payment of a huge ransom, first putting it to the torch. The city was then removed a league from its old site to the mouth of the Río Grande, where it has since remained.

The Frenchmen had yet to grow used to the curious habits and modes of a tropical colonial city, differing, naturally, from one of the Continent. Charles-Marie de La Condamine was accustomed to being in the grand salons of Paris, but here he was received, even in houses of distinction, by ladies who greeted him while lolling at ease in their hammocks. Women had formed too much a part of this life for him not to observe that in Panama the women ". . . wear a kind of petticoat, which they call 'pollera' . . . and on their body a very thin waistcoat . . . which, however, they always lace to conceal their breasts. On their heads they put a cap of fine white linen, in the shape of a miter. Instead of shoes . . . they wear a kind of slipper large enough to contain only the tips of their feet. In the house their whole exercise consists in sitting in their hammocks . . . this is so general a custom that there is not a household without two or three. . . . In these they pass the greater part of the day!"

It took him some time to grow used to seeing women smoking. In Europe, where smoking was social and where a man could grow discursive over a pipe and mellow over a bottle, the practice was confined wholly to men and only to pipes. In America he found the passion for smoking universal — "The ladies and other white women smoke in their houses, a decency not observed by women of the other castes, nor by the men, in general, who regard neither time nor place." Ah, but the manner of smoking! "They rolled the tobacco into slender rolls and they put the lighted part of the roll into their mouths and there continue it a long time without its being quenched, or the fire incommoding them."

But there was more to do than to discourse with fine ladies while swinging in hammocks and smoking in reverse; there were the final preparations for the journey, and letters to be written to the Académie des Sciences.

Originally they had been granted two years in which to perform their measurements. La Condamine wrote to the treasurer, Couplet, that he did not believe that it could be done in the time allotted. They had sailed from France in May 1735; it was now January 1736, and they were yet to sail to Peru. He tried to give them as clear a picture of the Americas as analogy would permit, since only thus could those sitting in Paris form an idea of the immensity of their task.

"Along this isthmus run those famous chains of lofty mountains called the Andes, which, beginning at such a prodigious distance as the Tierra Magellanica, traverse the Kingdom of Chile, the province of Buenos Ayres, and thence through the provinces of Peru and Quito; and from the latter, contract themselves, as it were, for a passage through this narrow isthmus. Afterward, again widening, they continue their northern course. . . ."

He summed up the expenses, the cost of making tents and added protection for the instruments; he complained of the lack of co-operation of M. Pierre Bouguer, who seemed to want to make his own measurements independently, but it was impossible for him to conceal his enthusiasm for the impending adventure.

"We sail on the 22nd of February of this year of grace, 1736."

CHAPTER IV
Expedition to the Equator

"The *San Cristóbal* sailed on the high tide on the night of February 22, 1736. Winds variable and light. Passed Cabo Menglares on the 26th. Currents weak. Passengers limited to members of the Academía de Ciencia — Carlos de la Condamine, Luis Godin, Pedro Bouguer, etc., etc., and two officers of H.C.M. Navy, Don Jorge Juan and Don Antonio de Ulloa. . . . The fog is thick. . . ."

THE FOG IS THICK." This appeared not only in the salty scrawls of the captain's logbook: it was echoed ceaselessly by the Academicians. They desired to see this land which had been closed so long to foreigners, they wanted to look upon the towering hulk of mountains that was to be the scene of their labors. Six leagues off shore, and they had not even had a glimpse of the Andes. A curtain of fog had settled down upon the whole sea ever since they had left Panama, a curtain of mist that dropped a steady, cold drizzle.

In mid-afternoon of March 9, after rounding Cape Pasado, the frigate pushed its way slowly into Bahía de Manta, halfway between the equator and Guayaquil. Slowly rising upward, like a drop curtain, the mist dissolved . . . and there before the astonished eyes of the Frenchmen stood the great hulk of the purplish, rock-hard cordillera. It was breath-taking. Parts of it were still mysteriously interlaced with streamers of mist; ribbons of color began to glow green, then red, and then purple. The mountains rushed up from the coast in wonderful untiring sweeps to a most lordly climax in the snow-encrusted, cloud-piercing volcanic peaks, serene and overpowering.

"Six fathoms — four fathoms," shouted the leadman of the *San Cristóbal,* marking the depths of the channel.

"Steady," shouted the captain.

"Steady," answered the helmsman, as if he were repeating a litany.

The Academicians gathered along the bulwarks and watched the landfall of Manta. The majestic grandeur of that great hulking wall of the cordillera acted as a spell upon the expeditionists.

Manta appeared behind a parapet of the black filigree of palm fronds; purple blossoms blazed against the small white houses. Dominating the plaza, and in a semi-ruinous state, was a church topped with a giant crucifix. It was a dilapidated affair, the wattle and daub showing through the cracked white calcimine.

Weighted with ficus plants which entwined the tower, the slanting tiled roof was host to other plants which grew and blossomed without the need for earth. Through the swaying crowns of the palm fronds the equatorial sunlight fell in dazzling shafts on the unpaved street. A two-wheeled ox-cart stood beside the church.

The whole village was dreamy and indolent. The Indians sat by their small huts and followed the Frenchmen with their dark, lustrous eyes, slanted in a way to remind one of Mongolian princes. The women, naked save for a skirt which they wound around their middle, hung out of their windows with roving inquisitive glance.

At the orders of the Alcalde, one of the few white people of the village, they were invited into the Hôtel de Ville, and there were served with a bowl of chopped fruit — bananas, oranges, granadillas, cherimoyas — on a large ebony-colored table. This was followed by strong black coffee and bowls of steaming chocolate. It was an idyllic introduction to the Audiencia de Quito.

La Condamine voiced his satisfaction with his decision to begin the work on this coast, for a singular phenomenon supposedly made it ideal for measurements. The whole coast was semi-desert. Little or no rain fell. This condition, they thought, would permit an easy handling of the measuring chains of their surveying instruments and would render simple the setting up of signals to be used for the plotting of the triangles on which all their work in the Cordilleras would be predicated. Alas! They reckoned without the mist.

Only Pierre Bouguer elected to stay with La Condamine. The others — Louis Godin, the astronomer; his cousin, Jean Godin; Hugot, the watchmaker; Jussieu, the botanist; and all the rest, fell in with the counter-suggestion of Ulloa and Juan that they proceed to Guayaquil, where they would be housed as befitted their persons and calling and as bearers of the King's own passport.

Pierre Bouguer's decision to throw his lot in with Charles-Marie was a rather unusual gesture, since Bouguer and La Condamine had already had occasion to quarrel violently. A small man, with a meager soul, Pierre Bouguer was an exacting moralist, a rare bird in an age when one could be both savant and profligate without one status upsetting the other in the eyes of the intellectual world. Bouguer resented La Condamine. He resented his ease in the elegant salons of Paris, he looked askance at a gentleman who could pass from turning *bouts-rimés* in a lady's boudoir to a stirring mathematical defense of Newton's cosmic hypothesis. Bouguer's early education had deeply affected his life. He had been born at Croisic on the Loire three years earlier than La Condamine — 1698 — and educated at a Jesuit school in Paris. His interest turned to the positive sciences. He was an excellent mathematician, with a scarcity of ideas and a total lack of imagination. He was a close friend of the Cassinians, a lukewarm adherent of the Newton theories, and thus, one can understand, was opposed diametrically to La Condamine. He suffered, too, from a regrettable obsession. He believed from the beginning that La Condamine was trying to take all the personal glory, and this so warped his character that it led, in the end, to the ruin of some of the objects of the expedition. Bouguer said very frankly that "M. Louis Godin had more pretension than anyone else to be placed at the head of our company. . . . For my own part, I had, at first, no intention of having anything to do with the enterprise . . . but when several of the mathematicians or astronomers on whom reliance was placed found themselves in a situation . . . to be unable to give efficacy to their zeal . . . this determined me to conquer the repugnance which the weak state of my health had always given me to sea voyages. . . ." So the lighthearted, enthusiastic La Condamine was left alone with him of the jaundiced vision, Pierre Bouguer.

The frigate *San Cristóbal*, after taking on water and provisions, left Manta with the rest of the expedition for Guayaquil. There they arrived on the 25th of March, amid a deluge of rain and insects. On their arrival the Corregidor saw that they were housed as pleasantly as circumstances allowed. He sent off Indian runners at once to the Corregidor of Guaranda, an Indian village high in the Andes and close to the frigid, snow-mantled volcano of Chimborazo. That way lay the only route to the cordillera and the city of Quito, whither they were bound. To reach it, travelers were poled up the Río Guayas, upon whose banks Guayaquil was situated. Far up the river, where it had narrowed into a swift-moving stream between jungles and river rushes, was the town of Bodegas. There they waited in a palm-thatched *tambo* for the arrival of mules, which slid, fell, and tumbled down the narrow road that was cut in the side of the 12,000-foot-high cordillera. This was the road the expedition would be forced to take, a route that gave poor Hugot, the watchmaker, endless suffering when he thought of the damage that would be caused to his beloved instruments. It was not until May 6 that the expeditionists would leave the ancient city of Guayaquil (which had been settled by Belalcázar as early as 1535) and set off for the capital of the Kingdom of Quito. While they were deluged with the heavy rains of the *invierno* that make all roads impassable from December until April, La Condamine and Bouguer were already at work on the deserts of Manabí.

They had no sooner settled themselves in a village called Monte
Cristi, a league from Manta, than they were surprised to see coming toward them one morning a long line of Indians, led by a
"Regidor" carrying a large cane ornamented with a silver head,
his wand of authority. He touched his hat and inquired — in a
language that he earnestly thought to be Spanish — if they were
the "measuring men." When assured that they were, he handed
them a letter. It informed them that His Excellency Don José de
Olabes y Gomara, Commandant of Puerto Viejo (a village some
miles farther inland) extended to the French mission his welcome, in the name of the Viceroy. The Indians he sent were instructed to perform whatever task the gentlemen desired.

So they chose "a more commodious station as an observatory at
about a third of a league from the village." There La Condamine
and Bouguer, with the help of the Indians, erected a primitive
observatory. While Bouguer sat with his eyes glued to the telescope, La Condamine experimented with Huygens's pendulum.
But this was the labor of Sisyphus, because, with the heavy *garúa*
fog settling on the coast, the sun was visible only in the evening,
never in the morning. This deprived them of "the correspondent
observations of which we were in want." A cloudy sky, a falling
misty fog, prevented them from observing the eclipses of the
satellites of Jupiter. Only a break in the weather permitted them
to observe the end of the eclipse of the moon on the 26th of March
1736, and from that circumstance they were able to fix the position
of this coast, the most westerly of South America. That bearing
became the base of the eighteenth-century maps of the continent.

Pierre Bouguer thought it useless to go on and suggested joining the others in Guayaquil, but La Condamine urged that they
continue seventy miles northward to the equator to make their
first observations on the "line." Bouguer reluctantly yielded. They
got together their Indians, tied their instruments onto mules, and
made their way northward along the deserts of Manabí.

The littoral was crowded with the chalk-white bones of whales
and sea lions. It was a regular ossuary. There was an endless
parade of pelicans and boobies and gannets fishing off shore in
the blue pellucid sea. The beach between the littered whale-
bones was covered with comminuted shells, the glare of them as
bright as sunshine on snow. Back of the long serpentine beach was
the calcareous desert, studded with palmetto shrubs and mesquite,
with patches of yellow and blue shrubs. Hidden by scrub were
occasional shallow lagoons, the nesting-place of flamingoes and
herons. For the rest, the land was practically barren, inexorable,
and without life other than the birds. In the east, against the dark

spurs of the Andes, was the purple shadow of forests. At intervals a river would spring from distant forests and cut its way through these aridities to the sea. Here the world would go tropical.

The natives taught them how to use the flux and reflux of the tides so that they could travel close to shore, along the sand, and avoid the tangle of cactus in the deserts. They passed Charapoto, where a small settlement of Spaniards was found; they crossed the Río Chone. The desert had ended. Now the coast was swathed in jungles, interspersed with grass savannas. By April 1736 they were established on Cape Pasado, a peninsula that jutted farther out into the Pacific than any other part of the continent.

They remained there a fortnight, while Bouguer struggled with the refraction of light and La Condamine began to lay down the meridian of his map of Ecuador. There were some irritable days. Food was bad and, what was more, scarce. And the insects began to plague their tempers. The piume flies bothered them most. A dozen at a time, no larger than a pinhead, would land on a bare part, gorge themselves on blood, and leave behind a dot of ex-travasated blood which was as irritating as the prick of a needle. Cockroaches swarmed over their provisions, stingless bees hung onto their hair to drink the exudate of their bodies. Sauba ants, large, red-bodied leaf-cutters, moved over the ground in an interminable procession. Mostly they cut leaves, which they dragged off toward their underground nests, but when leaves were not to be had, they marched in the dusk and laid siege to the sparse provisions of the expedition. At night there were mosquitoes and enormous flying cockroaches, the size of mice. And as if this were not enough, their toes were filled with niguas. Had he been in Paris, La Condamine might have thought he suffered from the gout; his feet pulsated, throbbed; but here in the province of Quito — the Indians looked at his feet and told him he had *niguas*.

"They are shaped," he remembered, "like a flea, but almost too small for sight. It is a great happiness that their legs have not the elasticity of those of fleas, for could this insect leap . . ." La Condamine hated even to contemplate it. "They live mostly in the dust. They insinuate themselves into the soles of the feet, or toes, and pierce the skin with such subtlety that there is no being aware of them." Once its "lodgings" are taken up deep in the skin, the nigua sucks the blood, "forms a nest covered with a white integument, resembling a flat pearl, and there enlarges the nest in the toe. There is an absolute necessity of extracting them. . . ."

All these annoyances gave rise to "humours" and aggravated the differences in the psyches of the two Frenchmen. La Condamine had heard of the Río Esmeraldas, and that its ascent would bring one to the inter-Andine plateau of Quito. He believed that they should take this route, so as to enlarge their horizon and give them greater knowledge of the country. Bouguer, on the other hand, thought that they should return at once to join their colleagues in Guayaquil. The irritation of the ceaseless plague of insects, and the unpalatable food, gave impetus to their tempers. La Condamine had made up his mind to continue; Bouguer to return.

They both, doubtless, had their say. But after the argument a wind blew away the insects, a soft breeze came up, and slowly their tempers cooled.

It was a night such as exists only in those latitudes, a night serene and beautiful, with every star mirrored in the water and reflected back as in a looking-glass. The Southern Cross hung in the sky. Sirius gleamed redly among the other stars and seemed to send the softest light into the sea. Pierre Bouguer was observing the transit of Venus through his telescope; La Condamine, by a flickering lamp, behind the drop curtain of a tent, was copying the figures of his experiments with Réaumur's thermometer. He finished it and, under the spell of the night, came out of the tent and looked upon the moon shining radiantly on the flat, unagitated sea and coldly on the forests at the spurs of the Andes. As the moon rose, the cicadas began their song, which sounded to La Condamine's Parisian ears like the scissor-grinders who kept their stalls on the Pont Neuf. Tiny frogs joined the cicadas, pounding away as if a hundred small hammers were striking an empty winecask. Then another sound joined in like the beat of the surf. It grew in volume like the staccato beats of a drum. The Indians heard it, too. They left the fire around which they were squatting. They put their ears to the ground. Horses! Who rode the night? The Indians suggested robbers, or, worse still, *cimarrones* (for the village of Esmeraldas was filled with Negroes), and slunk off; La Condamine carefully primed his pistols and waited. Then out of the shapeless night, into the light of the moon, came three mounted figures. Two stayed back, one figure advanced. La Condamine raised his pistols and then as quickly lowered them. He had no need of them; it was a gentleman that he faced. The stranger bent his knee, bowed, and said:

"Pedro Vicente Maldonado y Sotomayor to serve thee."

The Academicians looked upon the most extraordinary man that the Spanish colonies had produced in a century. Maldonado was a "product" of the Audiencia of Quito, born in Riobamba in 1704. Young — three years the junior of La Condamine — he was a good observer, a practiced mathematician, a clever cartographer; and he had, like La Condamine, an inquisitive mind. His bearing, his proud dark eyes, his hair combed back and braided in the manner of the period, belied the nature of his interests. Maldonado had traveled extensively in the jungles of his native province, completely indifferent to the hardships that such a life entailed. He dragged his surveyor's chain with him everywhere and had already completed a good part of the finest and most complete map ever made of the colonial province of Spain. For years, after quitting the Jesuit College in Quito, Pedro Maldonado tried to impress the Viceroy with the feasibility of opening the Esmeraldas-Quito route. This had been used, tradition insisted, by the Caras in the protohistory of Quito and it had been used by Sebastián de Belalcázar, the conqueror of Quito. Why not utilize it? Many had attempted it; most of them failed. Pedro Maldonado was certain that he would succeed. Within three years he had built a road from the town of Ibarra in the inter-Andine plateau, down the side of the Andes, to a section of the Esmeraldas River, which he called the "Puerto de Quito." He made numerous voyages up and down the river and at last convinced the authorities that it was an alternative route to the sea which might replace the long, involved road to Guayaquil. At a time when most men in the colonies languished and thought only of the past, Maldonado climbed mountains, braved rivers and the elements, and at the age of twenty-seven he was named Governor of Esmeraldas as a reward for his services. It was in this office that he appeared before the two Frenchmen quartered on the desert seacoast of Cape Pasado.

La Condamine had found his man. He knew it at once. Here was a native of Quito who could at last match his curiosity. Maldonado had all the eagerness and enthusiasm of restless intellects. In him were all the qualities of an explorer; he spoke French, Spanish, and the native language, Quechua. And his brother José Antonio Maldonado was a high ecclesiastical official in Quito. With his vast experience, his far-flung interests, his boundless curiosity, La Condamine could have asked for no better man. So when Pedro Maldonado said that he had hoped that they, or at least one of them, would honor him by going up the Río Esmeraldas and reaching Quito by his new route, La Condamine all but threw himself into Maldonado's arms.

It was agreed that Pierre Bouguer would take the heavier instruments with him to Guayaquil, while the Indians who had served as faithful guides and helpers would return to the Alcalde at Manta. So they parted: Bouguer to the south, to follow the others to Quito by the conventional mountain route; La Condamine and Pedro Maldonado to the north to take the Esmeraldas route.

[31]

The month of May 1736 marked the first anniversary of the expedition's departure from La Rochelle. The expedition was now
making its way up the sides of the Andes to the flat bare land of
the *páramos*. Over these frigid, wind-swept Andean moorlands,
dominated by snow-topped volcanoes which still rumbled and
groaned in the inner earth, the Academicians took their way to
Quito. All but one: for him the world was still green, for La Condamine traveled with Pedro Maldonado in the warm, luxurious
jungles of Esmeraldas.

By now they had arrived at the little village of Esmeraldas,
perched on the banks of the river only half a mile from where it
debouched into the Pacific. The vegetable world was green; the
human world, in Esmeraldas, black. Never had Charles-Marie
been so reminded of Africa and his youthful voyage with the squad-
ron of Duguay-Trouin to the Barbary Coast and the Levant, for
here on the fringe of the jungles the flesh was rich ebony. These
were Maldonado's subjects. Naked, black, pot-bellied children
played in the mud streets before their bamboo houses raised on
stilts. All about were extravagant arbors of papayas, mangoes,
bananas; and mixed with these in ardent hues were acacias, calla
lilies growing on trees, and passion flowers which, with other unseen blooms, made breathing a sensuous pleasure.

The Negroes had taken possession of the Esmeraldas coast in the
late seventeenth century when a slave ship had been wrecked on
the island-dotted coast. A war of extermination set in between
Negro and Indian. The Negro won: the Indians retired farther
into the interior; the Negro held the coast. Miscegenation had already set in. Here and there La Condamine began to observe
black skins becoming less black, bushy black hair taking on the
reddish hue of changing chromosomes.

What a joy it was to be among these people! At night they sang,
the soft tuneless haunting songs they had learned in past ages in
their African home. In the bright sunlight they rested in hammocks strung between the poles that held up their houses. Some
time during the day, La Condamine could not decide precisely
when, they set out to their fields of manioc and corn, pineapples
and beans. Everything here was casual. The earth was rich, the
seas generous, and the warm rains beneficent.

These very human people liked Pedro Maldonado, they were
eager to do anything he asked of them. They could spend much
time dawdling in the hammock, yet when there was need they
could pole up frightening, rushing rivers for hours at a time. So
the whole month of May was given over to the exploration of
Esmeraldas with the Negroes as *palanquines*. They went out to sea

in a small boat, north to the Río Verde. They ascended the river until they came to the houses of the Cayapas Indians perched high on its banks. They took observations; they enlarged their carto-graphic sheet; they plunged into the jungle, using each day as fully as if it were their last. By the time the month was well past, La Condamine would no longer start when the howling monkeys filled the forest with the whooping sound of Banshees. The rau-cous noise of the parrots that screeched at dawn, these flying rain-bows, the green and red *guacamayos,* were now the friendly avian symbols of the jungles that he had begun to understand.

It was a new education. America was unknown. La Conda-mine's mind had been conditioned to fill the unknown with all sorts of lugubrious phantasmagoria, but now, under the tutelage of Pedro Maldonado, he no longer feared that which he did not know. The beauty of the forest dissipated his last doubts. There was the toucan, the bird of the ridiculously long beak, which re-peated its song ceaselessly: *"Dios te dé, Dios te dé";* and the bell-bird, whose song was a single melodic note, the exact mimicry of a clapped bell; and the hummingbirds which hung in front of his very eyes, as filled with astonishment and rapture for this Parisian who walked the floor of the jungle as he for an iridescent bird, no larger than a full-bodied moth, which could hang suspended in mid-air by a violent beating of its wings. There were the trogons, beautiful and timid; the cock-of-the-rocks, a dashing ball of orange feathers with black wing-trim; and umbrella-birds with a chest pendant like a black velvet stock and a crowning topknot of head feathers that hung about its eyes like a black-fringed parasol.

The forest of America was not, he perceived, a land at all, it was an element — its inhabitants, arboreal. Jaguars crouched in the trees, monkeys hung from the vine-festooned limbs, frogs stuck to the trunks by means of suction pads on their feet. Every-thing depended on the green world of the tree. All of this became part of the Frenchman's new spirit.

Then came a new interest. The natives had brought him a strange piece of stretching "cloth" called *caoutchouc.* This was rubber. La Condamine became its modern discoverer. It fasci-nated him. He came upon leaf huts in the jungle close to where the sambos of Esmeraldas were tapping the rubber tree. The pale trunks were scarred with brown wounds from which dripped the white viscous "milk" which one day would build empires. He watched the sambos gather the "milk" from gourds fastened to the trees with coagulated "rubber" and was amazed at the manner in which the latex solidified. Having seen the Negroes pour the co-agulated *"jebe,"* as they called it in their patois, into plantain leaves two yards long, he thought of his quadrant. If this caout-chouc was water-resistant, why not make a case of it to keep his instrument dry? So La Condamine, in the fastness of the firefly-spangled jungle, fashioned himself a rubber pouch for his quad-rant. Unknowingly he became the first white rubber-manufacturer.

He was not, to be sure, the first to see rubber. It had been known to all the explorers ever since Cortés found the Aztecs playing the game of *tlachtli* with solid rubber balls. Nor was La Condamine the first to mention the rubber tree. It had been mentioned by Pietro Martyre d'Anghiera in his *Decades of the New World,* and by a Spanish chronicler, Juan de Torquemada, who wrote a "recognizable description" of one of the latex-yielding trees and an account of the tapping methods, and mentioned its numerous uses. But Torquemada's report, early in the conquest, a report calculated to arouse lively curiosity, fell on utterly deaf ears.

La Condamine's reports, however, attracted Europe's attention to rubber. His were the first scientific experiments, his the first mention of the hevea tree; he was the first to bring back samples of rubber to Europe.

It took five days to pole up the Esmeraldas River to Maldo-nado's landing which he called, a bit exaggeratedly, the Port of Quito. From that "port" Quito lay eighteen leagues skyward, and to reach it meant a tortuous climb of three days. Before they left Maldonado's "capital" they had gone to the emerald mines which lay on the River Bichile, no great distance away. From the "mine" came the emeralds called *umina-cuna* by the Incas, who had a great passion for them. And there the natives of Manabí, long be-fore the Incas dominated the coast, worshipped "an emerald the size of an ostrich egg, to which they had consecrated a temple."

The whole land seemed to breathe the mystery of forgotten cul-tures. There was hardly a day when the explorers did not come across ancient stone seats and monolithic grave slabs and small clay figurines decorated with cicatrized lines. Some of the seats were carved forcefully out of andesite with crouching human fig-ures as motifs. Others had animals as decorations. Their Indian guides told them that these stone seats were those of giants who once lived on the coast of Manabí. They had come down from the north — that is from the direction of Panama — in the ninth cen-tury, and were called Carás or Scyris. They established the city of Cará a few miles north of Manta, and during the passing cen-turies they carved the slabs, the stone seats, and built "giant cas-tles" which time and the rapine of man had destroyed. But the coast was too dry to support them. They found the great River Esmeraldas, as far north of the equator as Manta is south, and following its course; they climbed the Andes and penetrated the inter-Andean valleys. They there established the city of Quito. For four centuries the Carás, with their rulers, the Scyris, dominated Ecuador. Then they in turn were overwhelmed by the soldiers of the Inca Tupac Yupanqui, who finally completed the conquest of all Quito and made it a sub-capital of Cuzco in the year 1450. Yet when the Incas began to filter into this land and up the coast, the civilization that had flourished here was no more. Only small tribes of primitive folk lived on the rivers, hunted in the forests, and fished in the sea.

Pedro Maldonado knew well the peoples who lived within his jurisdiction, the Provincia de Esmeraldas. Along the coast were scattered settlements of black sambos; three primitive tribes dominated the jungles between the Andes and the Pacific. Close to the border of Nueva Granada were the Malaguas living their time-honored customs in small, isolated groups in cleared jungle spaces. Below them, toward the sea, were the Cayapas, a very intelligent, industrious tribe numbering 3,000 people, among his most docile subjects. They lived on the banks of rivers in small communities of houses raised on stilts. They were excellent weavers, superb fashioners of the dugout, and expert canoe-men. The third tribe into whose country they would soon enter were the Colorado Indians. A surprise awaited La Condamine, Maldonado assured him of that.

In the first three days, traveling in their forty-foot dugout, and paced by six black palanquines, they had covered more than half of the one hundred miles from the sea to Maldonado's Puerto de Quito. Packed in the canoe with their instruments were the now familiar bananas, long parsnip-shaped tubers called *yuca,* rice, and beans, and several chickens which, with legs tied, wiggled themselves into the shade under the passengers' canopy. There were also demijohns of a high smelling *masato-sum,* a liquid without which no Esmeraldeño traveled. Masato, which La Condamine would learn to drink, was made from boiled ripe plantains which, reduced to stinking mash, were put into a basket lined with banana leaves and allowed to ferment for three days. Then the mixture was spooned into a *tutuma* gourd, bored with holes like a colander. Out of this dripped the masato, pale and sugary. A few days sufficed to ferment it. In taste it was acid, agreeable, and alcoholic; its effect, volcanic.

In the fifth day of poling they had entered the country of the Colorado Indians. The Esmeraldas River had been widened by several other streams pouring into it. The current increased, the poling became labored. After the confluence of the Río Guaillabamba, a wide turbulent stream which poured down from the heart of the Andes, La Condamine noted the change in the jungle's topography. The swift moving water of the Esmeraldas, two hundred feet wide, was now confined between rock banks, and beyond were two walls of solid vivid jungle. These last days were without a breath of air, as they worked upstream on the gray river serpentining under the torrid equatorial sun.

A change had come over their sambo palanquines. They had long lost their simple gaiety. They were now sullen and resentful, for fear had command. They were almost a hundred miles from their aerial huts facing the Pacific, and in the very center of the territory of the Colorados, their hated enemies. Each task was performed with sullen resentment. In the glare of the fire the Negroes slept close together, their warm, half-naked black bodies breathing into the darkness at arm's length.

On the fifth and last night of the river journey, the sambos were active most of the night. As dusk gathered, the howling monkeys began their psalmody. The birds went silently to their nests for the night, and the vampire bats circled about on noiseless wings, hideous and menacing. The sky was ablaze with stars. Moisture hung in the cool jungle night as fragrant as crushed herbs. La Condamine could look up through the trees and without a chart pick out most of the constellations of the southern celestial theater. These five days had been well spent. They had mapped the courses of the Esmeraldas River and made numerous observations for their triangles of the equator. They had collected plants for Jussieu, the botanist, and picked up metal which, being neither gold nor silver, was called *platina*. La Condamine put it into his collections, and when it was finally examined by the metallurgists of Europe it became known that he had discovered platinum.

It was a night not quickly to be forgotten: the stars, the cool air, the deep scent of earth and jungle, the singing of the Negroes; the high conversation and the thoughts of these two men, Maldonado and La Condamine, who had been cast in different worlds. Pedro spoke of his home in Riobamba, at the base of the slumbering snow-capped Chimborazo. He spoke of his family, of the Indians on his hacienda, of the marvels of the Incan past. And La Condamine satisfied Maldonado's interest in Paris. They were as brothers now, possessed of a friendship carved from the same interests, enthusiasms, and the search for the unknown; theirs was fraternal feeling for the mysteries of the earth.

The next day they came to Puerto de Quito. Perched high on an embankment, a few miles above where the Río Toachi joined the deep-flowing Esmeraldas, was Maldonado's port, a cluster of houses on an embankment, buildings of split bamboo raised high above the ground, windowless and uninviting, with strange and memorable odors, evasive and sweetly pungent like the smell of rotting chocolate beans. The "port" was deserted. Royal palms, smooth-trunked and delicately fronded, gave grace and life to the three vacated buildings. The noon shadows of the huts were as deep as the stains of ink. The forest rose behind, like some soft and benignant Eden.

The sambos worked feverishly to unload the equipment; food, chickens, and instruments were thrown off as fast as their dark sweating bodies could accomplish it; then they were gone. Without a word, so overcome by fear that they did not wait for their money, they cast off, picked up their mahogany paddles, and disappeared in a rhythm of pounding sounds.

The explorers were alone. There was a faint sibilation of insects, a call from a toucan, a rasping crunch of some tree that fell to earth — then there was silence. It was cellar-cool in the jungles of Esmeraldas. Statuesque silk-cotton trees stood over them like buttressed giants. Nothing moved except the wings of a giant blue morpho butterfly which fluttered in the damp gloom of the forest. So entranced was La Condamine with the scene that momentarily he forgot they were alone, without carriers, in the grip of the forest. No sooner had he remembered this than out of the jungle poured a score of the most fantastic people he had ever seen; he stood face to face with the Colorado Indians.

They were small men, hardly coming up to his eyes, their nakedness garbed with but a single breech-clout. But their color! They were painted a brilliant scarlet from the bottom of their wide spreading feet to the top of their heads. Even the hair was red and made up into a most amazing coiffure. Stiff and thick with the dye, it came down over their eyes in a red screen. It was an amazing spectacle. They hovered on the fringes of the jungle, shifting from foot to foot like embarrassed children. Maldonado spoke to them in Quechua. One understood and translated his words into their own language, Tsátchela, and there followed a babble of voices when Maldonado indicated La Condamine as "a friend."

At the word "friend," the Indians surged forward like a wave engulfing a passive coast, seized the bewildered Charles-Marie by the free right hand, and pumped it up and down. "Friend." It was a sort of open sesame, a key to understanding. When the Indians had ceased shaking his hand, La Condamine looked ruefully at his coat and found himself covered with the red dye from their bodies.

There was a conference between the Quechua-speaking Indian

and Maldonado. He indicated with a sweep of his hand that he wished them to carry their equipment to Mindo, the next *tambo,* on the road to Quito. A buzz of voices, a rapid survey of the bundles that lay on the ground, and the Colorados agreed. Each one ripped off long strips of bark from near-by trees and twisted them deftly into rope, selected a bulky burlap-wrapped piece of cargo, tied the rope around it, slipped the strap across his forehead, and set off into the jungle.

The two explorers followed them. Their feet half buried in the black ooze of the Esmeraldean forest, they kept pace with the laden Colorados to the tune of the instruments of nature's orchestra. The wind rustled the leaves, the giant frogs somewhere in an uncharted lagoon gave out throbbings like a bass viol, cicadas ground away, pounding on the two membranes stretched like drumheads near their wings. The grasshoppers fiddled, producing their sounds by means of their toothed shanks, which they pulled across the edge of a wing. The jungle rang with these forest voices.

At dusk, in the light of myriads of fireflies, their tiny blue and yellow glow lamps burning with puzzling inconstancy, the explorers stumbled into the center of a clearing. In it was a gigantic palm-thatched open house, a *yaa* of the Colorados. Here, it was announced by the oldest Indian, who grinned at them through stained teeth, they would spend the night, and begin the climb of the Andes at dawn on the morrow.

An entire family of Colorados, two or three women (for the tribes were polygamous), a husband, his children of all ages, lived within this dwelling. The first part of the *yaa* was open, the second section closed. A fire, the traditional three-logged fire, was burning in the center. Although it was cold and damp, the people seemed to cover themselves only with light cotton coverings, which were made on the simple loom at which one of the women worked throughout the evening. Around the clearing were planted bananas, a trefoil-leaf-shaped plant called *yuca,* some chili peppers, and pineapples.

Spread as if by some subhuman sense, the Colorados received word of the arrival of Maldonado and La Condamine and they poured into the house throughout the early night. All were dressed alike. A skirt with broad bright stripes of red and black was caught about the waist with a reddened sash and fell to just above the knees. All had the same reddened hair with the coiffure arranged so that it fell down over the eyes. Large silver bracelets were on their wrists, and, most curiously, in the tip of the nose was inserted a short wooden plug. The nose had been perforated for the inclusion of a singular silver ornament which some were wearing. All were friendly and curious. Since he could not speak with them save through gestures, La Condamine looked on and wondered. The houses of the Indians, he learned through Pedro Maldonado, were never put close together; each one was at least half a league from the next. There seemed to be no chieftain in the tribe; the father of each *yaa* was the master of the fate of his household. Yet all the people spoke the same language, had the same customs, and were friendly and co-operative with the others.

La Condamine slept the sleep of the exhausted and rose at dawn. The new day was but a thin solution of the night. The fog was as opaque as the *garúa* that had covered their ship on its downward passage from Panama. The Indians fed them boiled bananas and grilled agouti flesh, and gave them copious draughts of a drink called *malakchisa;* they then set off with them into the jungle.

Henceforth the road ascended. The world ended and began in rain. Rain fell regularly and unremittingly, usurping the sun's place as the measurer of time. Above it was green, below it was black in the thick mucky sediment of jungle loam. Ceiba, cedar, and walnut trees towered above the rest, their roots awash in the black earth. Little sun penetrated the dense forest; mud and fallen trees in succession macadamized the trail except where a strong running brook crossed it and converted it into a quagmire. As the road grew precipitous, it became, at best, a gully worn by the passage of men and beasts. Where it was level, it was worn by the equable step of mules into deep transverse ridges called *camellones,* after their vague resemblance to the humps on a camel's back.

The explorers advanced, slipped, fell back, rose again, and dug their feet deeper into the loam of the jungle. At night they slept in hastily erected ranchos, shelters of *bijao* leaves woven into a sort of lean-to. In the morning they drank of the thick yuca gruel the Indians had brought, and set off for another day of rain and mud. Drenched and miserable, hungry and exhausted, La Condamine's only solace was that he had protected his Hadley octant and other instruments in the rubber cloth he had found at Esmeraldas.

On the third day of climbing they stumbled into the Tambo de la Virgen. Not long after them the faithful Colorados trudged in, the red dye washed from their bodies by the rain. They dropped their cargo and stood around the fire for only a brief moment, their teeth chattering with cold at the 3,000-foot altitude. This was not their world. They were worried and ill at ease. Pedro Maldonado, sensing this, went to his stores and returned with gunpowder, needles, shot, and a long machete for the leader of the group. Pleased that they had been paid at all for the difficult journey, they seized the hands of La Condamine and Maldonado, pumped them up and down in farewell, and ran out of the house in a sort of dog-trot.

The Tambo de la Virgen had been erected by Pedro Maldonado as a halfway station between Puerto de Quito on the Esmeraldas and the village of Mindo in the cordilleras. Its single grass-thatched house was occupied by a family of sierra Indians. They lived as Charles-Marie imagined troglodytes once lived. The yard was a sea of mud and manure in which naked children and pigs alike sported. The dwelling had but a single room, occupied by the whole family, which bred like lemmings. It was a horrible hole without window or fire, dark, dirty, and damp. The food that they were given was an unpalatable potato soup called *locro,* whose one and only virtue was that it was hot.

As soon as they had dried their clothes they were off once more on the road to Mindo. They were above the dense jungles now. At this 3,000-foot level the verdure had begun to change. Gone were the thick matted forests and tightly laced lianas. La Condamine could already trace the different isometrical zones by the change from the lowland jungles to the subtropical zones. He did not need his thermometer to tell of the drop in temperature, for he could see how the laws of decrease of heat were plainly written on the slopes of the cordilleras. On the hot, steaming plains there were bananas and palms; as they rose, these thinned out and tree ferns took their place; losing these as they mounted in fog and rain and oozing mud, they found the cinchona trees, bedewed by the cool clouds of the *garúa.* Trees became smaller and lost their tall straight trunks, becoming twisted and gnarled. Then shrubby plants appeared, sprinkled here and there with red and purple gentians and geraniums. There were stunted trees covered with thick moss which waved in the breeze like great patriarchal beards. More and more the alpine flora replaced that of the tropic jungle.

The skies were gray, the fog swept by in successive blankets of opaque whiteness, permitting them to see only the vague, blurred silhouette of the Andes, the great cordilleras that La Condamine had come so far to measure. Where the earth was cleared of its dwarfed plants, it was rich and black. In the clearings the mountain Indians had planted corn, beans, potatoes, and sugar cane in light green masses. But these people were not the free-laughing denizens of the jungles. The sierra folk were taciturn and melancholy. Their faces seemed to be hidden by a mask, and the bronze visages that held their jet-black eyes were as lifeless as those of a dead fish. Their homes, called *huasipongos,* were made of adobe, sun-baked earth, roofed with thick grass. Inside, the houses were dark and filthy. Charles-Marie learned to avoid them. Death lurked there, the unseen death of fevers and plagues. They were glad to be off, glad to be beyond Mindo on the way to Nona, in the high cordilleras, away from the stench of the village into the raw cool countryside.

At Pedro Maldonado's insistence, Charles-Marie had assumed the dress of the mountain people. He wore the light straw hat of the country, his stockings, now in tatters, had been traded for a pair of woolen pants, and his great gray coat, now out of character, was replaced by a poncho, a llama-wool blanket which had been split in the center and passed over his head. At first he tripped over it; then he learned to gather it up as he scrambled over rock and earth clusters.

Charles-Marie found it difficult to keep pace with Maldonado, who had been reared in these heights. He found a good excuse to stop frequently to take measurements. On June 4, near Nona, the liquid in his apparatus showed an altitude of 4,000 meters, (12,000 feet) I He had never been so high in his life. His head rang, his ears buzzed, and his heart now was beating as if it would tear itself from its moorings.

They were now higher than the line of vegetation. The land was as a desert with titanic rolling rondures, broken with deep chasms. Except for thick tufts of ichu grass, the woolly leaves of frailejon, and the prickly arms of cacti, the land was naked. It was freezing.

After they had passed over the crest of the Andes they came into well-traveled lanes and acquired horses. For the rest of their way the land was a checkerboard of neatly laid-out farms, separated one from another by gray-green thick-stemmed prickly *cabullas.*

Near Quito the fog lifted, and before them in clear majestic grandeur were the peaks of the Andes. It was, Charles-Marie vowed to all the saints, the most imposing and magnificent spectacle in the whole world. For they could see fifteen snow-covered volcanoes rising from the gray-green of the Andean world. There before them was the peak of Imbabura, then Cotacachi, the grand Cayambi, rising above a small village at its base, and so down the line past Altar and Corazón and Cotopaxi to the greatest of them all, the sky-piercing Chimborazo.

In the valley of Añaquito, sandwiched between the volcanoes of Pichincha and Cotopaxi, was a great swath of green earth, and here he could see, in the blue haze that still enveloped the Andes, rows of houses, the pinnacles of churches, and the massive white structures of convents. The city seemed to nestle in the very arms of the belching volcanoes. This was Quito, ancient citadel of an ancient people.

Here in this high valley was the home of the Indian of the Andes. Here he had lived for centuries, forming himself into great tribal kingdoms that were divided into *ayllus,* self-contained territories. Here he grazed his communal flocks on the long ichu grass, strange animals like the llama, guanaco, and alpaca, all tamed from the wild creatures of the mountain. Here in this small parcel of communal land he raised corn, cassava, calabash, potatoes, camotes, and oca. Here he worshipped the sun-god and built gigantic sundials. Across the chasms of the Andes he built roads. He manufactured subtle clay pottery and devised cyclopean fortifications.

By the year 1450 the Incas of Peru had developed, then knit together, all the Andes from Chile to Colombia in one great, complex kingdom, an empire whose heart was Cuzco. In 1535 Europe was upon them, Europe in the person of Francisco Pizarro and his one hundred and eighty lustful, gold-loving, devoutly Catholic conquistadores from Spain. Besieged by horse and ordnance, the Inca empire dropped apart. Within seven years the conquistadores had destroyed the Peruvian armies, conquered the country, garroted the Inca, wiped out the Indian plan of communal *ayllus,* and rebuilt their ancient cities. Colonists replaced conquistadores. Time rolled on and the conquest of the great Andean empire was complete.

Such thoughts as these must have been in La Condamine's mind as he gazed down upon the city of Quito. Maldonado looked upon Quito in utter ecstasy, his eyes as reverent as those of a Moslem on his first sight of Mecca, or those of the Peruvian Indian as he looked at Cuzco, heart of the old Incan empire. After a year of travel Charles-Marie looked at long last upon the city on top of the Andes which was to be the scene of his labors. He allowed his eyes to follow the lovely green contours of the valley, and he heard, as in a dream, Pedro Vicente Maldonado saying softly:

"There it lies, Charles-Marie — there is Quito."

CHAPTER V
The Conquest of the Heights

THE INHABITANTS of Quito turned out in a magnificent welcome to the "measurers of the arc." Church bells were rung; *cholo* children, dressed in gaudy blue tunics, guided by their keepers, the Dominicanos, waved bright-colored flags; Indians danced and played panpipes, and a whole retinue of the *"muy altos"* of Quito rode out to meet the Academicians on their arrival from Guayaquil. At the head of the welcoming party was the President of the Audiencia, Don Dionisio de Alcedo y Herrera, a most cultured and diligent administrator, along with many other *"personas distinguidas."*

The expeditionists were completely taken aback by this welcome; they knew it was a compliment far above their rank. Yet such was the extravagant sentiment in this strange Andean world where every white man was a *caballero,* every instrumental concert an *opera,* every man with the elements of education a *savant,* everyone showing devotion an *angel.*

The earth-measurers were provided with apartments in the Palacio of the Audiencia, where they were entertained, as Don Jorge Juan noted, "for the first three days with great splendor, during which we were visited by the Bishop, the oidores, the regidores, the canons, and all other persons of distinction, who seemed to vie with each other in their civilities toward us."

No one seemed to know why this delirious welcome was extended to a group of scientists whose objectives could not be plumbed even by the most advanced citizen of Quito. Enough that they were fresh from Europe; enough that they carried a letter from His Catholic Majesty the King. No one in living memory could recall a time when there was such a round of merry-making, such festivities. The city had not known such excitement since 1546 when the first white women arrived in Quito.

The munificence of the inhabitants, the solidity of the architecture, the superb churches utterly astonished the Academicians, who had no idea that such a place would be found in the remote Andes. It was the largest and most beautiful city they had seen since they left France. There were receptions and dances, at which the men, being young and late from Paris, excelled. Couplet was never nearer to heaven in his life than when he was permitted to show the latest steps to the young Quiteñas. In a letter to his mother he wrote ecstatically:

"Every part of the dress of the women of Quito is covered with lace. . . . Their hair is made up in tresses, which they form into a sort of cross on the nape of the neck; they tie a rich riband, called a *balaca,* twice around their heads — with the ends forming a kind of rose at their temples. . . . The people are very charming. . . . We live in the Presidential palace at the Plaza. . . ."

"At the Plaza" — it became a new word to the Frenchmen and with a new meaning, for the Plaza was the heart of Quito. It was an enormous square in which there was a garden, tastefully planted with tall palm trees, and around it were grouped all the elements of the Audiencia — the religious, administrative, and commercial edifices which housed the organizations that kept the wheels of empire turning.

Created an Audiencia by Philip II in 1563, San Francisco de Quito was, as were most South American cities, subservient to Lima, the seat of the Viceroy. In 1736 it had a population of about 35,000 souls, who were, as Antonio de Ulloa suggested, divided into "four classes." The Spaniards numbered about 6,000 which was one sixth of the whole. The mixed bloods (called *cholos*) were one third of the entire population; the pure Indians formed another third, and the Negroes the remaining sixth. Dress was by rank and color. A gentleman dressed much like one in Spain, in a black cloak reaching down to his knees, tight-fitting knee-breeches of the period, silk stockings, and a dress sword. The cholos in general wore the "blue-cloth" of Quito, and though "the lowest class of Spaniard, they were very ambitious, distinguishing themselves from them either by the color or fashion of their clothes." The Indians, who formed the bulk of the population of the whole country, dressed like most South American Indians of Quechua stock, in white cotton drawers which came down to the calf of the leg, while a shirt "in the form of a sack with three openings, covers their naked bodies down to the knees."

The streets beyond the Plaza Mayor were ill-paved or not paved at all. Not far from the Plaza began what Ulloa called the "troublesome declivities." Persons of rank, denied the use of carriages because of the rough cobblestone streets, had to distinguish themselves by having an Indian carry an elaborate parasol over their heads.

The Indians, the travelers soon found, were little more than animated automatons; at worst slaves, at best dray-animals. Their treatment very much preoccupied the Spanish contingent, Jorge

Juan y Santacilla and Antonio de Ulloa. They had been sent along not only to assist the French expedition and keep an eye on its activities, but also to write a confidential report on the administration of the colonies. Here in Quito was laid the basis of that famous report called *Noticias Secretas de América*. Its pages brought the King unimpeachable evidence of the misery which the Indians suffered at the hands of the officials and of the clergy.

The policy of colonial goverment was, in its intentions, as enlightened as any known in Europe, but the governmental mechanism was cumbersome. The Council of the Indies, which ruled America, was too far from its subjects to be aware of conditions, and distance and geography intervened, as Means remarked, "like an invisible but impenetrable wall between the Crown's functionaries and its subjects." Don Jorge Juan found that the Corregidores used every possible stratagem to wring money from the Indians. If the Indians were absent from their homes at the time of taxation, they had to pay double indemnity. So long as they gave their taxes in the form of the usufruct of their lands, as in the times of their Inca, life was not too oppressive. But when the Viceroy insisted that they pay tribute in gold, "the money-complex was," as Means wrote, "introduced to a people entirely devoid of pecuniary behavior."

Indians who were weavers were locked in the cloth factories of Quito at dawn, with a task of so many yards to weave that day. At midday the doors were opened to allow their wives to bring them food; then they were locked in again to work until darkness stole over the earth. If their task was not finished, Juan and Ulloa noted, they were "punished with greater indignity than could be practiced toward the most delinquent slaves." * Forced labor, enforced taxes, ruinous working hours, high prices, all contrary to the Laws of the Indies, were taking their toll. The Council in Spain was warned, and the warning passed unheeded. A lack of courage within the King's Council prevented it from anticipating the eventual Indian revolt led by Tupac Amaru within fifty years of these *Noticias Secretas*.

So already the Spanish contingent was dipping behind the façade of colonial Spain and finding that the magnificent exterior hid many lamentable and sordid bits of social masonry. All that they observed, all that they heard and dug out, these young men of Spain put into their truly encyclopedic notebooks. History, geography, natural history, the caste of society, rituals, customs, all that was very quaint or very ridiculous, diseases, pharmacopœia, industries, systems of construction, methods of planting, the

---

* *Noticias Secretas de América*, p. 276.

manner of coastal seamanship . . . nothing escaped the intelligent curiosity of these young Spaniards. It was the most complete picture that Spain ever had of its colonies. But all these observations did not come upon Juan and Ulloa at once; they were accretions over a long period of time. For the moment they were enjoying, as were all the Frenchmen, the glory of this ancient Andean city.

After three days of festivals the "honeymoon" period of the Academicians was over. The people of Quito, having now seen these strange beings called "natural philosophers," henceforth spent their time trying to find out the *real* reason why they had come to the ends of the earth.

"A few of the first days after our arrival," writes Don Jorge Juan, "were spent in making proper returns for the civilities we had received from all persons of rank. . . . We began to deliberate on the best methods of performing our work . . . during which time Charles-Marie de La Condamine had arrived on the 4th of June by way of Esmeraldas — and Pierre Bouguer six days later."

"To deliberate on the best methods" took no little time. For, as the Academicians saw with awe the giant snow-capped volcanoes, the earth cut by deep fissures, they wondered where and how they would begin. To initiate the work, they had first to measure an exact base with a six-foot iron bar called a *toise*. Such a base line, on which all the other triangles would be predicated, had to be of the greatest exactitude. Now, where in this perpendicular land could they find a stretch of land reasonably level for the distance required?

Meanwhile a second expedition of the Académie des Sciences, under Maupertuis, had departed from Paris for the Gulf of Bothnia to carry out the measurements of the two degrees of the meridian. Just about the time that Maupertuis and his group, in July 1736, were making their way through the ice-studded fjords on the way to Lapland, the expedition at the equator was moving on to its objective. Pedro Maldonado had found a locality near by, on the plains of Yarqui, four leagues northeast of Quito. There, between the villages of Caraburo and Ayambaro, they could lay down their base line.

So at last they were to begin the work of determining the shape of the earth. There were more fiestas to give the "earth-measurers" a proper farewell. It was all very merry. Then, on their way to the plains of Yarqui, young Couplet suddenly fell violently ill. He insisted upon going on when it was obvious to all, especially to Pedro Maldonado, that Couplet had the *paludismo*. On the 17th of September he collapsed. The fever, doubtless malaria, had completely consumed him and left him pallid and wasted. Dr. Jean Senièrgues, the expedition's physician, tried bloodletting and some other simple remedies by which the man of the eighteenth century cajoled himself to health or death. But Couplet grew too weak to respond, and died without ever gaining consciousness. It was a deep blow to all, especially to La Condamine, in whose care the Treasurer of the Académie had placed his nephew's safety. After having observed the funeral decencies toward the remains of Couplet, the "earth-measurers" turned toward their work.

They had first to map the land over which they were to lay their path of triangles. This occupied them for some months. Captain Verguin of the Navy, with Jean Godin des Odonais as his chain-bearer, began to map the vicinity of Quito. Pierre Bouguer, with Morainville, the naval draftsman, went north of the equator to undertake the cartographic operation there.

La Condamine, Maldonado, Juan, and Ulloa fell to measuring the base-line on the high cold plains of Yarqui. As most of the land was sterile and desertlike, the heat during the day was almost unbearable, even though they were at 8,000 feet of altitude. At night the temperature dropped to freezing, with cold winds sweeping down from the snow-capped volcanoes that surrounded them. The explorers, unused to such violent changes, were laid low one after another. One Indian became ill and died, and this caused the remaining helpers to decamp, leaving the gentlemen for a time without a single servant. Louis Godin, the astronomer of the expedition, was constantly ill; Pierre Bouguer was in a pique and knew no restraint; M. Hugot, the instrument-maker, complained of the cold and the return of his Parisian chilblains. Only La Condamine and Maldonado possessed the fortitude, buttressed with unquenchable enthusiasm, to keep the men at work.

Suspicion, too, was in the air. When members of the *Consejo de Quito* journeyed out to see what these Academicians were doing, they were amazed at what they found. Some of the expeditionists were measuring the earth with theodolites and taking the transit of the stars with Hadley's octant. Others were walking across the scarred face of the Andean earth with the iron *toise*. The treasure-obsessed Quiteños took this for a divining rod for locating buried Inca gold. Aroused, believing that the Frenchmen were looking for buried riches, they carried their suspicions back to the President of the Audiencia.

Unfortunately for the Academicians, the learned Alcedo y Herrera no longer held this office. He had resigned his post and gone off to Cartagena, and in his stead was one Don José de Aruajo y

[47]

Río, a swollen, bigoted official whose knowledge of the realm that he governed was limited to a stroll in the Plaza. Aruajo y Río began to make difficulties. He interrupted the men in their work, he kept inspectors on the field, he questioned the servants. The situation grew intolerable. The Academicians decided that Don Jorge Juan and La Condamine should go to Lima, to the Viceroy, and place the matter before him. La Condamine also wanted to arrange for the finances of the expedition through his letters of credit. So they now had to take a thousand-mile journey down the Andes, by horse, by foot, and by palanquin, to plead with the Viceroy for his support. But La Condamine thus saw more of the country than had been originally planned.

Such interruptions were incidental to measuring the shape of the earth.

CHAPTER VI
Death and Triangulation

AFTER EIGHT MONTHS' ABSENCE in July 1737 Don Jorge
Juan and La Condamine returned to the plains of Yarqui. They
had accomplished their purpose. La Condamine's purse was swollen from his monetary transactions, and Jorge Juan carried a letter from the Viceroy to the President of the Audiencia which
ordered that the "natural philosophers" be permitted to carry on
their work uninterrupted. In their absence the others had completed the measuring of the base line. They were now ready to
undertake the next phase of the work. They would have to carry
a chain of triangles from the two ends of the five-mile-long base
line to the north beyond the town of Ibarra, and to the south
toward Cuenca. The triangles would cover more than three degrees of latitude, a distance of 200 miles.*

Now they had to become mountain-climbers. The party was
split into two groups. Louis Godin directed one company, with
Lieutenant Verguin of the Navy and Morainville, the draftsman.
They were to climb the mountain of Pambamarca, to the east of
the base line. The other party, of La Condamine, Pedro Maldonado, and Antonio de Ulloa, was to climb the volcano of Pichincha, which dominated the Valley of Añaquito. They were to exchange signals from their respective peaks fifteen miles apart, and
from their simultaneous observations the triangles of the series
were to be laid down. Thus began the work that was to take years
to complete.

They scaled Pichincha, and for twenty-three days they lived on
top of the 16,000-foot volcano that had brought so much destruction to Quito. At night the thermometer dropped to freezing; in
the day the sun baked the volcano until they had to shed most of
their clothing. Where the gray pumice-lava did not break from
the ground, Pichincha was covered with tough, tall ichu grass;
gray-green lichens covered the rocks. Snow-beds lay in the volcano
fissures. It was a place to have inspired Dante. From it they could
look down on the city of Quito, 7,000 feet below. Like Thor, they
were above the lightning, the thunder, and the rain that drenched

* Technical discussions of this work are to be found in La Condamine's
works: (1) *Mesure des trois premiers degrés du méridien* (Paris, 1751); (2)
Histoire des pyramides de Quito (Paris, 1751); (3) *Journal du voyage par
ordre du roi a l'équateur* (Paris, 1751).

the valley. Every day at a prearranged time they tried to pick up the signal of the other party on the height of Pambamarca. But most of the time drifting fog banks intervened. Their food consisted of rice and fowl, brought to them from below by a daily concourse of Indians. And even these people, although paid four times as much as they would have got below, would not remain. At last they made their observations and passed on to the next objective.

The difficulties continued, from mountain to mountain, desert to desert. They climbed the plains of Changalli. They scaled the sides of the giant Fujiyama-shaped Cotopaxi just at the time it was shooting flames 2,000 feet into the air. Mountain after mountain they climbed in the thin air, across the earth pocked with the ravages of earthquakes. Blasted by winds, beaten by hail, the Frenchmen wandered from one frigid mountain station to another. The animals, the landscape, the small mice, the llamas, the bears, even the Indians, had the same gray color as the landscape. Over this wild topography, scarred by gaping craters and abysmal *quebradas,* the intrepid Frenchmen dragged their chains, their theodolites, their barometers and measuring rods.

For two years, from June 1737 to June 1739, they carried on triangulation work, through illness, desertion, and ceaseless bickering, until their triangles brought them to the town of Cuenca, nearly three degrees south of the equator.

Two years of work on this moonscape! There was scarcely a part of the whole Ecuadorian Andes that they had not traversed, measured, drawn, and mapped. Scarcely a point where they had not made experiments with Réaumur's thermometers and worked on the declination and dipping of the magnetic needle, on the swiftness of sound, on Newtonian attraction, on the length of the beat of Huygens's pendulum at different heights from the sea. Now at last, four years after leaving Paris, they laid down the chain of triangles from which they could deduce mathematically the shape of the earth. To them would come the honor of being the first. . . .

Then came a letter from the Secretary of the Académie des Sciences, M. de Fontenelle. He begged to inform them that the expedition to Lapland under M. Maupertuis, along with Clairault, Camus, Lemonnier, and the Swedish savant Celsius, had completed its mission and had returned, after eighteen months, with the measurements of an arc of 57' amplitude. They had found that the world was actually an oblate spheroid as Isaac Newton had suggested. Voltaire was right when he shouted and roared: "They have flattened the earth as well as the Cassinis."

A terrific disappointment. To have gone through all these physical difficulties for four years, and now to find that Maupertuis had already confirmed Newton's hypothesis! Some wanted to stop then and there. Louis Godin was offered a post at the University of San Marcos in Lima; Hugot had married and wanted to settle in Quito; but La Condamine held them together with a spirited discourse on the glory of science.

How quickly the time passed! There was no way to mark its passage. Each day was like yesterday. Yesterday was duplicated by every other yesterday. Here the world is in perpetual equinox, seasonal change is insignificant, and one does not count the days. It was already June 1739, and they were just now laying down the last of the triangles, the line of which was fixed to the tower of the Cathedral in the little town of Cuenca, 200 miles south of Quito.

By this time suspicion toward the Frenchmen and their motives was the common talk of the whole of the Audiencia. At first it was a mere breath skimming the ground like a swallow; then rumor went from mouth to mouth. Calumny stood upright, rearing its head, hissing, swelling and growing visibly. These men were looking for the treasures of the Inca, they were making maps of the country to furnish to the English. Everyone felt the hostility, even the Spanish contingent. Wrote Antonio de Ulloa:

"Some people here admire our resolution. Others cannot tell what construction to put upon our perseverance. Even those of the best parts and education among them are utterly at a loss what to think. They make it their business to examine our Indian servants concerning the life we lead when we are in the high Andes. And the answers they receive from the Indians only tend to increase their doubts and astonishment. The serenity in which we live on high mountains swept by wind and hail . . . the tranquillity and constancy in which we pass from one scene of desolate solitude to another only feed their suspicions. . . . Some consider us little better than lunatics. Others impute our whole proceedings to the fact that we are endeavoring to discover some rich minerals or buried treasure. . . . When we inform them of the real motive of the expedition it causes much astonishment. Their ignorance of its importance would not suffer them to give credit to what we said. . . ."

At first the explorers thought the people of the Audiencia excessively simple. Then, as the hostility grew and the suspicion became annoying, they grew angry over it. But no one thought that all this would lead to death.

The earth-measurers, resting from the vigors of their last stay upon the wind-swept paramo of Azuay, took a house in Cuenca. All of them occupied the same apartment. Lower in altitude than

Quito, Cuenca was then a city of 20,000 inhabitants, mostly Indian, with some cholos and a sprinkling of whites. Typical of the Andean cities of colonial times (and almost equally so today) the Frenchmen found the city "classed among those of the fourth order . . . its streets straight and of a convenient breadth, the houses of unburnt brick tile . . . and mostly of one story."

Cuenca was ancient. It was long the province of a great tribe of Indians called the Cañari, the buffer state between the encroaching Inca legions of Tupac Yupanqui and the empire of the Quitus farther north. For a century the Inca's legions hurled themselves against the wall of resistance offered by the Cañaris. At last, in 1425, they were overrun and "to do the Cañaris special honor, and also to strengthen his hold upon their country and to cause his renown to spread throughout these regions, the Inca Tupac Yupanqui caused to be built remarkable roads provided with inns, storehouses (*tambos*), post-runners and for his own convenience, the Inca erected sumptuous palaces, as well as strong fortresses and imposing sun-temples." *

On the outskirts of Cuenca was the great citadel of Tumipampa. When the conquistadores took over in 1571, it was promptly leveled, and its well-chiseled gray slabs were used to build the edifices of the Spaniard.

Cuenca, the second city of the Audiencia, was also one of its most isolated. Roads were poor, commerce was trifling in comparison with that of other cities of its size. Its society was personal in the extreme; everyone made it a point to know all about everyone else. Jorge Juan found the people "differing somewhat in their genius and manner from those of Quito; particularly in the most shameful indolence, which seems natural to them so that they have a strange aversion to all kinds of work. The vulgar are also rude, vindictive, and, in short, wicked in every sense."

Could this have been the reason behind the death of Dr. Jean Senièrgues? Now, while the expedition rested in the environs of Cuenca, *M. le docteur* began to give free medical treatment to such as applied to him. Among his patients were members of the Quesada family, an old family dating from the conquest, a family enhanced by a very spirited, fine-looking daughter, aged twenty, named Manuela. She had been engaged to Diego de León, a handsome guitar-strumming Cuencaño, but some time during the romance he had abandoned her and married, instead, the daughter of the Alcalde.

For Cuenca this was a scandal of the first magnitude. The town

---

* Philip Ainsworth Means: *Ancient Civilization of the Andes* (New York, 1931), p. 268.

was small, talk was the life-blood of the city, and Manuela was exposed to the clacking tongues of the gossips. The Quesada family sought *M. le docteur's* advice on the affair. He, as a man of the world and a Parisian, would be of assistance to them in their disgrace. So Senièrgues offered to carry to Diego de León a not too delicate proposal that he settle a sum of money on Manuela, since none now would marry her. The Frenchman carried out this mission, obtained Diego's promise of a settlement, and thought that so far as he was concerned *l'affaire Manuela* was at an end. But Don Diego was deeply insulted, his honor sullied. He refused to keep his promise and no settlement was forthcoming. Soon it was bandied about the cobblestone streets of Cuenca that Diego considered himself released from all obligations, because Dr. Senièrgues was now so intimate with Manuela that this gave the lie to her plea that no man would have her. When this came to the ears of the doctor his rage was uncontrollable. He met Diego de León on a narrow street and challenged him to a duel forthwith. Diego suggested pistols, Dr. Senièrgues swords. Getting nowhere even in this impasse of unrequited honor, the Frenchman, whose anger was now beyond all bounds, unsheathed his sword and lunged at Diego. But he caught his foot on the cobblestones, missed his mark, and fell headlong into the street. People surged up to disarm them and the whole populace became aroused. The likable Senièrgues fell into disgrace, and with him the whole company of earth-measurers passed into social limbo.

The Alcalde of Cuenca now fed the flames of the embroglio by bringing into it the authority of his good friend the Grand Vicar, whose "only virtue," remarked La Condamine, "was his indifference to sex." His pastoral letters, read at Mass, were actually polemics against the persons of the Frenchmen. This served to further enrage the popular feelings; all had taken sides in Manuela's affair in an alarming manner.

La Condamine was much agitated. He got Jorge Juan to speak to one of the Jesuits of Cuenca who happened to come from the same province of Valencia as himself. The Jesuit tried reconciliation between the various factions, but he plowed the sea. Matters continued in this state until the 29th of August. On that day the whole town turned out for a bullfight in the main Plaza. Dr. Senièrgues, in brash defiance of a people smoldering with anger, appeared in one of the boxes with Manuela Quesada and her father, a gesture of extreme boldness considering the passions of the city against him. The crowd had no sooner settled itself when a man named Neyra, a friend of Don Diego de León's and master of the bullring, rode up to the Quesada box and flung off some remarks in its direction. Senièrgues rose up and made a reply with so much spirit that Neyra, thinking he was about to be attacked, backed off quickly, to the accompaniment of loud hooting from the crowd, who disliked his lack of bravura.

Thereupon Neyra turned and announced that as his life had been threatened, the bullfight was suspended. The people, deprived of their one favorite sport, were instantly furious, shouted: "Death to the Frenchman!" and flowed onto the field. Things had now taken an ugly turn. Dr. Senièrgues gallantly leaped from the box, pistol in one hand, drawn sword in the other, and faced the crowd. La Condamine, followed by Bouguer, Captain Verguin, and all the others, surged to his rescue, but before they could get to him, the crowd fell upon him with lances, swords, and rocks and stabbed and pelted him to death.

There was much to-do about the affair. La Condamine sent a man off at once to Quito to insist upon the prosecution of those involved. The tumult was so great that the expedition had to be given refuge in one of the monasteries of Cuenca. To top off the tragedy, Joseph de Jussieu, who had collected the plants of the Andes for years, lost his whole collection through the ignorance of his servants. It had represented five years of toil in a region where Dante's Inferno would have seemed like the Elysian fields. Jussieu was so affected by the loss that he became giddy-pated. He never fully reclaimed the use of his senses in his lifetime.

The murder of Senièrgues created diplomatic difficulties. France and Spain were now allies, yet bound only by a tenuous treaty which anything might unhinge. The killing of a Frenchman by a Cuencan mob could do much to harm it, especially as the Alcalde of the city, the Vicar of Quito, and other people of family were involved in it. La Condamine spared no one. He demanded examinations, he named the murderers. There were *declaraciones, extractos, cartas,* and *testigos,* and then finally, after many months, the verdict — *última repuesta.* The courts named Sebastián Serrano, the Alcalde of Cuenca, Diego de León, and Nicolás de Neyra as the murderers. But justice was casual and personal, and the accused were never sentenced. It enraged La Condamine. He pushed matters so far that Pedro Maldonado, who knew the temperament of his people, suggested that his friend desist for his safety's sake. But one of the first books La Condamine published on his return to France was about the murder of their doctor under the title of *Lettre à Madame — sur l'émeute populaire excitée de la ville de Cuenca.*

The death of Senièrgues, and the loss of Jussieu's plants with the consequent unseating of his reason, did not help the progress

of measuring an arc of the meridian. Then, no sooner had these
affairs quieted down, than an envoy of the Viceroy of Peru burst
into Cuenca, looking for the Spanish captains. War had been
declared upon Spain by Great Britain! Vice-Admiral Anson was
on the high seas to attack the Pacific coast of South America. The
Spanish *capitanes* were ordered to come to Lima to look to its
defenses.

The determination of the shape and size of the earth was growing complicated.

CHAPTER VII
Pyramids on the Moon

Two notable wars were fought in South America in the year 1741 — the War of the Pyramids and, as the other was facetiously called, "the War of Jenkins's Ear."

There had been an undeclared war between England and Spain for more than a decade, growing out of England's desire to trade with the colonies and Spain's refusal to allow anything more than the so-called *"navio de permiso,"* the one English ship permitted to call annually at Puerto Bello. There was much smuggling. The Spanish Guardia Costa, when it caught the smugglers, submitted them to the usual routine tortures, lashings, hangings, garrotings, and decapitations. Word of these proceedings was received in England with a crescendo of indignation, yet it did not excite the Commons until the appearance of Jenkins.

Master Mariner Robert Jenkins came back from the Spanish Main minus an ear. The imperialists who wanted a formal declaration of war on Spain had a good exhibit in Mr. Jenkins. They arranged his appearance before Commons, where he displayed a dull red jagged scar where his right ear had once been. He told with lurid details of how it had been pulled from his head by the Guardia Costa who had captured him on a "trading expedition" to South America. He related all the well-known, thrice-told atrocity stories, concluding with his own, dramatically raising before the startled Commons his erstwhile ear suitably preserved in a bottle of yellowish-colored spirits. With a flourish he told how, as they tortured him, the Spaniards shouted: "And we will do the same to your King."

This was the master touch. Feeling ran high. Intelligence was brought before Commons that Spain and France had concluded a definitive treaty; moreover that their combined fleets were at anchor in the harbor of Toulon. Aroused, Commons acted. They declared that Great Britain was at war with Spain, whereupon William Pitt, who had engineered the war, brought out a plan of action based on the famous "Western Design" of Oliver Cromwell. It called for a terrible blow to all the vulnerable points of Spain's colonial empire, so swift and with so crushing a devastation that she could never rise again. England instead of Spain would then dominate the Americas.

Vice-Admiral Vernon, as the plan unraveled, was to sail with a tremendous armada first against Puerto Bello, gain and occupy that port, proceed to Cartagena and take that citadel, and then attack Panama from the Atlantic. Meanwhile another armada under Admiral Anson would sail round Cape Horn, raze Spanish shipping in the Pacific, and simultaneously attack Panama from the west. Anson set out first, but not in secrecy, for Spanish spies in London and Portsmouth were fully informed of his sailing. Word was sent to Spain. Out flew Admiral Pizarro with six ships of the line in pursuit. He followed Anson down the South Atlantic into the cold treacherous waters of the Antarctic, only to be caught in a terrific storm which either sank or disabled the whole defensive expedition of the Spanish. Admiral Anson, too, was not without loss. Some ships foundered; H.M.S. *Wager* was wrecked in Tierra del Fuego. The other ships limped into the Pacific, where they succeeded in capturing the island of Juan Fernandez. There they repaired ship.

Soon the whole Pacific coast knew of the impending attack. Don Jorge Juan and Antonio de Ulloa, called from their earth-measuring tasks, rushed down to Lima to repair the defense of its port, Callao. There they waited for four months. After receiving no other report of action, they left again for Quito to join their French colleagues. Yet no sooner had they gained the eminence of the Ecuadorian cordilleras than Admiral Anson swept down upon the port of Payta, Peru. Surprised by the attack, the Spaniards retreated, attempting to burn what they could not hide. The English "obliged" the Spaniards by putting the torch to the rest of the city. But they found 12,000 doubloons secreted in bales of cotton. They held a few of the city's *"muy altos"* for ransom, but it was plain that they would get no more from this desert port.

The "Western Design" had miscarried. From a prisoner Anson learned that Vernon had attacked Cartagena a few months before and had been overwhelmed by that fort's defense. His assault had been formidable: 50 ships of the line, 135 transports, 2,000 cannon, 28,000 men, greater even than the Invincible Armada. Cartagena had only a few thousand defenders. The hero of the battle had been but half of a man, Don Blas de Leso, the military governor of Cartagena, one-eyed, one-armed, one-legged, who for fifty-six days urged his men on to great feats of heroism. So sure had Admiral Vernon been of victory that he had even minted medals to be worn by his men on the taking of the city. "Spanish pride toppled down by Vernon," read the device. But it was Vernon who was "toppled." He left half his ships, 18,000 dead, and Cromwell's "Western Design" behind and fled to the West Indies. This ended Anson's plan for attack on Panama.

Now the whole Pacific coast was in arms. Juan and Ulloa came down from the Andes again, took charge of the siege forces at Guayaquil, and waited for the British attack that never came. Instead, Anson moved on to Acapulco in Mexico, captured the treasure ships of the Pacific fleet, circumnavigated the globe, and returned to England with £500,000 of loot.

Thus ended the "War of Jenkins's Ear" for the moment. Yet its reverberations continued long afterward in the high mountain fastnesses of the Audiencia de Quito. The threat had been a real one — real enough to wake the colonists from their wonted inaction. But they now saw enemies everywhere! These Frenchmen, for instance. They had been here six years measuring, drawing maps, taking angles, experimenting with strange instruments — what was their purpose? It was rumored that M. Louis Godin sat in a room in Quito going over a sheaf of figures and diagrams. He was supposed to be plotting the shape of the earth; but was this really what he was doing? And M. Pierre Bouguer sat on a mountain north of Quito looking at the stars — what was he doing?

"For what," asked a gentleman of Quito, "could induce gentlemen, well born and of high station, to lead such a dismal life, uncouth and uncomfortable, climbing mountains, passing over celestial deserts, looking at the stars, for any other reason than earthly profit?" All that they were doing was nothing more than a trick, a labyrinthine confusion to throw the people of Quito off the track. Still more suspicious were the actions of Charles-Marie de La Condamine and his friend, Pedro Maldonado. They were building, it was rumored, some sort of pyramid at the points where they had first measured the base line between Caraburo and Ayambara. *Por Dios,* even more! The pyramids were to have a fleur-de-lis at their pinnacle and those were the arms of Louis of France!

So began the War of the Pyramids. The opening shots were fired by Don Jorge Juan as soon as he had returned from Guayaquil. Rumor had already seeped down to that port that La Condamine had erected some pyramids which — well, Don Jorge would see for himself when he returned to the cordilleras. When he did, the War of the Pyramids began. Rumor had for once been correct. While Juan and Ulloa were called away to Lima after the murder of Dr. Senièrgues, La Condamine and Maldonado repaired to Ayambara and Caraburo to erect permanent markers. Charles-Marie had long anticipated that they should do this. The matter had been discussed in the Académie before their departure and it had been decided by the secretariat that "the base line should be marked with monuments of a permanent nature." So

Charles-Marie designed the pyramids. Hugot, when he saw what work their erection would entail, exclaimed for them all:

"Pyramids here? It would be like erecting pyramids on the moon!"

La Condamine set to work. In order to get water to the bare moonscape region of Ayambara, he had to construct a canal two leagues in length. A kiln had to be erected to fire the bricks; the slabs on which the inscription was to be etched had to be raised from quarries in the deep fissures of the Andes. Where the earth had not a proper base, wooden piles had to be forced down. It took months to erect these graceful pyramids at either end of the base line at Ayambara and Caraburo. No sooner was the work finished than the storm broke.

The Spaniards looked at the inscriptions and turned purple with rage. For not only had their names been left out (only the names of La Condamine, Bouguer, and Godin appeared as the measurers of the arc), but there was no credit to His Sovereign Majesty of Spain! Even more reprehensible, each pyramid was decorated at its top with an enormous fleur-de-lis, the coat of arms of the kings of France!

A serious controversy convulsed Quito. Louis Godin suggested compromise; La Condamine, certainly in fault for neither consulting the Spaniards nor including their names, remained adamant. Maldonado, as usual, sided with La Condamine. This was an expression of his contempt for the Spaniards, whom he called *chapetones.*

The antagonism between the European Spaniards and the creoles, though of the same blood, was almost as violent as that between the native racial groups of America. Antonio de Ulloa thought the creole possessed of "excessive vanity and overbearing manners," especially toward the *chapetones* when they first arrived. Penniless and forlorn in the new country, they worked hard, but even when these same people gained, through their industry, their place in the Andean sun, the "low condition in which the creoles first knew them is not wholly effaced from remembrance." These Spaniards then "espouse the cause of their countrymen, the creoles support their side equally vigorously, and thus the seeds of dissension spring up." From the practical side of the argument, the energy of newly arrived Spaniards was such that the creole women preferred to be allied with them rather than those creoles born in the colony. Indolence and sloth, then, were the complaint of the *chapetones* against the creole. But Pedro Maldonado was at pains to point out to the Spaniards, with great sarcasm, that Spain's colonial system reserved everything for the mother country; that it would allow few industries to function in the colonies; that nearly all offices, religious, civil, and military, were given as plums to favorites of the crown. Rarely did a creole arise above the indolence which was the natural outgrowth of such a system. He, Pedro Maldonado, was the exception.

Bitter words were exchanged between these two men of different worlds, Maldonado and Ulloa, and it helped to deepen the now irreparable schism. Louis Godin did his best to make a compromise. There was no doubt La Condamine was wrong in excluding the names of the Spaniards from the tablets that marked the pyramids, but these oversights could be corrected. The War of the Pyramids, however, went on. Juan and Ulloa brought suit against Charles-Marie de La Condamine personally over the wording of the tablets on the pyramids, over their shape and form, over the decorations that appeared upon them. As originally conceived, the pyramids had only a practical purpose; now they had become personal and political. La Condamine was summoned before the Fiscal of Quito. As usual, in all things in the Audiencia, everyone took sides. Since the war with England there had been a recrudescence of chauvinistic feeling; excessive patriotism was the norm of the day. Many who had never cared a fig about the work over which the Frenchmen had expended so much time and so much money were now vitally interested in the outcome of the suit between the Spaniards on one hand and the Frenchmen on the other. In some remote part of the Andes, La Condamine had placed two pyramids bearing French arms, that was all they knew. Did this mean that the King of France laid claim to Quito? La Condamine was now accused not only of omitting the names of Juan and Ulloa, but of conduct that hinged on the heinous offense of *lèse-majesté*!

For the better part of 1741–2 La Condamine defended himself against the suit of the Spaniards. Since he knew that the Fiscal of Quito did not very much care about whether or not the names of the Spaniards were included in the dedicatory tablets, his defense was based first on what offended them most — that is, the fleur-de-lis that adorned the top of the pyramids. So La Condamine pointed out that these were merely the arms of the house of the Bourbons and they could not possibly be derogatory to the dignity of Spain, since both royal families were branches of the same house. These same lilies he had seen on several façades of the churches of Quito. With regard to the names on the inscription, he would be willing not only to place the names of Juan and Ulloa on the slabs, but to place them above the names of the Academicians.

So dragged on the legal proceedings. There were intermittent testimonies, appeals, recesses, dissimulations, indecisions, and procrastinations. Documents rose almost as high as the volcanoes that surrounded Quito. La Condamine flooded Paris with letters and appeals, and these, having wide currency, focused the eyes of many on the problems of colonial Spain.

The expedition now had come to the point of dissolution. M. Louis Godin announced his intention of accepting the position of astronomer to the University of San Marcos in Lima. His work on the expedition had been completed, for his mathematical calculations from the series of triangles showed beyond doubt that the earth-planet bulged at the equator. Meanwhile his cousin Jean Godin des Odonais, whose part in the expedition had been a modest one (that of chain-bearer to the geodesists), was much in love. Every available moment he was free from carrying the measuring chain over the Andes or erecting signals on the hail-pelted mountains, he went to Riobamba. While studying the languages of the natives, he was introduced by Pedro Maldonado, who was a *"natural"* of Riobamba, to Don Pedro Manuel de Grandmaison, a well-placed creole of French extraction. A friend of the Viceroy, he had been made the Corregidor of Otavalo and was doubtless a gentleman of parts. But in the eyes of Jean Godin he had a greater virtue. He was the father of Isabela, an attractive girl of thirteen who had a marvelous facility of tongues: she could speak Spanish, French, and Quechua. At first he was attracted to her because of his interest in language. Then soon, under the gaze of her dark eyes, the only language that interested him was that of love. Although she was only thirteen and he thirty, her father gave his consent, and so, in the little pueblo of Guzmán, near Riobamba, under the frigid canopy of snow-encrusted Chimborazo, Isabela de Grandmaison y Bruno was married to Jean Godin des Odonais, chain-bearer to the Academicians. When the news of the impending marriage reached Quito, the lawsuits were put in abeyance and the whole company of Frenchmen rode down for the wedding. Hugot, the watchmaker, left his own bride in order to attend, for he had set up shop in Quito, deciding to wait there until he could see how the wars then raging between France and England would go. Pierre Bouguer put on his best manners for the wedding. Captain Verguin also came. Even Jussieu and Mabillon, whose minds now wandered unhindered in that Elysian field of the giddy-pated, were there.

What was meant to be a happy time turned out to be tragic, for soon after the ceremonies the enterprising naval draftsman, Morainville, was killed. He had helped design a church near Rio-

bamba. As he was climbing up the scaffolding to work on the façade of the church, the whole thing collapsed and down went
Morainville to perish beneath a pile of rubble and baked Andean
earth.

The death of Morainville caused a severe depression in La Condamine. They had been seven years in the Andes. Couplet was
dead, Senièrgues murdered, Morainville killed, Jussieu and Mabillon crazed beyond repair. Hugot and Jean Godin were married
and Louis Godin had gone off to Peru to take over a post at San
Marcos. The expedition now was virtually disbanded, but there
was still one confirmatory observation to be made. Pierre Bouguer
and La Condamine decided to compose their differences long
enough to effect it before they returned to France. They returned
to Quito to hear the last arguments in the suit over the pyramids
and to prepare for their last astronomical observations.

While in Quito, La Condamine had fixed one of the meridians
of the triangles they had laid down at the foot of the sumptuous
new Cathedral which the Jesuits were building off the Plaza
Mayor. They had permitted him to put an inscription at the base
of its richly decorated rococo façade.

This gave La Condamine active contact with the Jesuits, and
through the efforts of Father Maldonado, the elder brother of
Pedro Maldonado, he gained entrance to their secret archives.
There he saw the original of the first map of the Amazon made by
Padre Samuel Fritz.

This map, with its tangling lines of rivers like a skein of wool
unwound by a kitten, aroused his interest. Although he had been
buffeted by eight years of work and hardship in the Andes, La
Condamine now desired to duplicate the work of Father Fritz. He,
too, would sail down the Amazon! He consulted the map again.
It was most detailed, showing the broad 3,000-mile Amazon coursing down from the Andes, down through the nameless jungles
and myriads of streams to the Atlantic. Many villages had place-
names. There were the names of tribes, of river-courses tolerably
accurate, showing that Padre Fritz had used his twenty years on
the Amazon to the full. Most of the missions of the Upper Amazon
had been under the control of the Jesuits, who operated what was
to all intents and purposes a theocracy among the Indians. Among
these jungle people Padre Fritz had worked. Yet he did not have
modern instruments; he was not a cartographer. Besides that, the
Amazon was an intriguing adventure. No Frenchman had ever
descended it. La Condamine was allowed to copy Padre Fritz's
Journal; he was given a copy of the map, and he carried letters of
introduction to the Jesuits in charge of the missions. Maldonado

The death of Dr. Jean Seniérgues by a mob in the bullring at Cuenca. Dr. Seniérgues, physician to the La Condamine expedition, can be seen beating off the mob that is attacking him. The black-cloaked *policia* in the foreground prevent the other members of the expedition from interfering with the assassins.

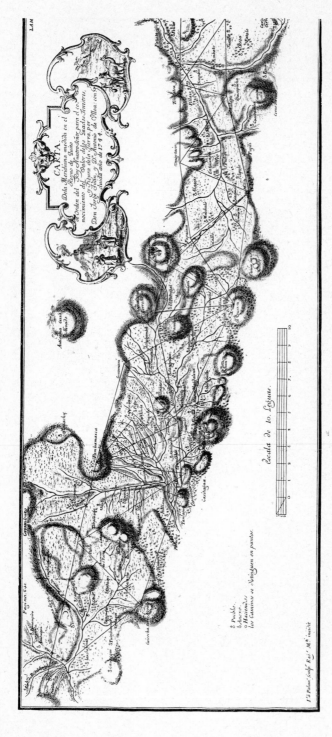

The triangulations to determine the true shape of the earth. This complicated series of triangulations covered over three hundred miles and took the members of the expedition of the Académie des Sciences the better part of nine years (1735–44) to lay down. From these measurements came the proof of the Newtonian hypotheses of the true figure of the earth.

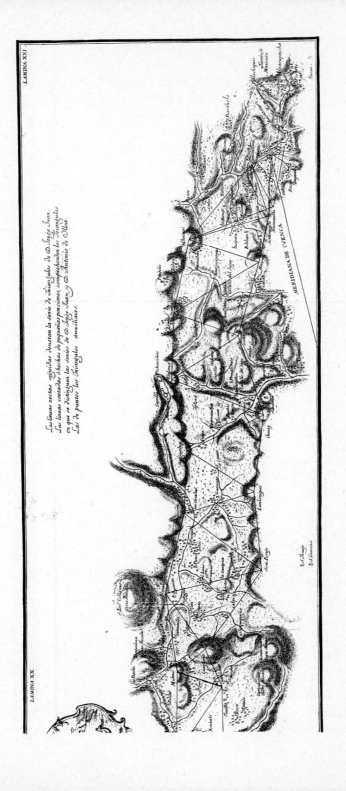

Las lineas rectas seguidas denotan la serie de triangulos de D. Jorje Juan.
Las lineas costeadas ó hechas de pequeñas porciones, comprehenden los triangulos
en que se distinguen las series de D. Jorje Juan, y D. Antonio de Ulloa.
Las de puntos los triangulos auxiliares.

MERIDIANA DE CUENCA

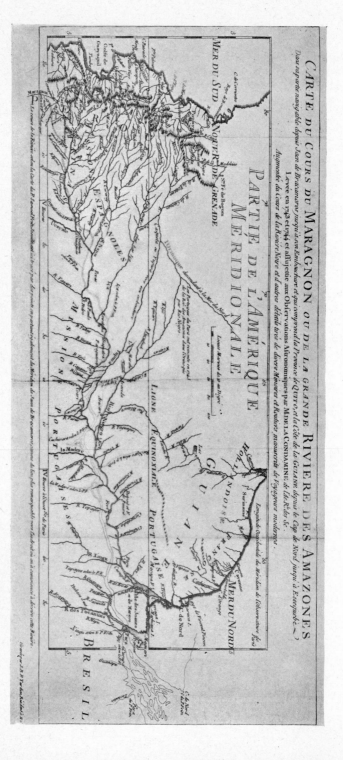

The first scientific chart of the Amazon. It was made by Charles-Marie de La Condamine during his descent of the Amazon (1743–4).

agreed to go with him; they kept spiritual company with Orellana, who two hundred years before had stood on the Amazon and said: "Having eaten our shoes and saddles boiled with a few herbs, we set out to reach the Kingdom of Gold."

As for Pierre Bouguer and Captain Verguin, after the final astronomical work they were to go out by way of the Andean road from Quito to Santa Fé de Bogotá, thence descending the Río Magdalena and ending up in Cartagena, the same city at which they had arrived in 1735.

In 1742 the decision came from the Fiscal of the Audiencia respecting the pyramids, which they had almost forgotten. It had been determined that the names of the Spanish explorers should be inserted and the offending arms of France obliterated from the top of the pyramids, as well as from the stelæ that held the inscription. For La Condamine and Maldonado it was a diplomatic triumph. They had reason to congratulate themselves on the outcome of the suit, but the triumph was shortlived. Six years later the Council of the Indies, dissatisfied with the moderation of the Real Audiencia, ordered the monuments destroyed and completely obliterated. Thus, for a few dubious omissions and commissions, the whole basis of the work was historically removed.*

* The history of the pyramids on the moon went on for another century. The Marquis de la Enseñada, responding to appeals made by La Condamine, rescinded his decision to have them destroyed. He even made up a new inscription to be placed on the pyramids, which read:

"In the reign of H.C.M. Philip V, King of Spain and the Indies, agreeable to the request of H.C.M. Louis XV and in condescension to the Royal Académie des Sciences, Louis Godin, Pierre Bouguer, and Charles Marie de La Condamine, members of the Académie, were by command and munificence of our Most Catholic Sovereign, sent into Peru to measure the terrestrial degrees under the equinoctial in order to obtain a more accurate knowledge of the figure of the earth. Antonio de Ulloa and Jorge Juan, members of the Royal Navy, were sent to accompany the expedition, from the purse of M.C. Philip V. The base line from Yarqui was established at $6,272\frac{551}{726}$ Paris toises in a direction North of L. 25' 30" in the month of November 1736."

But all this was too late; the monuments had already been destroyed.

In 1836 Quito (then the Republic of Ecuador) had them restored under the orders of President Rocafuerte with this inscription: "The French Academicians, Messieurs Louis Godin, Pierre Bouguer, and Charles Marie de la Condamine, sent by Louis XV, King of France, under the Ministry of M. Maurepas, erected these pyramids in the month of November 1736; they were destroyed by command of the King of Spain, and rebuilt one hundred years afterward in November 1836 (on the exact points determined by the French Academicians) by order of his Excellency Vicente Rocafuerte, President of the Republic," etc., etc.

Yet these were pyramids in name only; the structures themselves were all low square piles of bricks, whitewashed and covered with a pyramid roof of

And now, in the hail-driven month of March 1743, the expedition had come to its final chapter. La Condamine paced nervously in front of his tent pitched in a hollow of the treeless paramo at Yarqui, near Cuenca. The time had come for the final astronomical calculations. Jean Godin rode in from Riobamba to keep his friend company on his last frigid mission, to help him to compute the final confirmation of the shape of the earth-planet. Pedro Maldonado had already left on his way down the Amazon, taking the route down the Río Pastaza. Only these two, Godin and La Condamine, remained on the mist-filled Andes waiting for the paramo fog to clear. At last La Condamine's telescope breached the mist and he fixed it on the same star as Pierre Bouguer was doing 200 miles north on the equator. La Condamine's observations had been made; now to await those of Bouguer. Then at last came an Indian *chasqui,* a relay post-runner. La Condamine opened the letter, looked at the figures, and quickly sat down to compare them. In cold, precise language, but scarcely repressible happiness, he entered in his journal:

"The arc has been measured! M. Bouguer at the northern extremity of our meridian had made a series of observations, as had I, two degrees south of the equator. The intermediate between our two zeniths was effected by us both on the same night. By these simultaneous observations, we attained the singular advantage of being able to ascertain precisely and beyond dispute the real amplitude of an arc of the meridian of three degrees. . . ."

"The arc has been measured! . . ." At the end of the work he had at last measured this base of verification and found the length of the arc of direct measurement to have differed from the calculated astronomical length by less than two feet.

"The arc has been measured," and now he was going home, home to Paris by way of the Amazon, descending its full 3,000-mile length. Going home after eight years of incredible labors by way of the most dangerous route in all the world. . . . Jean Godin embraced his friend and wished him Godspeed. He thought, too, to remind him that he would follow him down the Amazon shortly with his wife and to advise the various stations at which he would stop of his coming so that he could be sure of facilities for his wife.

So La Condamine disappeared over the barren, wind-swept Andes of Ecuador, riding beside his two servants with his mules burdened with an eighteen-foot telescope. He avoided Cuenca,

tiles. A picture of the restored "pyramids" was given in 1890 by Edward Whymper in *Travels amongst the Great Andes of the Equator,* p. 292.

since the assassins of Dr. Senièrgues were anxious to meet with him also. He passed Giron, revictualed at Loja, the quinine center, remained there long enough to collect some quinine plants and seeds — for he envisioned planting the trees in France — then descended into the Amazon basin.

La Condamine was about to open the treasure-chest of the world — the Río Amazonas. . . .

CHAPTER VIII
The Dark River of Tragedy

At Borja on the Amazon La Condamine stood on the fringe of a new world. It had taken him four months to come down from his mountain camp at Yarqui, passing around Cuenca, through Giron, over to the mines at Zaruma, and then down the walls of the cordillera to sun-bathed Loja, the realm of the quinine trees. There, procuring guides, he set off by foot, horse, and canoe, down the precipitous sides of the Andes into the Upper Amazon. By June his trek through the dripping verdure of the jungles ended at Borja, a village of leaf huts grouped around a church ornamented by a giant iron cross. The Río Amazonas plunged by its very door. Rivulets coursing down the sides of snow-capped volcanoes, streams gathering moisture-laden fog on their way down the sides of the Andes, poured into and became the swelling mountain-spawned Marañón. Above Borja the Marañón plunged through a break in the Andean way, the Pongo de Menseriche, and with the roar of a Niagara spread out over the flattened land to form the Río Amazonas.

Charles-Marie de La Condamine expanded in this new realm of nature; the unhappy years in the cordilleras, the years of bickering, of herculean tasks of measurements, seemed now of little consequence. He looked over the never ending jungles and wrote: "At Borja I found myself in a new world, separated from all human intercourse, on a fresh-water sea, surrounded by a maze of lakes, rivers, and canals, and penetrating in every direction the gloom of an immense forest. . . . New plants, new animals, and new races of men were exhibited to my view. Accustomed during seven years to mountains lost in clouds, I was rapt in admiration at the wide circle embraced by the eye, restricted here by no other boundary than the horizon. . . ."

At Borja he made contact with a Jesuit to whom he had letters of introduction, who not only arranged canoes for his trip down the Amazon, but agreed to accompany him to the confluence of the Río Huallaga. The priest had spent many years among the Indians and had collected much material; he was so won over by the eager curiosity and the indelible Condaminean enthusiasm that he pressed into Charles-Marie's hands, before they left Borja, a chart upon which were marked the missions of the Spaniards, along with a description of the Indians and their language. Then they stepped into the canoes, paddled by bronzed, naked Indians, and were swept down the Upper Amazon.

A few hundred miles down, they came to the Mission of Nauta on the left bank where the Río Huallaga, a gigantic torrent of water, joins the Amazon. Some leagues up that river was the missionary village of Laguna, and there La Condamine found his good friend "Don Pedro Maldonado, Governor of the Province of Esmeraldas — who had been waiting for me six weeks." La Condamine was deeply attached to Maldonado. He made this most evident by writing: "To this nobleman, as well as to his two brothers and his entire family, I owe a public acknowledgment for all the distinguished civilities our academic detachment experienced at their hands during our long stay in the province of Quito. He, as well as myself, on his passage to Europe, felt disposed to proceed down the river of Amazons and had taken the second of the three routes for descending the Río Pastaza; after many dangers and great fatigue he had been fortunate enough to arrive at Laguna six weeks before me, notwithstanding the period of his departure from Quito, which was nearly the same as that at which I left Cuenca. He had made requisite observations as he traveled along, with a compass and a portable gnomon, and this enabled him to describe the course of the Río Pastaza. . . ."

Together these two scientific explorers, beset by all the dangers, the difficulties, and the thousand and one bedevilments that explorers must face on the Amazon, went down the mighty river. Even then the trip was not as dangerous as it would be a century later. In their time missions were spread along the rivers, the Indians gathered into and about them, and a system of mission hostelries was set up so as to help those who descended the river. Even with all his multitude of interests, La Condamine did not forget to mention at each mission where he stopped that shortly his friend Jean Godin would follow them down with his wife, Isabela.

La Condamine and Maldonado traveled on virgin scientific ground. In the two months that it took them to be swept down to the Atlantic they put every moment to work. They measured the variations of the dimensions of the river, they plumbed its depths, its rate of fall, the swiftness of its current. They corrected the chart of Padre Fritz and made a general map of the Río Amazonas so correct that, in general, it has remained unchanged. Thus La Condamine provided himself, as he remarks, against "the tiresomeness of a weary, though tranquil, voyage through a country in which the continued sameness of objects, however novel in themselves, tended to fatigue rather than please the eye. . . ."

Down, down they went, La Condamine remaining indefatigable. When he found the natives using "leaves or roots which when thrown into water have the faculty of intoxicating fish," he collected the plant and became the European discoverer of *varvascu,* or barbasco, which contains the alkaloid known as rotenone, widely and extensively used as an insecticide. Then he early discovered, like so many other travelers before and since, that most of the Indians used a black resinous poison on the tip of the arrows which they hurled from their blow-guns. "Notwithstanding that we had fowling pieces, we scarcely ever, in going down the river, ate of game killed by other means than these arrows." La Condamine did not take this as just one more insoluble phenomenon. "There is no danger," he goes on, "in eating of the flesh killed by such means — for the venom of this poison is only mortal when absorbed by the blood. The antidote is salt, but of safe dependence — sugar." He had heard this from the Indians, and taking nothing at its face value, he made experiments on the poison and its alleged antidote, sugar. He shot a chicken with an arrow dipped in curare, pulled out the arrow, a few seconds later administered sugar, and the chicken "exhibited no sign of the least inconvenience."

Below a village called Manáos, on the right bank of the Amazon where it is joined by the dark waters of the Río Negro, his interest shifted to another phenomenon. Indians and padres alike told him that that same Río Negro was connected by a canal with the white waters of the Río Orinoco, which flowed through Venezuela. This, if true, was an important geographical phenomenon, since the whole of the Amazon and Orinoco valleys would then be connected by waterways. After talking to Indians who confessed that they had used this mysterious canal and to padres who received them, La Condamine became certain of the connection. "The positive certainty," he wrote, "of an existing communication between the waters of the two rivers . . . is a geographical fact. . . . It has been generally suppressed in those maps by modern geographers as if by common consent, and treated as chimerical by those who were supposed to have the best means of information. . . . Yet where does this communication between the Orinoco and the Amazon take place?" This was to touch off a whole century of exploration. For when La Condamine was to ask this rhetorical question in his discourse before the Académie des Sciences, and it was printed in his *Relation abrégée d'un voyage,* the Spanish government and Brazil contended over the control of this hypothetical canal.

Then, too, La Condamine continued to investigate the rubber

plant. He had first seen rubber growing in the province of Esmeraldas in the Audiencia de Quito, and now he saw the rubber trees along the entire length of the Amazon basin. He marveled at the way "when fresh it could, by means of molds, take any shape given to it, at pleasure." Down the river he gathered the syringes and "pumps which the Indians made of rubber, which among the Omaguas are a very common utensil." These he brought to Europe, along with chunks of coagulated rubber, and so began the history of that product which changed the industry of the world.

By the 19th of September, four months after he had left Cuenca, La Condamine arrived with Maldonado at Pará, the city which was the entrepôt to the Amazon. In a few days a vessel picked them up and they moved northward to the French colony.

After a short stay in Cayenne, where he studied the sea cow, planted the seeds of the quinine he had brought from Loja, and visited the spot where Jean Richer had first made his experiment in 1672 on the inequality of weights under different parallels, La Condamine and Maldonado took passage to Europe by way of Holland. In the spring of 1745 they arrived in Paris, the same Paris from which the Academicians had departed ten years before. There they met Pierre Bouguer and Captain Verguin. La Condamine received a letter from Jean Godin des Odonais written from Cayenne. It said briefly that he had left Riobamba in the Andes in March 1749 and had traveled down the Amazon, and that he had arrived at French Guiana four months later. He thanked him for advising the padres of his coming. He did not go into the suffering of his 3,000-mile trip down the stygian Amazon; he did not have to. La Condamine was thoroughly acquainted with its horrors. The purpose of Godin's voyage was to acquaint himself with all its difficulties and to obtain a vessel so as to ascend the river and to bring down his wife with her retinue of servants.

To people used to living in a country of relative civilization such an action would seem on the point of lunacy, and Jean Godin admitted it in his letter to Charles-Marie:

"Anyone but you, sir, might be surprised at my undertaking thus lightly a voyage of 1,500 leagues for the mere purpose of preparing accommodations for a second, but you will know that travels in South America are undertaken with much less concern than in Europe; and those I had made during the twelve years for reconnoitering the ground for the meridian of Quito, fixing signals on the loftiest mountains, in going and returning from Cartagena, had made me perfectly a veteran."

In his letter to Charles-Marie, Godin enclosed one to M. Rouillé, the Minister of the French Navy, asking that it be delivered as soon as possible. He asked M. Rouillé to assist in sending recommendations to the court at Lisbon so as to "enable me to ascend the Amazon, for the purpose of proceeding to my family and bringing it back with me by the same channel."

La Condamine sought out the Minister at once and delivered the letter, along with an eloquent address on the debt and duty France owed Jean Godin des Odonais for his now fifteen-year sojourn in the Americas. M. Rouillé indicated his intention to be of assistance. At the same time La Condamine also visited Senhor de la Cerda, the Portuguese Minister in France. Thus began one of the strangest odysseys in America's history.

It began in the twilight of M. de La Condamine's life, that period beginning about 1750, an age marked by a violent upsurge in Anglo-French rivalry, the epoch of Voltaire, of Diderot and the Encyclopedists, that age of reason when men grew politically restless, when human suffering laid the preludes to revolution. It was in this age of aristocratic artificiality, when royal mistresses played shepherdesses, when bewigged gentlemen in silken stockings warbled ten-syllabled couplets into the perfumed ears of overdressed ladies, that the haunting tragedy of Mme Godin stalked across the stage of Europe. Her jungle hegira, one of the most remarkable episodes in the whole history of South America, played in its tragic way a superlative part in the opening of that continent. Those who would not read of the War of the Pyramids, of the assassination of Dr. Senièrgues, who died in a Cuenca bullring, or of the "figure of the earth" in elaborate mathematical language, could and did read of the tragic voyage of Mme Godin.

Years passed and still there was no action on Jean Godin's request to the Portuguese and French governments. Believing that he would help himself if he ingratiated himself with his government, Jean Godin began to draft some elaborate speculations on the seizure of the Amazon. These he sent to Choiseul, the Minister of Foreign Affairs, by the hand of a missionary returning to France. In this document Godin des Odonais suggested the manner in which the French, now smarting from defeat in North America, might seize the whole Amazon. He suggested the tactics, how and in what manner a fleet operating from French Guiana could take all the salient points of the Amazon and control it henceforth as a route to the entire South Seas. This was a dangerous document from one wishing the aid of the Portuguese government. It is excusable in Jean Godin only because he saw the great riches of the Amazon lying untouched. He thought them incapable of development in the hands of the Portuguese and Spanish. But that document was to play its part in the tragedy, for Choiseul never acknowledged its receipt and an *idée fixe* settled down upon Godin: he believed it had fallen into the hands of the Portuguese. Impatient of waiting for a vessel to be dispatched to him, he built one himself, but no sooner had he essayed the first leagues of travel than he was overcome by the idea of possible Portuguese treachery. He returned again to Cayenne.

Delay piled on delay. Then, out of the blue of the Atlantic, one day came the rumor that a ship was on its way to him. That rumor took form on the 18th day of October 1765, when a Portuguese galiot arrived at Cayenne, equipped at Pará by order of the King of Portugal, manned with thirty oars, and commanded by a captain of the garrison of Pará. "His instructions were to bring me to Pará, thence transport me up the river as high as the first Spanish settlement to wait until I returned with my family."

For this he had waited fifteen years, a third of his life. He made preparations for the trip, then just as suddenly ceased them — he was overcome with an old suspicion. Was this a trick? Did the Portuguese want to seize him, with his plans for capturing the entire Amazon? He invented all sorts of pretexts for not going. He feigned illness, he invented delays. Still the galiot remained. The captain had a royal command — he was there to see that it was carried out. This very tenacity made Godin the more suspicious. Now the matter grew complicated. Fiedmont, the French colonial Governor, not knowing the reason for Godin's mental aberrations, began to suspect his motives. Abusive letters were exchanged between the two. Finally Fiedmont ordered the Portuguese vessel to sail. Godin had to make up his mind, so he sent in his stead one "Tristan d'Oreasaval, a person whom I had known long and in whom I had confidence."

A packet of letters was to be carried to the Father General of the Jesuits in the province of Quito and to the Superior of the missions of Maynas, who were to equip the canoes for the descent of his wife, Doña Isabela. Tristan was to go directly to the main mission at Las Lagunas. There he was simply to deliver those letters to the head of the mission, who in turn would send them to Riobamba in the cordilleras. Tristan was then to wait at Las Lagunas until he had a direct communication from Mme Godin and then send it down the Amazon to Jean Godin.

So instructed, Tristan d'Oreasaval left for Pará and thence up the Río Amazonas on the Portuguese galiot. It was the year 1766, the same year that Spain was expelling the Jesuit order, and the Spanish were settling California. Jean Godin waited.

Eight months later the galiot had come to Iquitos, the highest point of river transportation. As instructed, Tristan had delivered his letters, but not to the monks at Las Lagunas. Instead he had given them into the hands of a dark-bearded missionary, who delivered them, not to Riobamba, but to Quito. There they passed from monk to monk, who each in turn read them. The letters were never delivered to Mme Godin. Yet gossip, that strangely curious mouth-to-mouth, ear-to-ear, subhuman communication, began to send its news down the Andes. At last it seeped into the little village of Guzmán, near Riobamba, where Isabela de Godin had waited patiently over a span of fifteen years for such a communication.

"Your husband," whispered the rumors, "has dispatched a Portuguese galiot to take you down the Amazon. It lies now at Las Lagunas. I heard it from Señora X, who got it from the curé, who was told by . . ."

Enlivened by this news, Mme Godin sent a servant to Quito to inquire about the letters. The monks professed ignorance of them. It became known that they were lost. But was the vessel there or was it not? Doña Isabela must know, so she sent her servant Joachim (a Negro whom she had purchased from an intolerable slavedom) over the Andes, down the Amazon to Lagunas to see if the rumors that she had heard were true. Joachim came back after two years of travel to announce:

"It is true, *su Merced,* the vessel is there and your husband, although ill, is alive in Cayenne."

That is all Mme Godin needed to set about to prepare for her journey. Twenty years! Even in the Andes there is metamorphosis. When young, Isabela de Godin (née Grandmaison y Bruno) had been a handsome woman with deep brown eyes, an oval face, prominent cheek-bones, laughing lips that gave her face a wildwood, voluptuous expression. Now in 1769, beyond the age of forty, her once voluptuous bosom had lost its appeal, her face, although still young, was matured by the tragedy she had suffered, as well as the strain caused by the separation of more than twenty years from her husband.

Isabela de Godin was a remarkable woman. She had been cloistered all her life in the cold, remote citadel of the Inca and Spaniard. Since Jean Godin had left, all her children — four of them — had died from the repeated scourges of the tropics — malaria, yellow fever, and dysentery. Now in middle age she was called upon to take a journey that no one, even in the fullness and freshness of youth, could look upon except with unmitigated horror, a journey down the whole of the Amazon.

She disposed of her property and put what she did not sell into the hands of her brother. She selected those to accompany her, arranged the recitation of prayers for the repose of her soul, and in October 1769 was ready to leave. As an extra precaution her father, Don Pedro de Grandmaison, decided to precede her to arrange for such comforts as he could devise. Although aged, Don Pedro was a vigorous man; for in this Andean world once one survives the epidemics of typhoid fever, bubonic plague, smallpox, yellow fever, malaria, and dysentery, one becomes practically immortal. Such was Don Pedro. He went through the town of Baños, where he arranged to have a sort of palanquin made so that his daughter could be carried on the shoulders of the Indians, and at points along the trail he arranged for caches of food. This he did until he reached the outpost of God, the mission at Canelos, seven days' journey below Baños. There he arranged with the Dominicans in charge to give all the succor that a woman of family could expect. With the help of the padres he sought out Christianized Jivaro Indians who would be willing to paddle the canoes of Mme Godin's party to the next mission of Andoas, down the Río Pastaza. There other canoes could be produced to go down to Las Lagunas where the Portuguese galiot still swung at anchor.

Convinced that he had anticipated every emergency and had overcome all the forseeable difficulties, Don Pedro and his party obtained canoes and proceeded down the Pastaza 400 miles to Las Lagunas. But before he left, he dispatched a letter to his daughter, who was waiting at Riobamba.

"Hija mía," he wrote, "all is in readiness. Canoes and men to paddle them are waiting at the village of Canelos. The roads are bad. Keep down the amount of baggage and the members of your party. The canoes and space therein are limited."

"Keep down the members of your party." When that message arrived, Mme Godin was hard-pressed. For no sooner had her father left than three Frenchmen who had just arrived from the South Seas heard of her contemplated trip down the Amazon. They came to Riobamba and begged to be allowed to go with her.

Mme Godin was easily led by her heart to have compassion for others. These men (whoever they were, for history tells us little about them other than that they were Frenchmen) gained her sympathy when one of them told her that he was a physician and that he would be able to administer to her during the long, arduous trip. So Mme Godin consented.

The expedition now included her nephew, aged twelve, two

brothers, three chola women servants — Rosa, Elvia, and Heloise — the three "Frenchmen" from the South Seas, the Negro Joachim, and a whole company of Andean Indians. Well equipped, led by guides who knew the roads along the gorges of the Pastaza canyon, they left the cordilleras late in the year 1769.

The seven days of travel from Riobamba to Canelos were, as expected, horrible. The rain was heavy, the mud of the roads seemingly bottomless. The voices of the rain-soaked jungles, the noise of falling branches, the crashing of trees, the swinging crunch of the lianas, the slithering snakes, the cry of the bellbird, the bark of the howling monkey, made an ensemble of jungle noises which added to the fear that already possessed them. Yet they felt that these seven days would be the hardest. Once at Canelos and in canoes, they would sweep along the broad Amazon and be in Las Lagunas by the new moon. But something got to Canelos before them.

Smallpox!

The month previous, when Don Pedro had stopped at Canelos, one of his men — a cholo of the Sierras — was infected with the *viruela*. Among the Indians, with no backfire of resistance, the pox traveled like a forest fire. Within days Canelos was decimated. Those who did not die fled. These Amazon denizens, bedeviled by twin curses, the germ and the gun, knew but a single answer to both — flight. Thus, when the expedition of Mme Godin, mud-splattered and exhausted, stumbled into the mission of Canelos, it came to a village deserted. Where they had expected to be welcomed by both priest and Indian, they were met instead by the invisible specter of death. Houses were still smoldering from fires set by the Indians, who believed that fire would purify the air. Even the large mission was gutted. They set up their camp among the ruins of the mission. That night the whole retinue of mountain Indians deserted.

When courage returned, the men of the party searched the jungle environs for some of the inhabitants of Canelos. A league from the gutted village they found four Indians, and these they brought back to Mme Godin.

Danger had suddenly transformed this small, middle-aged woman into a dynamic soul. She took complete charge of the party. Where the others cringed before the dangers that lay ahead and lamented their fate, she, with an indomitable will, sought a solution to their dilemma. She had no intention of returning to the cordilleras after all these years of waiting. She questioned the Indians in Quechua and learned that they were the only ones left of the village; the others had died or taken to the jungles. She engaged their services, paid them in advance, and then turned to face the next problem. There was only one large canoe and a balsa or raft; they could not take the greater part of the food they had brought. Mme Godin kept her own counsel with a gentle deprecatory obstinacy, holding her lips tightly pressed to keep back the tears that welled in her dark brown eyes, but she had made her decision. The balsa, manned by two of the Indians, held most of the food and equipment; the rest of them crowded into the forty-foot dugout.

The first day was uneventful. The insects bothered them, there were some difficulties with the canoe, as the Frenchmen had little experience in paddling it, but it seemed now that at last they would manage. The first night the Indians suggested spending on the high, verdure-festooned bank, since the Pastaza was too full of debris, rocks, and cascades to travel at night. To this Mme Godin agreed. The next morning the Indians were gone.

Deserted in the Amazon jungles! The Frenchmen were for going back, but Mme Godin reminded them that she had not undertaken all this journey to turn back, and besides, to paddle against an eight-knot current would need the arms of fifty strong men. They were now about five days from the next settlement of Andoas, and Mme Godin suggested that they themselves try to navigate the balsa and canoe. Since it was obviously the only thing left them, they made ready to descend the river.

The Pastaza here was half a mile in width, deep and swift-flowing. Hemmed in between two walls of silent jungle, the river moved along at the rate of five knots. Two factors were needed to descend it successfully — great skill and great luck — and Mme Godin's party had neither. The balsa, guided by the Grandmaison brothers, was first into the river. Once in the current, it was wafted along at the rate of speed of a horse's canter. Pierre, one of the "Frenchmen from the South Seas," suggested himself as pilot for the canoe. In the first hours he sat back on the flattened stern, steering the craft between floating roots and trunks, and whistling at the dolphins as they leaped from the water and broke the still, tropical air. At midday, while most of the others were asleep, a breeze blew his hat off. He reached for it, lost his balance, and fell into the Pastaza. No sooner did he bob to the surface than he was struck on the head by a floating log, and thus Pierre of the yellowish skin was swallowed up in the dark river as if he had fallen through a trapdoor.

Death dogged them the rest of the day. The course of the river became more filled with rapids and more dangerous. They had one narrow escape after another. As the day ended, just when they had decided to put in to the bank for the night, the canoe struck a floating log, dipped its bow into the river, and rolled on its side. All of them were thrown into the stream. Only the fact that they were near the bank saved them.

Joachim, the Negro, kept close to Mme Godin, helped her when she seemed to weaken, brought her to shore, and then saved the others. He even brought back the canoe. On the edge of the forest they built a lean-to and thatched it with strong, tough bijao leaves that grew on the river's bank. There they collected as much of their goods as was not ruined by the water. They had saved little of their food. One of the Grandmaisons shot some turkey-like fowls; these, along with boiled manioc tubers, made up their meal. About the fire that night they discussed what their next step would be.

The "doctor" who had expected to be wafted along in the retinue of a great lady suddenly found himself in a dubious position. The longer they delayed, the less grew his chances. He suggested that he and one of his companions, a silent, moody fellow, along with the ebullient, good-natured Negro, Joachim, take the canoe and make their way to the mission of Andoas, some hundred miles away. There they would secure help and come back with the canoes and paddlers to bring them out. Eugenio, Doña Isabela's younger brother, did not like the suggestion. This would take from them their only means of travel. Yet as no one had any other suggestions, and as Mme Godin sat with head bowed, her silence became a manner of consent. So the "doctor," his companion, and Joachim struck off in the only canoe. They left behind them four women, three men, and a boy of twelve, none of whom had ever been in a jungle or had ever come to grips with the raw specter of nature. Death's holiday was over.

What does one do in the jungle as hours become days, and days become weeks? What does one do when the provisions shared by eight people begin to dwindle and disappear; when despair turns to hate; when love for one's kind is reduced to the point where food and food alone is life's one supreme desire? At first one tries to improve the lot of all, and then that effort degenerates with time. As the animal struggle for existence begins to insinuate itself, man ceases to be a man — he is at best an animated stomach. So it was with Mme Godin's party.

In the first week they did not conserve the corn, the beans, the flour, and the bacon that they had brought from Riobamba, since they believed succor to be at hand. In the second week the remaining Frenchman (left by the "doctor" as a sort of hostage) was aroused at seeing Doña Isabela's servants bathing at the river's edge; there followed days of passion and rape. Yet in man, once hunger takes possession of the scene, love assumes its place merely in the general phenomenon of nutrition. So on the banks of the Pastaza passion metamorphosed into hunger, and food became the only reality of the group perched on the high, verdure-splashed banks of the jungle river.

Mme Godin during the first week seemed oblivious of the tide of passion that flowed about her. Joaquín, her twelve-year-old nephew, was ill and wasted, and she spent much of her time trying to nurse him. But how long would they be able to endure this? The men hunted and gathered wood, and the women sought tubers and birds' eggs on which to feed. At night came the mosquitoes and the black piume flies, the small blood-sucking *jejenes*, which pricked their skin and swarmed on their unprotected flesh. They itched and scratched until the blood flowed and until most of them were half-mad. The Frenchman's lust for the six olive-tinged breasts of the chola women left him completely; now he was assailed by the fear of darkness which pulsed through him in the black of the jungle night. One night he awoke and saw a vampire bat sucking the blood out of his toe. He screamed as if the devil himself had taken hold, and went utterly berserk. The nerves of the others, laid bare by the ceaseless presence of death, broke; the camp was thrown into an uproar. When dawn came with the screeching of parrots and the yelp of monkeys, Mme Godin decided that they had waited long enough. A month had passed. There was no word from Andoas. Perhaps Joachim and the Frenchman had perished in the river. Perhaps? They could no longer speculate. They must act. Mme Godin ordered her brothers and the Frenchman to make a balsa. This accomplished, they piled the remaining bits of their cargo on it and pulled their own wasted bodies into its center, and the three men, acting as polers, pushed it out into the Pastaza.

The women sat in the center with the sick boy. The two brothers stood at the end to pole. They had scarcely propelled the raft into the swirling Pastaza when it struck a half-submerged tree, the balsa was rent apart, and all of them, the two brothers, the Frenchman, the young boy, Mme Godin, and her three women servants, were thrown into the river. All their remaining provisions, their ragged clothes, and all that was once part of a sumptuous expedition were swept away irrevocably. They saved themselves only with the last residue of their strength. Even as they pulled themselves up the steep banks, Joaquín was already moribund; without opening his eyes, he died that night. Most of them were too far gone to shed tears. They did not even possess the strength to bury him.

Rosa, the eldest of Mme Godin's servants, died in her sleep. Heloise, in a delirium, walked off and never returned. There was no food, and even had there been, none had the strength to prepare it. Even as the oldest Grandmaison brother told his beads in anticipation of death, he expired. The Frenchman and the other brother were already dead; ants crawled over their open, sightless eyes.

Mme Godin lay between the rapidly putrifying bodies of brothers and servants, her brown eyes still glistening in her livid face. Like some noisome perfume, the cadavers spiced the jungle air. She had resigned herself to death. Yet two days later she was still alive. Something within her, some hidden impulse, animated that small, emaciated body. She thought of Jean Godin des Odonais, the handsome young man who had left Paris on a great expedition when only twenty. She thought of the young man who had married her, sired her children, and had now for twenty years lived in French Guiana waiting for her to come down to him. These thoughts, she confessed later, seemed to pour strength into her wasted body and they acted upon her like some sovereign balm. With new-found strength she raised herself unsteadily from the ground; with a knife she cut off the shoes of her dead brothers, fashioned these into crude sandals, picked up a machete in one hand, supported herself with a staff in the other, and, without so much as a glance behind at the seven dead bodies, she stumbled into the jungle.

Doña Isabela pushed through the jungle of vegetation in the dreamless reality of a somnambulist. As she trudged forward, she thought she heard someone calling, someone calling her name, but she had heard those voices before. On she went, flitting through the jungle like a wounded white morpho butterfly. Her rich dark-brown hair had turned white, her olive-tinged skin, drawn and depigmented, gave her the look less of a woman than of a ghostly apparition flitting between the buttressed giants of the jungle.

A woman of gentle soul and gentle birth, alone and lost in the most dreaded jungle in the world.

It had been a real voice that had shouted the name of Mme Godin, and the voice was that of Joachim, the Negro slave. He came to the spot where he had left her party weeks ago, and even as he paddled up in a giant canoe he shouted her name. His black face wreathed in smiles, his simple, valiant Negro soul expanding under the knowledge that he was about to rescue his *patrona,* he had paddled up from the mission of Andoas in a canoe manned by four Indians. Delayed by the machinations of the "doctor," who

Isabela Godin des Odonais, the heroine of the terrible saga of the Amazon. From a facsimile of a portrait painted for the Godin family.

had no intention of returning, Joachim had gone to the padres and told them of the plight of Mme Godin and her party. They had given him a canoe, Indians, and supplies. Now eight days of paddling up the Pastaza had brought them to the spot he had left weeks ago.

He shouted. There was no answer. He thought that he heard something crashing through the brush along the side of the river, and shouted again. There came no answer. He rushed up the embankment, fell upon the lean-to which he had built for them — and there before him on the ground were the shapeless forms of decayed bodies. The stench was nauseating, some of the cadavers were already gone beyond all recognition. He saw the bodies of women and that told him the whole story — all were dead. Joachim fell to his knees, quickly mumbled the prayers for the dead, offered their souls to God, and then fled back to his canoe with all the abject terror of the primitive. He told the Indians what he had seen, and the canoe felt the breath of stirring life and animated terror. The black and brown bodies, glistening with sweat under the equatorial sun, pulled heavily on their paddles to put distance between themselves and those decaying bodies on the banks of the Pastaza. At they paddled in rhythm, the blades struck the edge of the canoe with a thump-thump-thumping like a message being tapped from a signal drum. And message it was. All down the river into the mission, to the Indian settlements, came the tragic message: "Mme Godin and her party are dead. All perished in the jungle."

Joachim paddled down to Las Lagunas to carry the tragic news to the father, Don Pedro Grandmaison. The elderly gentleman was overwhelmed. At one blow he had lost his daughter, two sons, and a grand-nephew. Through a torrent of tears he wrote the sad news to Jean Godin, who after twenty years still waited in Cayenne. But there was no need of such a letter. Jean Godin had heard. Already, as if on the wind, the story went down the long, serpentine-flowing Amazon to Pará, across the ocean on the decks of ships, into the stinking piers and counting-rooms of Marseille. A Frenchman, Jean Godin des Odonais, who had left on an expedition of the Académie in 1735 to measure an arc of the equator, who had waited twenty years for his wife to join him, had now lost her. Mme Godin was lost in the horrible jungles of the Amazon. The rumor carrying the news of the tragedy reached Paris and came to Charles-Marie de La Condamine. It was a tragic dénouement to all his efforts to arrange for their safe passage. While France was being brought to the brink of revolution, while she was convulsing over Voltaire's *Candide*, while the Boston Massacre gave the final impetus to the American Revolution, the story of Mme Godin went its appointed way through the salons of Paris.

The story of Mme Godin was still current in Paris in 1770 when Joseph de Jussieu returned from Quito; it was still remembered when a young "natural philosopher," Alexander von Humboldt, came to Paris in 1799. For fifty years the story was told and re-told until at last it appeared, draped in a sort of Chateaubriandesque romanticism, in the pages of the *Magasin pittoresque.** Yet the story was merely enhanced by its miraculous dénouement — for Mme Godin did not perish in the jungle.

Mme Godin wandered for nine days after leaving the rotting bodies of her companions on the banks of the Río Pastaza. How she endured it she never could recall. She lived on palm cabbage, tinamou eggs, some fruit of the cherimoya; yet what really kept her alive was her unquenchable spirit.

On the ninth day she discovered three Shimigai Indians sitting around a fire on the banks of the river. They were so startled by seeing a white woman walking alone like a ghostly specter in the midst of the jungle that they were ready to run. But Mme Godin spoke to them in Quechua, some words of which they understood (for it was a lingua franca down these rivers). She indicated that she wanted to be taken to the mission of Andoas; then she collapsed. As tenderly as they could, the Indians placed her in their canoe and took her to Andoas, which they reached in the first days of January 1770. When they reached the mission, as she said later, "not knowing otherwise how to testify to my gratitude to the two Indians who had saved my life, I took from my neck two chains of gold (such as are usually worn in this country) of about four ounces' weight and gave one to each of them. . . . But the missionary, in my very presence, took possession of the chains . . . gave the poor Indians in lieu of them about three or four yards of coarse cotton cloth. . . ."

Mme Godin was outraged by such conduct. Still so weak that she could not stand without support, her eyes flashed, her body trembled in moral indignation. To cheat these Indians who had saved her life, to take gold necklaces from them in exchange for four pieces of material was robbery of the worst kind. She denounced the padre as unworthy of his cloth and demanded a canoe and provisions to continue on her journey. So weak that she had to be carried to her canoe, Mme Godin gave eloquent testimony to the spirit that had kept her alive. An Indian woman, on her way to Lagunas, gave her a cotton petticoat to clothe her nakedness; she

---

* An issue of 1854.

had nothing else but the "soles of the shoes of her dead brothers, converted by her into sandals."

On her arrival at Loreto (where the missionaries had transformed the jungle into a small thriving settlement) she found that the tragic story of her travels had preceded her. Seeing this small woman, wasted and worn, still facing a long journey down the Amazon, Father Romero, the chief of the missions, told her that if she desired, he could send her with full security back to her home in Riobamba. To which Mme Godin replied:

"I am, Padre, surprised at your proposals. God has preserved me when alone amid perils in which all my companions perished, in my wish to rejoin my husband. Having begun my journey for this purpose, if I were not to prosecute my first intention, I should esteem myself guilty of counteracting the views of Providence and rendering useless the assistance I have received from the two dear Indians and their wives, as well as the kindness which you, kind Father, have given me. . . ."

Thus Mme Godin.

Padre Romero sent off a message to M. Grandmaison informing him that his daughter, alive, was now beyond danger. The Portuguese galiot met her canoe and in it Mme Godin, with her father, sailed the 2,000 miles down the Amazon to the Atlantic and up along the coast of Brazil to French Guiana.

Jean Godin des Odonais, hearing of their coming, went out to meet them in a small boat and climbed aboard the galiot. With understatement so typical of the time, he said:

"On board this vessel, after twenty years' absence and a long endurance on either side of alarms and misfortunes, I again met with a cherished wife whom I had almost given over every hope of seeing again. In her embraces I forgot the loss of the fruits of our union; nay, I even congratulated myself on their premature death, as it saved them from the dreadful fate which befell their uncles in the wood of Canelos beneath the eyes of their mother, who certainly would never have survived the sight."

They remained for two more years in French Guiana, waiting for a vessel; a census taken in 1772 reveals Jean Godin des Odonais, his wife Isabela, Don Pedro, the father, and the Negro, Joachim, living in Godin's house on the Río Oyapoc. In 1773 they took ship for France and arrived at La Rochelle. Jean de Godin had been absent from Paris for thirty-eight years!

And there, waiting for them at the docks of La Rochelle, was Charles-Marie de La Condamine.

CHAPTER IX
The Triumphs of La Condamine

WITH THE RETURN of Jean Godin and his wife, the *"expédition dans l'équateur"* had officially terminated — that is, for all but Charles-Marie de La Condamine. What he had gathered in South America animated him the rest of his life.

No sooner had he set foot in Paris and prepared his discourse for the Académie on his descent of the Amazon (which was published in the same year under the title of *Relation abrégée*) than he began to lay down the outlines for all the other books that he would finish in the succeeding years, based upon the work that had been done on the equator. He was already up to his periwig in controversies: on the virtues of quinine, the efficacy of smallpox vaccination, the phenomenon of sound, the truth of the legends of the Amazon, the geographical basis for the connection of the Orinoco and the Río Negro. And while he was convulsed with these arguments and writing the accounts of the journeys that opened up South America, he had time to see that his good friend Pedro Maldonado was elected a member of the Académie des Sciences as well as of every other brilliant scientific society in Europe. In 1748 Pedro Maldonado went to London to be present at his election to the Royal Society. La Condamine's pride in his protégé was boundless, and he was as delighted as Pedro Maldonado, but their joys were shortlived. Maldonado, who had since childhood lived through every scourge known to man, who had traveled through the wildest country in the world, whose knowledge of his own people had much to do with the success of the La Condamine expedition, suddenly fell ill with the measles. At the age of forty he died in London.

In Paris once more, Charles-Marie, whose whole being made him incapable of jealousy, was set upon by Pierre Bouguer. Having published an account of his part in the expedition in a technical book, *La Figure de la terre,* Bouguer used its pages to ridicule La Condamine and his part in the expedition. The jealousy that had jaundiced the character of Bouguer for ten years now knew no bounds. He regarded La Condamine *"comme un ennemi de sa gloire."* On every hand he saw La Condamine accepted in the salons of the great, walking arm in arm with Voltaire; he saw him elected a member of the great scientific academies of the world —

Berlin, St. Petersburg, Stockholm; he listened to his discourse and realized that its warm enthusiastic delivery was correctly calculated to arouse interest.

Never had South America a more ardent champion than La Condamine. There was not a savant in all Europe with whom he did not correspond, not a book appeared that he did not know and read, not a journal that did not carry something of his writings. He wrote of rubber, he experimented with the samples that he had brought back, he introduced it for the first time to the scientists of Europe. He experimented with curare poison, the black viscous active agent of Amazonia's flying death. He experimented with the use of sugar and salt as antidotes, repeating his trials at Leiden in the presence of the celebrated philosophers van Musschenbroek, van Swieten, and Albinus. Not content with merely collecting the poison, he had collected the plants from which it was made and described its manufacture.

And if writing, lecturing, experimenting on material from South America was not enough, he became the champion for inoculation against smallpox. He took up the controversy when it was frowned upon by church and medicos alike. There was a personal touch to this; he had had the pox when young, his face still bore its scars. When, in Pará in 1748, he saw a Carmelite friar successfully inoculating his Indian charges for smallpox, he was stimulated to try to make his own country adopt the practice. From the rostrum of the Académie he lectured on the need for it, in the halls of fashionable salons he expounded the theme, to give publicity to it he even persuaded his family in the provinces to submit to inoculation. La Condamine had a champion in his old friend Voltaire, whose face also was scarred by the pox. "If we do not "inoculate in France as in England," he ranted, "it is because the English decide by calculation and we by sentiment. . . ." La Condamine fought for its adoption and was himself vaccinated against this scourge five years before Dr. Edward Jenner (to whom is credited the perfection of vaccination) was born. La Condamine's treatise on the pox was so well known that it was translated into Spanish and circulated in the Spanish colonies.

Then, when it was not rubber, curare, quinine, smallpox, physics, or chemistry with which La Condamine was busy, it was the science of measurement. He wanted the countries of the world to adopt a common standard of measurement — there were English miles, English feet, there were German leagues, Italian leagues, there were French measurements that agreed with none of these. La Condamine suggested the French *toise* as an invariable measure of length and as a legal standard. He argued, wrote, and campaigned until it was accepted; and from this evolved the French metric system.

All this activity, created and augmented by his experiences in South America, was having its effect. La Condamine was sick. Those who had known him as a young, handsome man would hardly have recognized him; ten years in America had taken their toll. Women who once swooned in his arms when he turned a pretty phrase now looked upon a man so deaf that he had to use an ear-trumpet, so paralyzed in his left leg that he needed a cane. His face had grown very thin, the cheek-bones seemed to burst through his skin, while the eyes had a glassy look under inflamed lids. The paralysis had gained so in the last years in Paris that, following the advice of friends, he sought his health in a journey to Italy. In 1757, at the age of fifty-six, La Condamine also thought of marriage. Partially deaf, half-paralyzed, he knew he was no longer a catch. But his niece, twenty years younger than he, venerated him; she felt it a duty to give him some happiness for the years he had left. On the trip to Italy La Condamine went to the Vatican to get the Papal dispensation for this marriage.

There was not much time for health in Italy. La Condamine visited Mount Vesuvius, which was in eruption. With the instruments that he carried with him for that purpose, he measured the buildings of the ancient Romans to try to determine their standard of measurement. He went to a cathedral at Genoa, drawn there by tales of the altar made of solid emerald. Having been to the emerald mines in the province of Quito, he believed that he could pass upon its authenticity. The priest stopped him just in time as he was scraping off a piece of a vase for chemical analysis.

In Italy, too, he began experiments with electricity to see if his paralyzed body might respond to electrical charges — and this was in 1757, almost half a century before Volta invented the electric pile. On his return to Paris a year later, he brought back no change in his health, but the Papal consent to marry his niece.

For the next six years, under the loving care of his young wife, La Condamine still further expanded his multitudinous interests. He knew no rest. When he could not appear at the Académie, because of the ever increasing paralysis, he read the reports; when his condition permitted him, he attended, ear-trumpet in one hand, cane in the other. His curiosity knew no bounds, and often it made him indiscreet; he wearied the other savants by his insistence on the efficacies of his various projects; but his faults were only the consequence of his qualities. And it was these qualities that the French finally recognized by making him one of the Forty

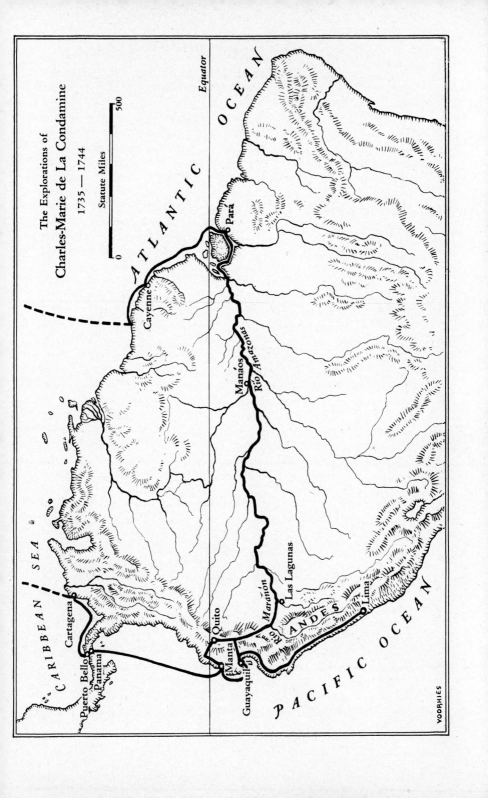

The Explorations of
Charles-Marie de La Condamine
1735 — 1744

Statute Miles

500

0

ATLANTIC OCEAN

Equator

Pará

Cayenne

Manáos

Río Amazonas

CARIBBEAN SEA

Cartagena

Puerto Bello
Panamá

Quito

Manta

Guayaquil

Las Lagunas

Río Marañón

ANDES

Lima

PACIFIC OCEAN

VOORHIES

Immortals. He was elected a member of the Académie Française in 1760.

After that his physical decline set in rapidly. By 1763 he was completely paralyzed. He knew his active life was over; yet this did not prevent him from dictating articles and books. These still continued to issue from his study. Europe now had more interest in South America, thanks to the work of La Condamine and to Voltaire's novel *Candide,* than it ever had, and when the haunting tragedy of Mme Godin stalked across the whole of France, with Charles-Marie as its agent, interest was raised to fever pitch. La Condamine, now completely paralytic, lingered on for six more years. He even tried to make his disease useful. He offered a prize of many thousand francs — the Berlin Academy to act as judges — to any physician who could discern the cause of his paralysis. Then when nothing came of this, he composed songs to assuage his pain. In 1773, the year before he died, he dictated a small pamphlet addressed to an anonymous M. * * * giving an account of the fate of those astronomers who participated in the requisite operations for the measurement of the earth in 1735: *Sur la Sort des astronomes qui ont eu part aux derniers mesures de la terre depuis 1735. . . ."* Of these Couplet, Dr. Senièrgues, and Morainville he listed as dead. Jussieu and Mabillon were crazed, their memories unequivocally lost. Hugot was living in Quito, Louis Godin dead at Cadiz; gone as well was La Condamine's enemy, Pierre Bouguer. Of the others only Captain Verguin of the Navy and Antonio de Ulloa, late Governor of the territory of Louisiana, were alive. And he ends it: "As for myself, M. de La Condamine, you can consider me only half a man. . . ."

And that half succumbed in 1774, a deaf, paralytic gentleman, whose genius and whose insatiable curiosity and enthusiasm re-opened the New World. In his last gasp he passed the future exploration of the continent he had opened to one Alexander von Humboldt, at that moment aged five, then playing in the castle gardens of Tegel bei Potsdam.

PART II

❖❖❖❖❖❖❖❖❖❖❖❖❖❖❖❖❖❖❖❖❖❖❖❖❖

CHAPTER X
Humboldt's America

H IS EXCELLENCY Don Vicente Emparán, Governor of the
Province of Nueva Andalusia, was delighted to have Baron Alexander von Humboldt and his companion, the *citoyen* Aimé Bonpland, in Venezuela. Having finished his welcoming discourse to
the travelers, he turned to examine their passports. As they were being read, Humboldt allowed his gray eyes to roam about the room,
over the shoulder of the Governor and out on the tumbled city of
Cumaná. The recent earthquake had all but leveled the ancient
city; it lay lovely and luxurious, half-buried in ruins. The mountains of Nueva Andalusia in the background were veiled in the
mists. The Castle of San Āntonio stood guard in the harbor, delightfully camouflaged by the fronds of coco palms; behind it was
a solitary white hill, reflecting the great mass of tropical sunlight. Humboldt could see the palm-leaf houses of the natives, the
vast savannas studded with cylindrical cacti, and the dazzling
white shore of the warm pellucid sea, and to enliven the scene,
egrets, pelicans, and rose-pink flamingoes flew by with the pre-
cision of convoyed galleons. Humboldt was drinking in this delectable scene when, hearing a voice, he shifted his eyes back to
the room. In halting French Don Vicente was reading his passport:

". . . We, Alphonse de Santos-Rollin, Chamberlain to H.M.
King of Prussia and Prussian Minister Plenipotentiary to the
French Republic, beg and require all whom it may concern to
grant free and safe pass to:

"Friedrich Heinrich Alexander, Baron von Humboldt, born at
Berlin, age 28, five feet eight, light-brown hair, gray eyes, large
nose, rather large mouth, well-formed chin, forehead open,
marked with scars of smallpox. . . . *Traveling for the acquisition of knowledge.*"

His Excellency pursed his lips, looked up from the passport, caressed his black mustachios, stole a glance at Humboldt, and repeated under his breath in Spanish:

"Traveling for the acquisition of knowledge."

He studied with open boldness the face of Humboldt. Yes, the description fitted him precisely: twenty-eight years old, smallpox scars on his forehead . . . gray eyes . . . large nose. . . . Don Vicente was fully aware that there sat before him a most capable young gentleman. He knew that he and his companion, Aimé Bonpland, had come with the avowed purpose of ascending the Río Orinoco, but he had little idea to what extent this small young man would open the portals of South America to the world. Nor had Don Vicente the slightest idea of the thoughts that were coursing in the brain of Humboldt as he sat before him.

To Humboldt it was a dream realized, merely to be in America. An omnivorous reader, he had gulped down in succession the travels of the explorers, the conquistadores, and the world-encirclers. He had struggled with La Condamine over the wind-swept paramos, he had spilled youthful saltless tears over the odyssey of Mme Godin, he had thrilled at the descent of the Amazon, and he was fascinated by La Condamine's question: "There is a communication between the Orinoco and the Amazon rivers . . . but where does this communication take place?" Humboldt was in America to answer that question. Now, looking back, he could hardly pick the precise time when these things began to interest him. Perhaps his interest sprang from the very juxtaposition of the planets the year that he was born. It must have been an amazing year for the astrologers, that year of 1769, which saw born a dazzling collection of incipient luminaries — Humboldt, Napoleon, Wellington.

Humboldt's father, Major Alexander Georg von Humboldt, had followed the standard of Frederick the Great through countless battles and had won the friendship of that austere member of the *Aufklärung*. Often the King would come to the Castle Tegel at Potsdam, as much to bask in the charms of the Baroness von Humboldt as to see his old comrade in arms. For the Major had been fortunate in his choice of Maria Elisabeth. She was a French Huguenot whose family had taken refuge in Germany after the Revocation of the Edict of Nantes. She had been married first to a wealthy baron, then, after his death, she married the dashing Major von Humboldt, aide-de-camp to the Duke of Brunswick. To Georg von Humboldt she bore two remarkable sons, Karl Wilhelm, destined to be a great classical philologist, and Alexander, destined to be an explorer-geographer.

The first years of the brothers Humboldt were idyllic. They

lived through all the pageantry that that age produced, growing up
in the years that saw the beginning of the American Revolution,
and the inquietude that was stirred up by the readings of *The
Rights of Man,* printed by every clandestine printing press in
Europe. The Baroness wanted her sons about her, so their father
engaged a tutor, the famed Professor Campe, translator of *Robinson Crusoe.* Campe was imbued with the principles of education
conceived by Jean-Jacques. Lessons were given in the proper Rous-
seauan setting on the lawn of the castle, where the brothers were
inoculated with the spirit of responsibility and habits of discipline and study which were to serve them so well in their later
years. The high point in their childhood was when the King,
Frederick the Great, paid the Schloss Tegel a visit and came upon
them studying under the linden trees. They sprang up and stood
rigidly before him as he addressed himself first to the elder:

"What is your name?"

"Wilhelm von Humboldt, Sire."

"Age?"

"Ten years, Sire."

"That is a good age to enter military school. You shake your
head. You do not wish to become a soldier?"

"No, Sire, I wish to have my career in literature."

The King then turned to the other boy, aged eight.

"Name?"

"Alexander von Humboldt, Sire."

"Alexander." Frederick the Great pursed his lips. "Alexander,
that is a beautiful name. I seem to recall an earth-conqueror by
that name. Do you wish to be a conqueror?"

"Yes, Sire — but with my head."

Not long after that memorable conversation Major von Humboldt died, leaving his two sons in the hands of his Baroness. She
henceforth became the animating principle of their lives. She was
a "good European." A woman of rank who lived in a century
which did not believe that one nation's culture was superior to
that of another nation, who did not believe that any nation had a
particular culture of its own, she asserted that culture was European, despite its babel of tongues.

Alexander von Humboldt, thanks to his mother's influence, was
bound by no national barriers. Although German, he wrote in
French. He was equally at home in England, Spain, Italy, or Russia (all of whose languages he spoke fluently). He extensively explored the Americas. Never giving the kings of Spain reason to
believe that he served them ill, he none the less provided the intellectual spark for Simón Bolívar, who in turn launched the sec-

ond successful American Revolution. Tolerant, cerebral, a "latitude man," a little skeptical, without political passion, a little
worldly perhaps, but serene, graceful in manner, neat in thought,
eloquent in expression, sane in mind, and physically active — that
was Alexander von Humboldt.

His epoch was provocative; for he was nurtured in that period
which saw the demise of the monarchs of Enlightenment: Frederick of Germany, Catherine of Russia, Maria Theresa of Austria,
and Charles III of Spain. It was the age of the "great change."
With the rumblings of revolution, genius flowered. Mozart, Weber,
Goethe, and Schiller were the intellectual gods. There were new
forces loose in the world, forces whose depths could not be
plumbed.

The Baroness von Humboldt, with two sons to rear on this
protean earth, gave the direction of their education over to the
venerable Professor Kunth, friend, tutor, and financial adviser.
Under his direction the brothers Humboldt were sent to Berlin's
best Gymnasia. Alexander, who leaned instantly toward the natural sciences, was permitted to take instruction that would galvanize his interests. At eighteen he entered for a few months the
University of Frankfurt; at twenty he left for the University of
Göttingen, then the center of learning in physical sciences. There
the groundwork of Humboldt's life was laid under the most renowned teachers of Germany.

It was a glorious three years when curiosity and enthusiasm co-
alesced into science, the one channel of his interests. The world
was still young. There remained vast unknowns to tempt the most
timid of men. Everywhere science was battering down the walls
that medieval ignorance had built. Life then was a continual intellectual feast. Then there were the gay symposiums of students,
the sharing of confidences with Count Metternich (the future
Prime Minister of Austria), comradeship with the famed young
men of Germany: Stein, Forster, and the Counts von Hagen; days
of scientific excursions to test the knowledge gained in the classroom, which aroused the fever for travel.

George Adam Forster, it was, who fed the uneasy and ambitious
aspirations of Humboldt. Forster, then only thirty-six, had traveled
with his father on Captain Cook's second voyage around the
world and had himself written a masterly narrative: *Voyage
around the World on H.M. Sloop Resolution*. This book Humboldt gulped down with the rest. Man and author, Forster was his
inspiration and Humboldt's exploratory fever was turned into a
delirium. He never forgot those evenings when Forster held him
spellbound by his stirring narration of rounding the Horn and his

passage onto the soft, undulating bosom of the Pacific. "My *'philo-sophe aimable,'*" Humboldt said of him, "my most distinguished teacher and friend, whose name I can never mention without a feeling of the most heartfelt gratitude. Through his influence a new spirit in exploration was born."

The year the Bastille fell Humboldt finished his formal educa-tion at Göttingen. The world rang with the news of the Revolu-tion. Blood spilled across the German border. Hotels and spas filled with émigrés in flight from the revolutionary holocaust. It was a thrilling year. Yet there was more than the talk of revolu-tion and the death of kings, for Humboldt had accepted Forster's invitation to make a journey up the Rhine. It was a leisurely trip up to Die Lorelei and the upper Rhine, with geology as their primary interest. With geologist's sack and hammer, Humboldt chipped at the castle-studded cliffs, and from the material gathered on that trip came a youthful paper: *Mineralogical Observations on Some Basalts on the Rhine.*

Humboldt, following the lodestone of geology, proceeded to the one spot to which every student was going — to Freiburg and the classes of Herr Professor Werner. There, under that teacher's warm eloquence, Humboldt took instantly to the study of the earth. Werner had come from a family who for centuries had en-gaged in mining. His practical turn of mind, enhanced by great charm, gave him unrivaled leadership in geology.

In his classes Humboldt found a Señor Andrés del Río, who had come all the way from Mexico to absorb Werner's teachings and, as may be imagined, between classes del Río inflamed Alexander all the more in his desire to visit the Americas. Thus, while the "Friends of the People" in Paris lopped off heads and the sewers of the Bois de Boulogne gagged on the viscous oceans of blood, and while Burke and Fox argued on the merits of the Revolution, Humboldt and his fellow students were lost in the catastrophic geology of Werner.

The professor expounded the engaging theory that all existing rocks were deposited from primeval water, a "chaotic fluid," he explained in his best romantic manner. "The whole earth was taken to pieces at one time and dissolved in an all-embracing ocean," after which layers of inorganic material were deposited as the water evaporated or receded. No matter how absurd the dogma of the "Neptunists" (called so from the great importance they gave to oceans and chaotic fluids), the lectures of Werner stirred the imagination of Humboldt; he plunged into geology with both feet. He scaled the sides of mountains, he crawled among the feld-spars and hornblendes, he collected pyrites and apatites, and so proficient did he become that he was soon appointed assessor to the Mining and Smelting Department in Berlin. In 1792, he became Director General of the Mines in Franconia.

The aged Baroness von Humboldt died in 1796. This date marked the turning-point of Alexander's life. The voices of the sirens calling from America grew louder. Out of filial piety Humboldt had remained in and about Germany while his mother lived. Her death released him, cut his ties with the homeland. Now he was able to begin in actuality the program that he had so long cherished — to explore the world. He went to Jena to study astronomy and visit Goethe and Schiller. He studied the new sextant which he had made by Hadley in London. He went to Dresden to study under Köner at the Philosophical Museum, to become proficient in the use of astronomical and meteorological instruments. There he found his brother, Wilhelm, already a famed classical philologist, preparing to go as Prussian Minister to the Vatican. Wilhelm was about to leave for Paris, for that capital, with the rise of young General Bonaparte, was the key to the Continent. Before one left for anywhere, one first went to Paris for permission. It was a feverish summer. Preparations and illness alike absorbed them. Schiller, who was in Dresden with the Humboldts, wrote to Goethe: "Although the whole of the family Humboldt, down to the servant, lie ill with ague, they still speak of great journeys."

Wilhelm at last left for Paris, but Alexander stayed behind to arrange his financial affairs. He sold his part of the estate to the poet Franz von Kleist, which left him a modest fortune of 85,000 thalers. This he confided to the care of his old mentor Professor Kunth, who wisely loaned it out at four per cent interest, giving the young Baron an annual 3,400 thalers with which he might make his assault on the unknown world. Not a princely sum, but ample enough, and with Humboldt's connections sufficient to open his way. With financial matters arranged, he gathered up his instruments, his aspirations, and his connections and left by way of Salzburg for Paris.

By 1798 the Revolution had spent itself. And since the Republic had been choked to death by its own contradictions, there was nothing left but to restore the monarchy under a new dynasty. The waves of revolution had pounded at the immovable wall of inertia, but the spindrift lapped over the wall and produced, as if by reprisal, Napoleon Bonaparte. Napoleon, during the short reign of the Directory, had been victorious everywhere. He had beaten the Italians and the Austrians and was now back in Paris preparing himself for a gigantic undertaking — the conquest of

Egypt. For out of the Treaty of Campoformio an avalanche was set in motion: it buried Italy, it rolled on France, on all Europe. Everywhere there was war, chaos, misery, and a rain of blood. The Law of Conscription — part of the Napoleonic war without rules — was being proclaimed to the thunderous accompaniment of the roll of drums while young Alexander von Humboldt threaded his way through the streets of Paris. Mars was in command. Should anyone have mentioned a small book, *Zum ewigen Frieden* (*Toward Enduring Peace*), by Immanuel Kant, which had just made its appearance, he would have been thought quite mad; the people were blinded by the terror of their victories.

For Alexander it was a thrilling moment to be in Paris. Here were all the famed men of Europe — scientists, naturalists, botanists, the whole *Who's Who* of European learning. Gathered in Europe's capital were Cuvier, Delambre, Jussieu, Desfontaines, Laplace, Fourcroy. There were the museums, and wonderful things to see. Napoleon had collected art and science in the grand manner: Paris was bursting with the specimens that he had seized throughout Europe. Alexander met A. L. de Jussieu, author of *Genera Plantarum,* the greatest book on the classification of plants since that of Linnæus. He listened to the celestial discourses of Laplace, the author of *Système du Monde,* who had reduced the universe to so mechanical an action that he could boast to Napoleon: "My solar system has no need for a God." Those great men whom he did not meet in the academies came to his own home, for the house of the Humboldts had become a rallying-point for all cultured Germans visiting Paris. From his contacts Alexander learned that the Directory planned to send a vessel, commanded by Captain Baudin, around the world on a voyage of scientific discovery. Around the world! Why, that was just what he wanted. He sought out Baudin and laid his qualifications before him. He was chosen at once to be one of the scientific staff.

Alexander was in an explorer's heaven. The dream of a lifetime — to circumnavigate the globe. When the news percolated through the Parisian scientific circles that he had found a place on Baudin's vessel, he was visited by the venerable Captain Louis Antoine de Bougainville (now remembered mostly by the superb mauve and purple vine bourgainvillæa), who had circumnavigated the world in the famous man-of-war *La Boudeuse*. He had hoped to lead the new expedition, but he had fallen into disgrace (from which he has not yet recovered) at the Battle of Saintes and had nearly lost his head to M. le Guillotine in 1792. Bougainville had come to place in Alexander's care his fifteen-year-old son, whom Captain Baudin agreed to take with him.

Preparations had reached a crescendo; then suddenly they ceased. Orders from Napoleon; the expedition was to be delayed — for a year. Humboldt had scarcely time to measure the effects of this blow before another proposal came to him. Lord Bristol, Bishop of Derby, proposed an expedition to Egypt. His Lordship had a passion for Egyptian antiquities, as well as a princely annual income of £60,000 to satisfy it. Once again the exploratory barometer rose. Humboldt decided to go. He could board Captain Baudin's ship later, when it cruised in the Mediterranean. He accepted Lord Bristol's proposal, but with one reservation: he insisted on traveling at his own expense.

"I will preserve my independence," he explained, "and do not risk anything; I can then leave at any time if he should oppose me too much." There was no unconditional genuflection in Alexander.

Humboldt had wanted to go to the Americas; then he was to sail around the world; now it was an expedition to the Upper Nile. Arrangements completed, Lord Bristol passed on to Milan; there he was promptly and most unceremoniously clapped into prison. The hand of Napoleon again. The eagles of empire were about to leave for a campaign in Egypt, and no Lord Bristols were wanted about the Nile. By July Napoleon's legions had landed in Cairo, and within two months he had seized most of Egypt and won the Battle of the Pyramids. Now, in the role of visitor and civilizer, Napoleon sought to take up and expand the plan of Lord Bristol. Bonaparte, the conqueror of Egypt, would be the patron of science. He suggested that an expedition of one hundred and sixty of Europe's savants be fitted out to follow in his wake to collect and codify the wonders of Egypt.

Again Humboldt was chosen. He was asked to help search out astronomers and botanists to fill the scientific orders of General Bonaparte. So once more Humboldt threw his enthusiasm into the formation of an expedition. He sought out young, personable, capable scientists; he purchased equipment; he prepared a library. He was poised to set off for Marseille and Egypt, when once again fortune toppled his dreams. Lord Nelson destroyed the French fleet at Aboukir and established a blockade throughout the Mediterranean and the Atlantic. Now all avenues seemed closed. Then Humboldt met Aimé Bonpland, and the expedition to America came into being.

"How did I meet Bonpland?" asked Humboldt. "Why, in the simplest manner in the world. You know that when giving up the key to one's apartment on going out, one generally exchanges a few friendly words with the porter's wife. While doing so, I often encountered a man with a botanist's satchel over his arm — this was Aimé Bonpland. We spoke, and in this manner we were made acquainted." And so was born one of the happiest relationships of any epoch, a working friendship that was to endure for three quarters of a century.

Aimé Bonpland was, by profession, a doctor of medicine, but by interest a botanist. Good-humored and robust, he was cast in a very different mold from Humboldt. Tall, thickset and vigorous, with a tousled great head, Aimé Bonpland resembled the wine of France — a combination of gay vitality with a deep underflowing of richness and strength. Like Humboldt, he had been chosen to go on that ill-fated expedition of Captain Baudin in the capacity of botanist, and like Humboldt he was to go with the Army of the Nile. They found in each other consolation for blasted hopes. But more, they found complementary enthusiasms for reciprocal interests.

This new friend completed the botanical education of Alexander von Humboldt. For Bonpland under the influence of Lamarck, Antoine-Laurent de Jussieu and Desfontaines had developed a deep interest in natural history, chiefly botany. And at the Sorbonne he had met the venerable and muddle-pated Joseph de Jussieu, who in 1779 had returned to Paris from Quito after an absence of forty-five years. Despite his wandering mind, Jussieu managed somehow to impart an enthusiasm for the marvelous flora of the Americas.

Bonpland had still another contact with those intrepid Frenchmen who first stormed the unknown in South America. He was born in the parish of St. Bartholomew of La Rochelle, on August 28, 1773, the same month and year that Jean de Godin des Odonais and his wife, Doña Isabela, had returned from their tragic sojourn in the Amazon. Throughout his youth he had had this episode recalled to him. This too served to awaken his interest in America.

A doctor at twenty, Aimé Bonpland went to sea as naval surgeon for the French Republic. Then he tried private practice, but the lure of botany prevented him from becoming a successful surgeon; now, practice or no, he was a botanist. He, too, dreamed of accompanying an expedition; he, too, longed to fill his vasculum with plants from some luscious corner of earth. Never did two men meet with a greater harmony of interests. Alexander von Humboldt was one of those chosen beings in whom the forces of life are so abundant and so glorious that they overflow in every direction and invest whatever they meet with their own vitality. Alexander was the sun of the Humboldt-Bonpland system; all planets revolved about that radiance. Bonpland was without means; Humboldt had a considerable fortune. On their planned expedition Humboldt agreed to assume the study of the unity of nature, an inquiry into terrestrial phenomena and their mutual relationships. Bonpland was to take other fields. He was an excellent comparative anatomist, thanks to his medical studies, so he would collect the organic life, the flora and fauna. Thus, without contracts or written agreements, they became, by a sort of metamorphosis, the gemini, the Castor and Pollux, of the scientific world.

To Egypt, then, despite the British blockade!

Humboldt arranged with the banking house of Fould for a letter of credit in the sum of 40,000 francs. Then he sought a passport through the Prussian Ministry. It was sent to Talleyrand to countersign. Thus Humboldt, in his last days in Paris, had the opportunity of meeting this enigmatical man who continued to be Minister of Foreign Affairs under the Revolution, Directory, and Empire. They packed their cases and in the depths of night — for they did not wish intelligence to seep out that they had left — their chaise picked its way through the cobblestone streets, echoing with the rumble of artillery caissons. Somewhere along the route they picked up the Swedish Consul, Skiöldebrand, and made their way to the port of Marseille. Skiöldebrand had conceived the idea of getting them aboard the Swedish vessel *Jaramas,* which operated between Toulon and North Africa. It might, as a neutral, be able to slip past the British blockade. At Toulon they saw the frigate *La Hardie,* the vessel that was to have taken them around the world. Humboldt could not pass the ship without boarding it. With great emotion he wrote:

"The whole ship was astir, and all hands were on deck working the sails. It was to convoy merchantmen to Marseille. My heart swelled with joyous emotion as I witnessed the preparations around me, but when I descended to the cabin, the thought of Baudin's voyage completely overcame me. I lay for ten minutes in the window contemplating the bright vision of it. . . . I could almost have shed tears at the thought of my shattered prospects. . . ."

For two months the explorers prowled about the port of Toulon, waiting for the corvette *Jaramas* to arrive so that their passage to Africa might be effected. Then they learned that she had been driven onto a shoal, the bottom ripped beyond repair, their passage irretrievably lost. Political conditions no longer permitting them to remain in Toulon, there was but one place left to go — Spain. So they purchased mules, packed their bulky instruments on the backs of this one transport agent that never failed, and crossed the Pyrenees. By mere accident they had set in motion the skein of fate that would bring them to the Americas.

By January 1799 they were riding over the mountain passes, deep with snowdrifts. They passed onto the flat tablelands of La Mancha, scene of the famous exploits of Don Quixote which convulsed the world. Then the road dropped down to the Mediterranean and took them to Barcelona. Trees were in blossom along their route. Nearing Valencia they came upon oranges and pistachios; roses, cactus, and holly bloomed and wafted their scents across the deeply religious earth.

Amidst the flowering jonquil and narcissus Humboldt attempted to work on the stars, but the rabble of Valencia were in an iconoclastic mood and he dared not take out his precious instruments. For the fever of unrest had come to Spain with the ascension of Charles IV to the throne.

Spain was the victim of the most wretched conditions: a fool for a King; the Queen's lover, Manuel de Godoy, for Prime Minister; the heir to the throne a semi-insane Prince fighting with his father, his mother, and his mother's lover. Godoy, the notorious "Prince of Peace," had first opposed the French Revolution; then he suddenly altered his course and entered a league with France through the Treaty of San Ildefonso. The Spanish fleets joined those of France in a concerted move against England. Disaster attended their combined forces at the Battle of the Nile; blockade followed. Commerce was interrupted. Spain was threatened on the high seas by England, in her colonies by the rising tide of republicanism, and across the Pyrenees by the specter of Napoleon Bonaparte.

Such was the state of Spain to which Alexander von Humboldt and Aimé Bonpland had come in order to find a small vessel that would take them through the blockade to Smyrna. Instead they fell into a miracle of fortune that changed their entire destiny, for Humboldt discovered that a dear friend of his family, Baron von Forell, was Ambassador of the court of Saxony to Madrid.

A distinguished patron of science and himself interested in geology, Baron von Forell turned a sympathetic ear to the frustrated explorers. He promised them his aid. Perhaps he could get them an audience with the King. The King! Then why not America? Yes, of course, why not ask for permission to visit the Americas! Would His Excellency see if this permission might not be granted? The Baron would — and did. Within a fortnight they stood in the presence of Don Mariano Luis de Urquijo, Spanish Secretary of State. An eager, sympathetic man who had seen the results of the expeditions that Carlos III had sent to the Americas, Count Urquijo was easily won to their side.

On March 17, 1799, supported by the Count de Urquijo on one side and Baron von Forell, the Saxon Ambassador, on the other, Alexander, Baron von Humboldt, was taken to the palace at Aranjuez. There he was presented to the King. He discoursed at length on his plan to visit the Americas.

"I explained to him," Humboldt said later, "the motives that led me to wish to undertake a voyage to the New World and the Philippines. I affirmed that although many expeditions had gone to the Americas, there was, except for the published works of La Condamine and Jorge Juan y Santacilla, very little published on the great regions of His Majesty's American colonies."

Impressed, King Charles asked that Alexander address to him a memoir on the subject, for Spain had a great love for the *papel sellado* and the written word. So Humboldt wrote a memoir on the "subject" for Count Urquijo, and the Secretary was won over fully. Within a few days he sent Humboldt a letter informing him: "The King has conceded the necessary permission by which M. de Humboldt may leave for America to continue these studies in geology and the other discoveries that he has proposed. . . ." Passports would be granted them. More, the King himself would provide them with a letter bearing the royal seal. What more could have been wanted? A few days later came La Cédula Real — a document signed by the King with the royal seal directing all the captains general, commanders, governors, lord mayors, and other officials to assist in every way possible the passage of this Baron von Humboldt through the land that is America.

Never in the modern history of Spain had so extensive a permission been granted a foreigner. Never had anyone been so honored. Never had anyone been shown such trust. They were not to be shackled, as La Condamine and the French Academicians, with two Spanish companions, had been. They were free, in the King's name, to wander all over his realm, to collect what they desired, see what they desired, and inquire into whatever interested them. How the soul of Charles IV must toss in limbo! For in giving this young gray-eyed "natural philosopher" carte blanche, he had given him a rod with which to beat him. Humboldt would see, Humboldt would write, Humboldt would inspire. And in the dissolution of empire a young man, Simón Bolívar, suffering from the *Weltschmerz* of his age, would seek out Humboldt in Paris — and Humboldt, mellow with travel and wise in statecraft, would point out that the Americas were ripe for freedom; all they lacked was a leader. And so this ardent young German Baron was to be not only the scientific discoverer of America, but one of the main-springs of the second American Revolution as well.

No sooner had they their passports than Humboldt and Bon-pland took to the museums of Spain to study what had already been collected in the Americas. They visited Casimiro Ortega, who had headed an expedition into Nueva España. They sought out Hipólito Ruiz and José Pavón lately returned from an expe-dition on which they had suffered the tortures of Tantalus to collect plants in Peru. Don Hipólito recited all the horrors — "heat, weariness, hunger, thirst, nakedness, gnats of every kind, tempests, earthquakes, plagues of mosquitoes, continual risks of being devoured by jaguars, bears . . . ambushed by thieves and savage Indians, treachery of slaves, accidents from precipices, the falling of branches from lofty trees, shipwrecks, the separation from M. Dombey, the death of Bruñete, the loss of collections and manuscripts by fire and sword and shipwreck. . . ."

And for what? To have all these natural-history specimens lie neglected. For there they sat in the dusty museum with their un-packed cases about them.

"No European government has ever spent more considerable sums to increase the knowledge of plants than the Spanish gov-ernment," wrote Humboldt. Yet, after all the work of collecting, little was ever published. South America was still vast, unknown, unconquered. The heart of Humboldt pulsated in anticipation. The enthusiasm of Bonpland was uncontrollable; he could hardly contain himself in thinking about their prospects.

They left Madrid in May 1799 for the port of La Coruña.

There *El Pizarro* was waiting for them, hiding its unpainted masts in the countless bare masts that studded the harbor. The captain was offhand and pessimistic. He did not think that they would be successful in running the British blockade. Observers from the watchtower of Sisarga had just sighted an English squad-ron at the mouth of the Tagus River. On all sides they were told that their ship would be picked up within three days and interned at Lisbon.

While final preparations were being made for the voyage, Bon-pland and Humboldt took long excursions from the stench of La Coruña into the heath-covered hills. Wherever they moved they fell under the shadow of a giant citadel, the Castle of San Antonio, whose medieval walls dominated the seaport. Humboldt knew that within those walls was confined the thrice-unfortunate Ales-andro Malaspina, the great Italian-born Spanish explorer who, like so many other Spanish explorers sent out by Charles III, met the sad fate of ingratitude and imprisonment. He had been sent on an elaborately equipped expedition in the ships of the line *Descubierta* and *Atrevida* and had expected the accolade of a returning hero. Instead, he got a dungeon. Malaspina was disgraced, his mind enfeebled, his piles of notes and manuscripts destroyed or lost; his monumental work remained unprinted for a century.

The thought of him induced no happy mood. "Our gaze was fixed on San Antonio de Castillo, where the unfortunate Malaspina was languishing as a prisoner of state. At the moment of leaving Europe to visit lands which he had explored with so much devotion, I could have wished for a theme less sad on which to occupy my thoughts."

Yet when the captain announced that *El Pizarro* would soon sail, all their melancholy disappeared, they turned their faces westward to America, the momentary depression was swept away. Humboldt dashed off as many letters as time permitted to von Moll:

"In a few hours we shall sail. . . . I shall make collections of fossils and plants. I intend to institute chemical analysis of the atmosphere and I shall make astronomical observations. My attention will be ever directed to observing the harmony among the forces of nature, to remarking the influence exerted by inanimate creation upon the vegetable and animal kingdoms."

On the 5th of June 1799 the *Pizarro* weighed anchor and sailed out into the Atlantic. By July 1799, ten days out from the coast of South America, Humboldt picked out the constellation of the Southern Cross, hanging directly over the 16th degree of longitude. He saw it with deep emotion and knew now that the dreams of his childhood were realized — "to be sailing under the Southern Cross."

On the 15th of July they made their landfall at Cumaná. Tall cacti, in the shape of candelabra, studded the dry hills near the sea. To the westward rose a long wall of cumuli, darkly blue and softly shaded, appearing like a great range of far mountains bulking upward on the rim of the world. The harbor was spotted with small sailing craft, their white sails reflected in the turquoise sea, a blue only broken when a huge iridescent tropical fish sprang out of the depths. The bay was filled with canoes. One skirted the *Pizarro* containing earth-brown Indians. Tall and bronze, they looked upon the vessel with the restless, stormy eyes of savages.

The city of Cumaná lay between the rivers San Antonio and Manzanares. Because of its excellent harbor it had become the port of call for all vessels (with proper papers, of course) at the mouth of the Río Orinoco. It was no longer necessary for ships to call first at Cartagena. Charles III of Spain had liberalized shipping and abolished coastwise restrictions. In a royal vessel, the port *capitán* came alongside. When he learned that there were "natural philosophers" aboard who carried the King's rubric, the magic wand of empire began to function: the King's name was a powerful talisman. In a moment they were whisked off the ship, and within the hour they stood in the presence of Don Vicente Emparán, Governor of the Province of Nueva Andalusia, the Captaincy General of Venezuela.

Their passports examined, the official reception over, the freedom of the country was given them. They took to the jungles, the savannas, the rivers in a delirium of excitement. "What magnificent vegetation!" Humboldt managed to get off in a letter. "We have been running like a couple of fools; for the first three days we could settle to nothing. We were always leaving one subject to lay hold of another. Aimé Bonpland declares that he should lose his senses if this state of ecstasy were to continue. . . ."

In this orgy of collecting Humboldt did not forget his primary purpose, to ascend the Río Orinoco to its source and discover exactly where that body of water made contact with the Río Negro. But the monks told him that it was raining up there now, and that they must wait until December to make their ascent. So they collected the birds, the plants, the insects of the region, and then in November set off for Caracas, Humboldt by sea, Bonpland by land.

Alexander, Baron von Humboldt (1769–1859), as he appeared at the time of his sojourn in Quito. Painted by a native artist in 1803.

Balsa raft of South America, as drawn by Humboldt. These immense rafts, formed of lashed balsa logs, were the sea transport of the Incas. They were the marvel of Europe and unknown by illustration until Alexander von Humboldt drew this hand-colored lithograph for his *Atlas*.

CHAPTER XI
The Llanos of Venezuela

Humboldt arrived in Caracas in company with the *cajón de España*. Debarking at the entrepôt of La Guaira, he took horse with the mule convoy that was bringing the mail-bags from Spain.

Caracas was a delightfully planned city, resting in a valley between two mountain spurs and, to use his words, "agreeably placed." Four thousand feet above sea-level, a little less than twenty miles from a port on the Atlantic, it was difficult to assault.

In Humboldt's time Venezuela consisted of seven "United Provinces." Only one eighth of its total of a million inhabitants were Indians, although there were over 200,000 Negroes, mostly slaves. It was a miracle to Humboldt how all these elements — the Negro, the Indian, the mestizo (half-Spanish, half-Indian), and the Creole — with all their varieties of flesh-tints, could be fused into a living, cultural symphony. These United Provinces were then known as the Captaincy General of Venezuela, an enormous mass of land, 400,000 square miles, pushed in like a wedge between Colombia and Brazil.

On its sun-baked llanos, in its towering mountains, between the courses of its vast rivers, there had been built up no great pre-Columbian empire such as had flourished in Peru, Ecuador, Colombia and Panama. The Indians lived in small roving tribes, Caribs and Arawaks, and they alone for centuries had populated the immensity of the llanos and the selvas. Then came that fatal day in 1498 when the caravels of the Admiral of the Ocean Sea swept by the mouth of the Orinoco and moved northward along the Atlantic coast. "I sailed northwards," Columbus wrote, "till I came to a very high mountain. . . . I believe it is impossible to ascend thither, because I am convinced that it is the spot of the earthly paradise, whither no one can go but by God's permission." If this was true, it did not take very long for the Spaniards to have "God's permission." The *terra nova* being divided between Portugal and Spain by the Pope, the viceregent of God, the Spaniards descended upon the "earthly paradise" like baronial lords returning to their fiefs. When the Spaniards informed a chief of the Zenus that the Pope had bestowed all these regions upon the King of Spain, the Indian had replied:

[101]

"Then your Pope must have been drunk and the King an idiot." *

A year after Columbus had discovered South America, a Captain Alonso de Ojeda sailed the main, followed the coast, and entered the great <u>Lake of Maracaibo</u>. On board Ojeda's vessel was Amerigo Vespucci, who had already declared that the land was neither that of Asia nor the isles of Japan, but a New World — *"Novum mundum appellare licet."* When they saw Indian dwellings raised on piles over the lake, it reminded them of Venice, so they called it Venezuela.

Since the land had been marked "Earthly Paradise" by Columbus, the Franciscan friars made it their special domain. Cumaná, near the mouth of the Orinoco, was the place they chose. And for the first years they did well among the Indians. Then, in 1519, at the same time that Hernán Cortés was laying siege to Mexico, Spanish slave-raiders slid in with the dawn, snatched a score of Indians from their homes, and fled across the Caribbean. The Indians at Cumaná gave the padres, whom they held as hostages, until the full moon for the return of the captives, and when they did not appear, they slaughtered the friars. This brought reprisals from the Spanish. The bloodletting in this "earthly paradise" would have gone on interminably had not the celebrated Bartolomé de Las Casas arrived. Upon this apostle to the Indians the leadership of Cumaná had been conferred by Charles V. Accompanied by three hundred laborers, in 1520 he began the first settlement of Venezuela.

To the north, however, around Coro and Lake Maracaibo, and without God's permission, another settlement was taking place: a settlement of Germans. During the conquest of the Americas, Charles V was so animated by ambition that it was not enough for him to be the greatest monarch of Europe; he must be the only one. As quickly as the ingots of gold poured in from Mexico, he spent them in indecisive battles. Hard pressed for cash, he borrowed from all the banking houses of Europe, and by the year 1529 he was so deeply in debt to the commercial house of the Welsers of Augsburg that he was forced, "not in consideration of the sums he had already received, but of those he further expected," to subscribe to the demands of the Welsers for a hereditary fief of the crown.

That fief was the northern part of Venezuela. At once there descended upon Maracaibo fifty German miners and three hundred Spaniards under the leadership of Ambrosius Alfinger. It took but

* As it appears in Fernandez de Encisco's *Suma de geographia* (Seville, 1519), page h4.

six months for the Germans to realize that the Welsers had received a bad piece of real estate; there was little gold. The German colonists, following the same pattern as the Spanish, turned on the Indians to wring out of them by force that which the earth would not yield. Soon Ambrosius Alfinger was liquidated. George von Speyer was sent to replace him, but the organization of the Venezuelan earth progressed no better.

It was about this time that the fable of El Dorado seeped down into their colony. Animated by these *sueños dorados,* they sent Nicholaus Federmann and a vast concourse of colonists and Indians to seek out the golden city. Months later, after a trek of a thousand miles through jungles and mountains, they made that famous ironical junction with Quesada and Belalcázar in the Andes of Colombia.

The German colony ended with the death of Philip von Hutten in 1541, leaving for posterity only the work of his brother, Ulrich, on the virtues of the infusions of guaiacum bark — *De guaiaci medicina et morbo gallico* — for the cure of syphilis. After that the fiefdom of the Welsers lapsed back to the crown, and the Council of the Indies did not permit again any transferring of Spanish territory to other nations.

By 1652 all expeditions against the Indians ceased. Civilization, it was decreed, should come through the missions. The Capuchins took over the missions near the mouth of the Orinoco, the Franciscans the middle section, and the Jesuits the upper arms of that great river. By the time Venezuela was established as a Captaincy General in 1777, the monks had reared thirty-eight towns on the Orinoco and had brought twenty-five thousand Indians under control. The "earthly paradise" had been finally settled with "God's permission."

When Aimé Bonpland arrived, Humboldt secured a house in an elevated part of Caracas. It was elegantly furnished. The windows and inside doors were covered with curtains of crimson damask; the seats were of simple tooled leather or else fantastically carved in Gothic style and heavily gilded. Such rooms were part of the equipment of every person of means, but were opened "with scarcely an exception only in honor to those who come to fulfill the tender duties of friendship or the irksome ceremonies of etiquette." In the instance of Humboldt and Bonpland, they were opened in the King's name. The people of Caracas outdid one another in their efforts to make the stay of the honored gentlemen a pleasant and profitable one. They had the opportunity of meeting everyone of position.

When they could escape from the overwhelming kindness of the people, Humboldt and Bonpland carried on their researches. The months of November and December 1799 were well spent. They climbed the mountains, they measured the air, they undertook elaborate researches on the temperature; Aimé Bonpland collected plants; and when the deluging rains prevented them from carrying on this work, they readied their equipment for the trip across the llanos and the ascent of the Orinoco.

Everywhere they found the people of Venezuela — white, black, or bronze — the very epitome of kindness itself. "We northern Europeans," Humboldt wrote to his brother, "have a strange extravagant prejudice against the Spanish people. I have been living on intimate terms with all the classes of society from the Capuchins to the Viceroy. I have become as familiar with the Spanish tongue as I am with my own. . . . All these people possess, in my mind, the elements of a grand character."

Yet he found some lamentable defects, and of these he wrote simply and easily, as objectively as if he were describing a jungle or a river. These observations were the foundation of his political understanding. He found these people "warm, convivial, of likable candor, of great simplicity of manner, although," he confessed, "they were apt to be suspicious and very annoyingly curious."

Race was the exposed nerve of Venezuela. The color of the skin itself was a badge of nobility. *"Todo blanco es caballero"* — "All white men are noble" — was their phrase. Everywhere in the colonies Humboldt found two kinds of nobility: first the Creoles, whose ancestors filled great stations, and whose "prerogatives were founded on the distinction they enjoyed in the mother country, Spain"; and secondly the descendants of the original conquistadores, who kept their social distinctions, but who had lost their political ones. Yet the color of the skin was the supreme test. Humboldt once heard a man, barefooted, scarcely able to cover his skin with suitable clothing, say: "Does that rich man think himself whiter than I am?"

Humboldt believed that when the colonists essayed an attempt at freedom, Venezuela would be the spot from which the first struggles would develop: "Every enterprise in favor of independence and liberty puts the national, or American, party in opposition to the men of the mother country."

Humboldt was a human geographer (a field of which he was the originator) already concerned with the political ataxia of the Captaincy General of Venezuela. He saw and marked out three stages of society, based on the three geographical zones of the country. In the first of these, the marginal jungle, was the Indian, a hunter, a casual agriculturist. He lived principally along river-banks and in the deltas and plateaus of the Orinoco. His stage of society was anarchical, antisocial; there was constant hostility among the tribes, as well as intermittent war against the monks and the military. Humboldt observed: "Everything in this stage presented a melancholy picture, where misery and privation were the essential elements."

In the second zone the llanos-dwellers dominated. Their lives were lived on the flat savannas of even temperature. Here cattle grazed unattended and here the pastoral life was lived mostly by pure-blooded *castillanos*. It was a decadent society where the food had little variety, where the *llaneros* were isolated by distance from one another, and where fine courtly manners were completely out of harmony with the primitive surroundings, the unnoticed quagmires of filth that surrounded their doors.

The third and last stage of society, also corresponding to its geographical zone, was the agricultural. Here the people were usually white, although touched faintly with colored blood. In the minds of the rigidly social Creoles, this class was touched too by commercialism. These people grew coffee and cacao. They were exporters of their products, they hired people, they arranged prices, they fixed markets, they had contact with people and with governments on the outside — they were, in short, politically minded.

The most important product of the agricultural zone was coffee. It had been planted first in 1795 on the precipitous slopes of the mountains, and its marketing was already beginning to show in the financial register of the Capitanía. Coffee was not native to the Americas. It had first been known to be planted in Ethiopia. Later Arab traders brought the plant down to Mocha in Arabia. The Arabs took to preparing the bean; contact with the Spaniards spread knowledge of it; soon it was transmitted to all Europe. By 1720 it had reached the Americas. The gold and silver was gone and there was a need for a firmer economic foundation in the Spanish colonies. Coffee, along with cacao, became the basis of Venezuela's new agricultural economy.

Cacao (which when toasted and ground becomes chocolate) had not been known to Venezuela until it was brought in by the Spaniards. Originally developed by the Incas under the name of *kakua*, it had reached Mexico centuries before Cortés. Benzoni, an earlier traveler in the Americas, said that chocolate "was a drink fitter for hogs than men." And Acosta, a friend of Humboldt's, wrote that the Americas "are fond of chocolate to excess, but it is necessary to be accustomed to that black beverage not to be disgusted at the mere sight of its froth, which swims on it like yeast on a fermented liquor." Carl Linnæus had named the cacao tree *Theobroma cacao*. It was Humboldt who described its cultivation and growth in terms which have never since ceased to be quoted through the years.

December marked the height of the dry season. The great grass savannas, fired by the *llaneros,* filled the night with flame, sweeping like currents of smoldering lava over the valley. The vivid steady light assumed a reddish tinge, and the Dantesque scene looked precisely like a volcano. This Humboldt and Bonpland saw when they climbed the Cerro de Avila, close to Caracas. The evening atmosphere thickened and the mountains were overhung with clouds — "streams of vapor clung to their evergreen slopes," Humboldt wrote. "Beneath the misty sky, I could scarcely imagine myself to be in one of the temperate valleys of the torrid zone, but rather in the north of Germany among the pines and the larches that cover the Harz mountains."

Yet now, with the burning of the llanos, they knew their time had come. It was February 1800, and time to be off to the Orinoco to "determine just where the connection between the Orinoco and Amazon waterbeds took place."

Stretching southward from Caracas for one hundred and fifty miles are the most remarkable plains of the world, the llanos of Venezuela. Neither prairie nor desert, they are intermediate between the two, depending on the seasons. Their flatness is the flatness of a windless lake; no rolling prairies, no undulations, no sandhills or ridges, but a flat, almost treeless plain covered with short grass, which stretches from the Orinoco deltas to the spurs of the Andes. There are only two seasons, the wet and the dry, regulated wholly by the trade winds that blow across them, east to west. The sun beats down with an annual mean temperature of 90 degrees and the sandy ground, thinly covered with grass, becomes oven-hot. The winds, fresh from the sea, at first lessen the heat. But then, as the trades become heated, the wind becomes like the brain-searing sirocco.

It was over these llanos that Humboldt and Bonpland, loaded down with their cargo, made their way. First they went by canoe down to the mouth of the Río Guarico and Cabruta, through the Teques Mountains, past the hot springs of Mariana; they circled the fertile banks of Lake Valencia to land beyond its shores in the Valley of Aragua. There they found a cheerful pastoral setting, the land checkerboarded with plantations of sugar cane and coffee trees on the hills; cotton growing in the hot treeless valleys. Every ranch house, with its red-tiled roof, was surrounded by clumps of trees, dwarfed and shaded by the huge arms of a giant ceiba. Here Bonpland collected the seeds of the *volador,* a plant which he called the *gyrocarpus.* It was a tree that excited their imaginations, since the winged seeds rode the winds with erratic motions like the gyrations of athletes at a *Turnverein.* They rode past the great estates of the Marquis de Toro, built around an ancient Indian community. The soft undulations of the field of sugar cane resembled the great meadows of France. Everything there breathed abundance. Everything seemed luxurious, although purchased, in Humboldt's mind, at a high cost — the cost of liberty for the Negro slave.

Beyond Aragua they came out upon the vast llanos. Cattle could be seen miles away, dotting the flat steppes like fly-specks. The grass now was dry as chalk; broad acres were black as soot from the fires that had swept over them. It was hard to believe that with the rains this whole vast plain would be transformed into a sea of green. Now in the dry season the rivers and creeks were dried up, the plants dead, and the grass reduced to powder. Humboldt found that even the "alligators and snakes remain buried in the dried mud until awakened by the first showers."

Yet the hospitality of the people never failed them in this land, a land more like the desolation of the sea than terra firma. At every small *hato* they were given a place to swing their hammock, there was a fire, and later food. Almost always the food consisted of a *sancocho* of stewed fowl, thin, dry cassava cakes watered down to make them palatable, black beans, roasted plantains — and the grand finale, a cup of pitch-black coffee, so strong as to keep the travelers awake half the night.

At Güigüe on the llanos they lodged at a tumbledown rancho with an old sergeant, a native of Murcia, bearded and toothless, his gnarled body scarred by wounds of a thousand Indian skirmishes. They found him to be a most original character. To prove to them that he had studied with the Jesuits before the lure of battle had taken him from the blackboard, he recited the history of the creation while the travelers rested. They listened to him call off the names of Augustus, of Tiberius and Diocletian, of all the popes since Peter. He named the pagan philosophers, Cicero, Titus Livius, Polybius, Boethius, and Cassiodorus.

Beyond the rancho of the old soldier they came upon the small cluster of red-roofed houses which was the village of Nueva Valencia. Here they were surprised to find white people working the fields of cotton and indigo. It was the first time since their arrival that they had seen *blancos* turning their hands to manual labor. But these people did it far from the village, since if they were to be found working with their own hands, a grave disgrace would fall upon them. Nothing else seemed to grow on these llanos but indigo and cotton, the fault, the *llaneros* said, of the leaf-cutting ants.

These large, reddish, sharp-spined ants, with enormous heads and fierce serrated mandibles, lived deep down in the earth. There they grew fungus gardens which they fertilized with the leaves they cut, and which yielded the food upon which the whole formicary existed. When a nest was cut open, Humboldt watched the ants drag along a piece of cut leaf, crawl down the hole, and give it to a smaller red ant, which crushed it, rolled it into a ball, and placed it on a large fungus head. Humboldt did not then have the scientific background to gauge the importance of all that he saw, but his curiosity was endless. He saw, actually, the first recognized instance of *symbiosis,* wherein ant and plant lived together upon the joint product of their co-operation. Neither plant nor insect could live without the other.

As the swarming ants had a particular love for exotic plants, the village of Nueva Valencia was almost wholly destitute of plant life. It is true that the monks of San Francisco tried at first to use some intelligent methods of eradication. They dug into the ant nests. They destroyed the fungus and the larvæ, even tried fumigating them; still the ants persisted. Failing in this, the monks at last advised the inhabitants of Nueva Valencia to choose some saint who would act as mediator and eradicate the plague of ants. The honor of choice fell on Saint Saturnin. The inhabitants insisted that as soon as the name of the saint was evoked and his first festival celebrated, the umbrella ants disappeared.

At each new village they met some new phenomenon. Halfway across the llanos, in the village of Barbula, they were told of the "cow tree," the *palo de vaca,* which like a cow gave drinkable milk. Humboldt's servant assured him that he drank its milk every morning. Even in this continent of surprises, this was too much. "So we approached," said Humboldt, "this *palo de vaca* with incredulity."

The tree itself was not impressive. It looked like the star apple, with its handsome leaves deep green and glabrous above and dark on the other side. It was covered with deep brown cicatrices from the knives of those who "milked" it — and Humboldt, not to be outdone, had his servant strike the cow tree for milking. As the sap of trees is often acidulous or poisonous, Bonpland looked askance as Humboldt filled a calabash with the white thick liquid, raised the gourd to his eyes in a mock toast, and essayed an experimental sip, then took a deep draught. It *was* like milk! There was an acidity about it, but although it had a thick consistency, its taste was perfectly creamy and agreeable. With amazement, Bonpland and Humboldt stood and gazed at this wonder of America. In a land that contained solemn shades of forests, majestic courses of rivers, and mountains wrapped in eternal snow, in a land that was filled with ruins of bygone civilizations, these two stood enraptured before a few drops of the sap of the *palo de vaca*. It must be made known to science. The leaves were collected and pressed, the tree described and drawn; it proved to be an Arto-carpus, a tree already widespread in equatorial America less than a score of years after the hardy Spanish explorers of the late eighteenth century had brought it there from Asia. It was a relative of the mulberries, and a close ally of *Ficus elastica*, a rubber-yielding tree. Little wonder that one Negro, after drinking too much of the *palo de vaca*, vomited rubber balls! The acid of his stomach had, in effect, coagulated the sap of the *palo de vaca* into gutta-percha.

Their guide, who by now considered himself the very genius of the marvelous, stated with great ceremony that if the señores were surprised at a tree that emitted milk, they should see the eels in the region of Calabozo. These, a yard in length, gave out shocks of electrical current strong enough to put men and horses to death.

Calabozo, more than halfway from Caracas to the Orinoco, was on their main route to San Fernando de Apure, from which river port they would continue by boat. It was only March; there were still many weeks of dry season before them. Why not stop at Calabozo? Since the cow tree was a fact, why did they not look into the story of electric eels?

The whole field of electricity was new and exciting. The mere mention of the words "electrical current" was enough to arouse Humboldt's interest. Only a few years previously Galvani and Volta had made their first researches and discoveries; and Humboldt himself, while still a student under Blumenbach, had written a youthful paper on *The Nervous and Muscular Irritation of Animal Fibers*. Now he had before him, if his guide's rumor was true, an excellent opportunity for the examination of animal electricity. In this way was discovered, so far as science is concerned, the famed electric eel.

At Calabozo, Bonpland and Humboldt were put up at a rancho, the usual rural house of the llanos, roofed with tiles and constructed like a barrack. Horses, pigs, dogs, and chickens indifferently entered and left the house as if it were a stable. There was a ceiba tree shading the ranch, with a huge trunk like a column, supported by what appeared to be four uniform buttresses. Under the ceiba Humboldt gathered his eel-catchers. The natives confirmed all that the other had said: the eels, many of them, lived in the small streams that flowed over the treeless llano. But there was caution in the way they spoke. "They are dangerous, señor, these *tembladores,* dangerous!" If a man merely approached within a league of where they were, they could send shocks so fierce as to make the earth tremble. Humboldt was forced to pay the natives two piasters (approximately a dollar) to go after them. He soon learned, however, that the abundance of the eels and their capture were two different things. Humboldt wanted them alive. There was a long consultation among the natives; then they went away to the corral and brought out horses. These, they said, would arouse the eels from the slime of the bottom where they were resting and galvanize them into action.

The thirsty horses, sadly in need of a good pasturage, were sent splashing into the water of the *tembladores.* The *llaneros* kept them in the center of the stream by standing on both banks so as to prevent them from returning. Some of the natives scrambled up the trees that overhung the river, armed with their long harpoons, while others stayed on the banks similarly armed. Soon the thud of the hoofs began to disturb the eels. Like a horde of angry, venomous serpents, they swam against the bellies of the horses and began to blast out their shocks. The horses, wild with terror, plunged about in the water trying to escape the electrical current. The shocks that the eels were sending out were of sufficient strength to send them to their knees; some of the horses, completely unconscious, slid under the water. Humboldt, on the bank, stood in awe before this display of natural force. After some minutes the horses, panting and weak, were allowed to stumble out of the stream and fall on the ground. There they lay breathing heavily. The electrical shocks seemed to travel along their abdominal nerves, depriving them of the use of their legs. Some of them, indeed, had drowned.

But the horses had not been sacrificed in vain. The *llaneros* had harpooned some of the eels. They were five feet long, with a fiercely formed head and waving elastic body. Humboldt had the squirming creatures laid on the ground for experimentation. As he walked by, he made the mistake of stepping on one. Immediately there shot through his body a tremendous electrical current. "I do not remember," he wrote, recalling the incident, "of having ever received from the discharge of a large Leyden jar a more dreadful shock than that which I experienced. I was affected during the rest of the day with a violent pain in the knees and in almost every joint."

The voyage up the Orinoco was put off for the next days while

Humboldt experimented with the electric eel, which he called *Electrophorus electricus*. He found the eel over three feet in length; five feet was not uncommon. It was a sinuous fish, elongated and almost cylindrical in cross-section, entirely destitute of scales. Its most prominent external feature was a continuous, ribbonlike fin extending from the head to tail.

What created the electrical current in the eel? To find out, Humboldt, with Bonpland's aid, began to dissect a specimen. He found the "organs of Hunter" and the "bundles of Sachs," as they were later named, which were responsible for the eel's dynamo. He found the weight of the eel equally distributed between the muscles for its locomotion and the bundles of fiber that produced the electric shocks.

Humboldt then turned his attention to the manner in which this electrical discharge is used. He found that the eel lies quietly on the bottom of the river, giving out little shocks now and then. But when something stirs it, it sends off heavy discharges which arouse the other eels in the vicinity. The water, being an excellent conductor of electricity, fairly sparkles with electrical force. The animal or fish that is unfortunate enough to invade an eel-infested stream is soon stunned, then set upon by all the eels near by.

When Humboldt wrote of the electric eels, all Europe gasped in astonishment. Never in all the years that America had been explored had anything come out so startling and so well explained. Humboldt was an indefatigable correspondent, and his letters, written to the learned men of Europe, read before societies, quoted at salons, and repeated in newsprint, excited an interest in the New World which had not been displayed since its discovery. But this was only the beginning. In March 1800 Humboldt and Bonpland had come at last to the swirling muddy waters of the Orinoco.

CHAPTER XII
The Orinoco Yields Its Secret

THE ORINOCO sprawls across the map of Venezuela like a mighty fishhook, the shank flattened out to form its delta, the point stuck thousands of miles somewhere in that shadowy, mystical highland of Brazilian Guiana. Midway between its two extreme points is its largest tributary, the Apure, a river which drains most of the Venezuelan llanos. And on its banks, eighty miles from its junction with the Orinoco and waiting to descend it, were Humboldt and Bonpland.

The tangled-bearded Capuchins, upon reading a letter of introduction from the Bishop of Caracas, set their Indian charges to work and within three days had transformed a thirty-foot dugout into a sailing vessel that was to carry the explorers up to the border of Brazil. The help of the monks was invaluable since the Supreme Ruler of the Orinoco was God. Or, since God did not exercise direct control, the agents of God, the Capuchin, the Franciscan, and the Jesuit fathers, controlled the river. For centuries they had exercised spiritual and, when occasion demanded, material control over the Orinoco and its inhabitants.

The president of the Capuchin missions gave them a guide through whom they might find the "canal" that connected the Orinoco with the Negro. "You will go down the Río Apure," he said, "until it joins the Orinoco; thence you will go up the Orinoco, past the missions of Atabapo. . . . When the force of the current of black waters hinders you from advancing, you will be conducted out of the bed of the river, through forests, which you will find inundated. . . . Two monks who are settled in these jungles will furnish you with the means of having your canoes drawn overland. . . . If your canoe be not broken, you will descend into the Río Negro. . . . There you will find the canal."

By most of the monks who had traveled on the river, the connection was accepted as a fact. Since pre-Columbian times the Indians had known — and used — the waterway between these two of South America's greatest rivers. It was known to most of the missionaries operating on these rivers in the eighteenth century. Charles-Marie de La Condamine could write with conviction: "The fact of the connection between the Orinoco and the Amazon Rivers no longer admits of doubt." But where, geographically, was this point? It was this question that Humboldt proposed to answer.

Arrowsmith, the celebrated nineteenth-century English cartographer, had put a great inland lake into his maps, a lake seventy miles in breadth, which was supposed to lie between the Amazon and the Orinoco. This imaginary lake had persisted since the time of Raleigh and his dream of El Dorado. In a sketch map made by that Elizabethan, the Amazon and the Orinoco appear as great rivers running parallel to each other, connecting nowhere and separated by an enormous inland lake looking something like a shriveled appendix. This body of water, which no one ever saw, was called the Lake of Manoa. These geographical misconceptions had persisted down to Humboldt's time. Arrowsmith had even advanced the supposition that the Lake of Manoa was the source of the Orinoco River. It was all too evident how little was really known about the geography of South America.

It was Columbus who had discovered the mouth of the Orinoco. The current it produced between the mainland and the asphaltic island of Trinidad was so powerful that his ships, with all their canvases spread and a westerly breeze, could scarcely make way against it. This desolate and fearful spot he called the Golfo Triste — the Bay of Sadness. When he saw the body of milky water pouring into the blue pellucid Atlantic, he exclaimed: "Such an enormous body of fresh water could only be collected from a river having a long course; the land, therefore, which supplied it must be a continent, and not an island."

But what continent? Asia, of course! "The grateful coolness of the evening air, the ethereal purity of the starry firmament," writes Antonio de Herrera in his *Historia general*, "the balmy fragrance of flowers, wafted to the Admiral by the land breeze, all led him to suppose that he was approaching the Garden of Eden."

A century later Sir Walter Raleigh was undertaking a gigantic expedition up the Orinoco "to the large, rich, and beautiful empire of Guiana and the Golden City of Manoa." Actually the lake of El Dorado lay on a conical summit in the eastern cordillera of Colombia, at eight thousand feet altitude, and was not more than a mile in diameter. But this little tarn was transferred by Raleigh's wonder-filled brain 2,000 miles eastward. Many an English merchant and many a prince lost their fortunes on that expedition, seduced by the honeyed words of: ". . . wearied feet, traveling ye know not whither, soon, soon it seemed to you, you must come forth on some conspicuous hilltop, and but a little way further, against the setting sun, descry the spires of El Dorado."

Raleigh and his men sailed up the Orinoco in small boats. As they advanced, the wind failed them and they were forced to paddle against the powerful current. The crews grew weak as the river "ran more violently against them." But Raleigh refused to return yet, "lest the world would laugh us to scorn." Some hundreds of miles upstream they attacked the Spanish fort of San Tomás, a castle which sat most strategically upon a mass of rock dominating the river. There in the struggle Raleigh lost his son, and there he set in motion — although he did not know it — the mechanism that would deprive him of his handsome head. He was stirred to poetical heights by what he saw on the Orinoco; of it he wrote:

"Guiana is a country that hath yet her maidenhood. The face of the earth hath not been torn, the graves have not yet been opened for gold. It hath never been entered by any army of strength and never conquered by a Christian prince. Men shall find here more rich and beautiful cities, more temples adorned with gold than either Cortés found in Mexico or Pizarro in Peru, and the shining glory of this conquest will eclipse all those of the Spanish nation. I never saw a more beautiful country, nor more lively prospects; hills raised here and there, over the valleys, the river winding into different branches, plains without bush or stubble, all fair green grass, deer crossing our path, the birds toward evening singing on every side a thousand different tunes, herons of white, crimson, and carnation perching on the riverside, the air fresh with a gentle wind. . . ."

No foreigner in colonial times again wrote of the Orinoco; Spain plugged up the gap. The missions took over; the Franciscans and the Capuchins and the Jesuits ruled the roost, and the Indians, unmolested by competing conquistadores, gradually settled down to a relatively peaceful relationship with the agents of God.

Then, in 1745, Padre José Gumilla wrote his fantastic book, *El Orinoco illustrado y defendido*. In it he denied with vehemence the existence of the Río Negro and Orinoco canal in haughty words: *"El Orinoco (no) hemos visto entrar ni salir (el) alto río Negro"* ("We have seen the Orinoco (neither) enter nor leave (the) Upper Río Negro"). But La Condamine in his discourse before the Académie des Sciences insisted there *was* a canal that linked the whole of the Amazon and Orinoco valleys. This stirred the Spanish government, which sent out an expedition under a Capitán Solano in 1754. He proposed to look for the connecting link, but of his 325 men, only thirteen returned; and so the geographical controversy lay waiting for its solution by Alexander von Humboldt. Was there a connection between these rivers or was there not? If so, where did it lie? The questions would soon be answered, for Humboldt and Bonpland were poised on the banks of the Apure waiting for the moment to set off.

Their launch was a sad imitation of that in which Cleopatra once sailed. Two and one-half feet wide, their ark had been made more commodious by a sort of latticework which the Capuchins had constructed over its gunwales so as to extend its width beyond its thick sides. It had a roof intended to be large enough to cover their persons; but their legs stuck far out, to be wet by the rains and bitten by the insects. On the latticework floor there were ox-hides and, to lend a jungle note, an enormous jaguar skin. While the black-cowled Capuchins lined the bank and looked with sat-isfaction on their handiwork, the Indians brought food for the expedition. There were eggs wrapped in banana leaves, plantains, live chickens with their feet tied together, large cassava cakes, toasted cacao beans, all piled in the forward part of the canoe where the four Indian paddlers stood. In the palm-plaited "cabin" the Capuchins placed oranges, tamarinds, and for the dark days ahead some bottles of sherry. For trade goods (money was un-known to the Upper Orinoco Indians) they brought tobacco in broad dark leaves, fishing tackle, firearms, and casks of brandy. On March 30, 1800, while Napoleon was being proclaimed First Con-sul, the expedition set off to discover the canal that connected the Orinoco and the Amazon valleys. As their pilot, standing in the stern, sent the canoe out into the torrent of yellow water, the Ca-puchins lined the banks and shouted:

"*Vaya, vaya con Dios.*"

The Orinoco is divided, like Cæsar's *omnia Gallia,* into three parts. The main part, from the delta westward 400 miles, is wide, deep and swift-flowing, navigable for deep-drafted vessels up to the little town of Caicara. It flows through open, level llanos crowned with gigantic outthrusts of rock that look like Rhenish castles. Here are shifting sandbars on which the unwary may be marooned and exposed to sudden, unannounced *chubascos* that sweep down with the force of a hurricane. Above Caicara village is the Río Apure, which drains most of northwestern Venezuela and rolls down to make its juncture with the Orinoco. The Apure is choked with ugly boulders around which the waters seethe and spin and boil. The third part of the Orinoco comes directly from the south, flowing from the jungle-studded sierras of Mount Duida, which is its source, 300 miles to the Mission of San Fer-nando de Atabapo, then nearly as far again to its junction with the Apure. Over a thousand miles in length, formed of thirty-six monstrous tributaries and over two thousand streams and rivulets, the Río Orinoco extends its hydrographic system over 270,000 square miles, almost the area of the Kingdom of Spain.

Down the largest of the tributaries, the Apure, the small *lancha* was being tossed about like a pea in a paper bag. Even though the Indian crew was skillful, the boat, crudely fashioned, was clumsy. At every turn in the mile-wide river the explorers thought themselves in imminent danger of being swamped.

Then the river, falling less rapidly and leaving the *raudales* behind, spread out and grew calm. The llanos, which were its banks, became spotted with red-leaved suasco bushes and tall top-heavy palms, and animal life became more common. As they swept along, great flocks of rose-winged flamingoes, black-legged spoonbills, and snow-white egrets darkened the sky in wide-flung sweeps. Aimé Bonpland had never seen so many birds in all his life. His head was thrown back, watching the endless flights, until his neck pained. Sky, savanna, and river were now animated by living forms. "Animals of different nature," observed Humboldt, "succeeded one another. Alligators appeared on the banks, motionless, with their mouths open, while by them and near to them capybaras, the large, web-footed rodents that swim like dogs and feed on roots, appeared in bewildering herds, even lying among the alligators, seeming to know that these repulsive reptiles do not attack on land. Tapirs broke through the tall grass and slipped down to the Apure to drink." The toothless pilot, noting their interest in the animals, added his part; with a wave of his chocolate-brown arm he shouted: "It is just like paradise." But it was less like a paradise and more like the environs of the Styx as they approached the junction with the Orinoco.

An immense plain of water, current-tossed and wind-swept, something like a shoreless lake, shot up before them. White-topped waves rose to a height of several feet, caused by the conflicting currents and the winds. As they tossed over this inland sea, the air was rent with cries of herons and spoonbills, flying in files from one side to another. The paddling was growing difficult; the Indians hoisted a sail. It caught the trades, but it hardly sufficed against the current. And now mountains appeared on the shore, bursting through the llanos and casting a funereal darkness over the bare landscape. Three thousand or more feet high, rugged and forbidding, the verdureless mountains were a succession of peaks, domes, crags, and precipices, shadowed by a long, block-shaped bulk, beyond which were other jumbled peaks receding into the leaden horizon.

The Orinoco Yields Its Secret

By April 17, two weeks from their starting-point, they came to their first *"punta de la civilización,"* the Mission of La Concepción de Urbana on the Orinoco. The flat llanos had now disappeared; hills, bare and bald, were the dominant theme, pouring down, steep and precipitous, to the river's edge. A thin gallery of forest still fringed the banks, but the tablelands broke into sheer cliffs, "isolated bosses, knobs, and smoothly polished domes . . . monstrous rocks were thrown here and there in utter confusion." It was a weird, fascinating region.

At La Urbana their pilot and paddlers from the Apure turned back; they would have to get others who knew the streams ahead. While they raised this contingent, Bonpland went into the forest and was soon lost in an endless variety of new plants. He collected palms, orchids, grasses, and bamboos. He picked up the leaves of the achiote bush; there among the Cassias and Dioscoreas the botanic soul of Aimé unfolded like a star lily.

Having lost their boat with the pilot, they purchased a new canoe and got the Indians to fashion them a palm-plaited *carroza* at the stern — a sort of barrel-shaped contrivance in which men and goods were protected from alternate fiercely pelting rain and murderous sun. At La Urbana, too, they acquired a greater asset: they had the pleasure of a companion in the person of Padre Bernardo Zea, who, wishing to visit some other Padres on the river, begged permission to join them. The explorers acquired an open sesame on the river in his person.

Beyond La Urbana monstrous black rocks loomed before them. These were the sinister stones of Paluas. The lancha cut through the raging rapids, ripped past the black domes and the veritable labyrinth of inky steppes. As they whirled by this Stygian scene, Humboldt could think of nothing more fitting than the lines:

> Through me you pass into eternal pain,
> Through me among the people lost for aye,
> All hope abandon, ye who enter here.

"All hope abandon," at least all hope of comfort, for these malevolent cliffs of Paluas marked the entrance into a region of tiny insect fiends that exacted a blood tribute: *piumes* set upon them at once. An insect small enough to fly through a needle's eye, it could sting like a wasp and its puncture left behind a tiny globule of blood. Mosquitoes, flies, gnats, chiggers, ants followed, and were described briefly by the padre as *"la plaga."*

The plague was unusual even for the natives. One old Indian exclaimed: "How comfortable must be the people on the moon! She looks so beautiful. She must be free of mosquitoes."

[117]

Up, up, up the Orinoco they went, insects or no, paddling when they could, using ropes when the water was too swift, pushing in the narrows and portaging round the great *raudales* (rapids) . Up they went to the foaming junction of the Río Meta. The union of the two rivers Humboldt declared was a "great spectacle." Great rock castles, black and forbidding, rose three thousand feet over the tossing, stormy meeting-place of the Meta and the Orinoco. The force of the two streams created so many cross-currents and backwaters that the lancha was virtually suspended in the center of the raging river-torrents. Unable to make headway there, the pilot put the boat in to shore, taking advantage of the back-current thrown up along the bank. But they could no longer avoid the inevitable. To go up the river they had to enter the rapids.

The river grew frightfully turbulent. They came to the famous and much-feared *raudales* — the rapids of the Maipures. As they approached the rapids, which seethed and boiled as in a cauldron, the bowman sang out: *"Vamos con Dios."*

The pilot then sucked in a deep breath and answered: *"Y con la Virgen."*

Then once more as in an antiphonal chant, the bowman called: "And may the most Holy Mary accompany us!"

It was the final chant before they hit the boiling *raudal*. The boat was tossed about. The monkeys screeched, the canoe shook violently and they hit calm water again. Humboldt and Bonpland breathed normally once more.

About the extensive Maipures Rapids there are endless stretches of open savanna, broken by abrupt hills, some almost devoid of vegetation, others heavily forested; lines of forests followed the streams. There were more and more yagua palms, graceful, slim-trunked trees with drooping fronds, as well as chiquichiqui palms and the *palos de aceite,* big, smooth, yellow-barked trees that yielded an oil used in commerce. And in the background great barren outcrops of granite lay in nearly horizontal masses. This was one of Humboldt's collecting stations. They spent three days there in the small village erected by José Solano in 1754. They collected plants while their canoe was pulled through the rapids and their equipment brought on the backs of Indians around the cataracts. Here Bonpland added greatly to his plant collections. But the plague of insects was so overpowering that he was unable to arrange his specimens until the Indians suggested that he bring his plants to their giant conical oven. So Bonpland, as Humboldt recounted, "with courage and patience crawled into the hot *hornito* to be free of the insect plague, and there pressed thousands of plants."

Above the rapids of the Maipures, on their way once more, they passed the Río Sipapo, little different from the thousand and one streams that pour into the Orinoco, but Padre Bernardo Zea gave it great importance:

"It is the country of the Rayas Indians, whose mouths are said to be in their navels."

Now Humboldt and Bonpland, who had seen a cow tree, and electric eels, and spoonbills, were in a most receptive mood, but not for Indians with their mouths at their navels.

"Of a certainty," said the Indian pilot, "there are such Indians." He claimed that he had seen these acephali with his own eyes.

The padre said that the Indians were called *Rayas* because they were like the sting rays, whose mouths were near their tails. Humboldt was duly skeptical. The myth, thanks to his irony, has long been relegated to the realm of fable. A plausible explanation of the story is that the *Rayas* wore wide headdresses that covered their entire heads and shoulders, and painted faces about their navels. It was Sir Walter Raleigh who first began the nonsense by speaking of "Ewaipahomas, the headless warriors:"

"On that River Sipapo," he wrote, "which is called Caura, are a nation of people whose heads are reported to have their eyes in their shoulders and their mouths in the middle of their breasts and that a long train of hair groweth backward between their shoulders. The son of Topiawari, a lower Orinoco chief, which I brought with me into England, told me that they were the most mighty men of all the land . . . and had of late slain many hundreds. . . ." Thus Raleigh and his *sueños dorados*. Shakespeare picked up this legend and made it immortal by writing in *Othello:*

> And of the Cannibals that each other eat,
> The Anthropophagi and men whose heads
> Do grow beneath their shoulders.

Humboldt met with no acephali; only water, clouds, insects, and rain; days of poling and of portage that carried them up, up beyond the Jesuit Mission of San Fernando de Atabapo. So they went on day after day. A month had passed and, with them hardly aware of it, the Orinoco was transporting them to a new country. Again came the words of the Capuchin monk:

". . . You will go up and up. First past the Atabapo, the Temí, and finally the Tuamini. When the force of the current of the black waters hinders you from advancing, you will be conducted out of the bed of the river. . . . At Yavita you will be furnished with the means of having your canoe drawn overland. . . ." And as he had suggested, so it came to pass.

Thirty-three days after leaving the Capuchin mission at the Río Apure they had come to rest at the Mission of San Antonio de Yavita. Now, at this point there is a curious phenomenon that explains the connection between the Orinoco and the Amazon. At San Fernando de Atabapo, a distance of about 300 miles from the confluence of the Apure, the Orinoco makes a right angle eastward, then winds about the hills of the Sierra de Parima until it dissipates itself in a series of rivulets. But halfway between its source and where it turns eastward at Atabapo, there is a branch, the Casiquiare, a stream without a counterpart in the world, "whose existence," in Humboldt's words, "had been alternately proved and denied for half a century." The Casiquiare has not a reversible current; it is simply an arm of the Upper Orinoco which, instead of merely wandering around and then joining the mother stream, as do countless other arms and channels, gets lost on a low, wide plain and wanders over into the territory of the Amazon. There it joins the Río Guainía, rising far to the westward in Colombia, to form the Río Negro, the largest affluent of the Amazon from the north.

There is still another way to reach the Río Negro from the Orinoco, and Humboldt took this route so as to encompass the whole country. San Antonio de Yavita is separated from a stream called the Caño Pimichín, in the Río Negro drainage, only by a neck of land over which canoes can be dragged in portage. This is shorter than the Upper Orinoco-Casiquiare route, and it was for this reason that a mission was established there by the Franciscans.

Padre Ceresco, who had held the mission alone, was beside himself with joy at their arrival. "You will want for nothing at my mission," he told them. "You can have all the plantains and fish you want. At night you are not stung by mosquitoes. The longer you stay, the better the chance to see your stars. If your canoe is destroyed in the portage, we will build you another. . . . And I, Padre Ceresco, shall have the satisfaction of passing some weeks *con gente blanco y de razón! . . .*"

Portage rollers were made from the hard lignum vitæ wood, and on them the lancha was put when it was pulled from the water. It took twenty-three Indians a full day to drag the empty canoe through the jungle from one stream to the other. It did not break in the portage, but Humboldt stayed on, as much to please the padre who maintained this outpost of God as to allow Bonpland time to collect plants. And there were other observations to make. This road for portage had been built only since 1795 and it interested Humboldt. He unpacked his theodolite and began a survey of the ground. He believed that on the spot a canal could be

built connecting these two river arms. It would answer the problems of transportation. So Humboldt sat down amid the buzzing
flies and languid Indians and wrote a memorial to King Charles
of Spain, not only proposing the canal, but furnishing a plan for
it, with rough measurements. Nor was the political aspect of geography lost on him. He noticed that in an open country communication by river assists in a most definite manner to generalize
language and customs. Along the rivers there were a uniform
economy, monetary exchange, and culture. But on opposite sides
of a dense forest the differences would be great. He felt "that the
impenetrable forests of the torrid zone increase the dismember-
ment of a nation; such forests favor the transition of dialects into
languages and become the origin of national or tribal hatreds and
deep ingrained mistrust. . . ." Finally he philosophizes that ". . .
men avoid because they do not understand one another; they
mutually hate because they mutually fear."

Aimé Bonpland put all his collected plants into well-tied bundles, entrusted them to the hands of the returning Indians, and
then, three days later, trailing after the black-gowned monks, they
trekked over the jungle trail, following the windings of the forest
for four hours until they came to the camp at Pimichín. They
were now on the Río Negro.

Before them was an ancient boulder-decked country. Between
the parallels three and seven degrees north, and east to the Orinoco, stands one of the most ancient geological regions of the
world. Untold ages of erosion have worn it down, cut its ranges
apart, carved it into confused and fantastic masses. There are
mountains and hills, tall isolated peaks, huge flat masses shooting
up from rolling prairies, dense jungles. It is a chaotic land, an
amazing land, a land covering 200,000 square miles. In it the little
Casiquiare River joins both great river systems of the Orinoco and
the Amazon.

The morning was cool and beautiful as they floated down to
the villages of Solano and San Carlos. In the small grass-thatched
adobe huts at Solano, on the left bank of the Casiquiare, Humboldt and Bonpland unpacked their theodolites and sextants,
their thermometers and barometers, to set to work to determine
astronomically the point of connection of the two systems. But
Humboldt was not so close to the stars to forget the ground. He
drank in the tropical world like a poet: "Every object declares the
grandeur of the power, the tenderness of Nature, from the boa
constrictor, which can swallow a horse, down to the hummingbird,
balancing itself on a chalice of a flower." The animals and the

birds dominated the picture, and as often as Humboldt took himself into the "solitudes" at night to use his instruments on the stars, he felt himself eclipsed by the boas, the peccaries, the tapirs, the monkeys, the jaguars, which worked out their destiny with complete disregard for man. "This aspect of animated nature, in which man is nothing, has something in it strange and sad."

At last the determination of the connection of the Río Negro and the Orinoco was complete. Humboldt determined it as 2° 0′ 43″ north latitude. How exact and estimable this survey was, considering that his chronometers had not been set for years, is seen in a recent survey * where, with radio and perfect time sequences, the same region was determined as 1° 59′ 33.78″ north latitude. Humboldt was off a little more than a minute and wrong by only two miles on the Orinoco's length! †

This done, Humboldt turned his attention to the last remaining vestige of map-makers' imagination, the Lake of Guaiana. This fabled lake, out of which so many rivers, including the Orinoco, were supposed to arise, was said to be in a great low valley, eastward of the Casiquiare. Here the early geographers put the mythical Manoa Lake, on whose shores was supposed to be the fabulous city of Manoa, where lived El Dorado, the Golden Inca. With the expedition of Captain Solano, in 1754, the lake of El Dorado came again into prominence; it was then called the Lago de Parimá.

Humboldt had no difficulty in pronouncing fabulous these monstrous lakes, the sources of rivers and the repositories of gold. "I was able to convince myself on the spot — in the village of Solano and elsewhere — of the following facts, well known to the missions: that Don José Solano did not do more than cross the cataracts of Atures and Maipures . . . that astronomical instruments were carried neither to the isthmus of the Pimichín and the Río Negro nor to the Casiquiare. . . .

"Thus we see," he continues, "that the great Mar de la Parima (which it was so difficult to remove from our maps that even after my return from America it was still supposed to be 160 miles in length) was reduced by accurate measurements to two or three miles in circumference. The illusion, entertained for nearly two

* As given in *El río Negro (Amazonas) y sus grandes afluentes de la Guyana Brasileña*, by A. Hamilton Rice (1934), p. 13, footnote.

† To show the remarkable exactitude of Humboldt's work, he calculated that the Orinoco "according to [his] astronomical observations does not exceed 1,120 miles" (*Views of Nature*, London, 1850, p. 157) — less than two miles from the modern calculations!

hundred years, which in the last Spanish expedition, in 1775, for the discovery of El Dorado cost several hundred lives, has finally terminated by enriching geography with some few results. In the year 1512 thousands of soldiers perished on the expedition under Ponce de León to discover the 'Fountain of Youth' on one of the Bahama Islands, called Bimini, which is hardly to be found on any of our maps. This expedition led to the conquest of Florida and to the knowledge of the great oceanic current or Gulf Stream which flows through the Bahama straits. The thirst after gold and the desire for rejuvenescence — the Dorado and the Fountain of Youth — stimulated to an almost equal extent the passions of mankind . . . and geography."

Humboldt would allow no fabulous tale to exist without observing, weighing, and dissecting the matter, whether mite or mountain. It is easily understood why all this vast region is known as "Humboldt's country." Fifty years later another great explorer, a botanist, Richard Spruce, was to follow his trail, collect where he had collected, and express most humbly "the gratification I naturally feel, finding myself in *terra Humboldtiana*. . . . I could not look for the first time on the Orinoco without emotion, and I thought of the illustrious voyagers who more than fifty years previously [he was writing in 1854] had explored its course and the vegetable products of its shores."

Humboldt was famed then — but not in May 1800. On the shores of these desolate rivers he was thought to be a spy; and when a barefooted soldier of a Brazilian garrison saw him look through his telescope, he was certain of it. Suddenly at night Humboldt was arrested. He had followed his observations, and his triangles had carried him across the boundary that separated the territory of Spain from that of Portugal. Everything was seized — his records, his registers, his astronomical observations, his papers, his instruments, and his person. When asked what he had been doing, Humboldt explained that he was trying to prove that the River Casiquiare joined the Orinoco and the Amazon together.

"By the Good Mother!" roared the Portuguese Commandant. "You come all the way from Germany to do this? No one in the missions for half a century has doubted the communication between these two rivers!"

"Yes, yes," said Humboldt, "I know that. But the importance of my work is to fix, by means of astronomical observations, the course of the Casiquiare and particularly the point of its entrance into the Río Negro and that of the bifurcation of the Orinoco. . . ."

The Commandant stood there in amazement. He could not con-

ceive of a man of sense making so fatiguing a journey "to measure
lands that did not belong to him. . . ."

The Commandant knew his duty. Humboldt and his papers had
to be conducted down the Amazon to Pará, and on across the Atlantic to Lisbon. Now the matter had become serious. If this
Dummkopf had his way, he would ruin the whole expedition.
Padre Zea intervened. Aimé Bonpland, towering and threatening,
prepared to fall upon the hapless Commandant. At last he agreed
to send a soldier two thousand miles to Pará for "instructions."
But instructions never came, and gradually the storm passed and
Humboldt was released. Half a century later Humboldt was still
laughing at the contretemps. In 1855 he was made a Knight of the
great Brazilian order on account of his arbitration between Brazil
and Venezuela respecting a large section of Amazonian territory.
"Formerly," he laughingly wrote, "they intended in Rio de Janeiro
to arrest me as a dangerous spy and to send me back to Europe; the
order drawn for the purpose is still shown there as a curiosity. Now
they make me an arbitrator. I, of course, decided for Brazil," he
went on ironically, "because I wanted the large decoration; the Republic of Venezuela had none to confer."

Like a tropical storm the suspicions blew over and the expedition now threaded its way down the boulder-strewn river and back
to the Orinoco. They did not return the way they came, which
would have occasioned a four-mile portage, but continued down
the Casiquiare canal, passing little villages like Capybara, a collection of scattered leaf huts in a low-lying forest where great
beds of balsa wood stood like a phalanx. Gradually the water was
becoming less black as they neared the confluence of the Orinoco.
Opposite this point where the Orinoco forms its bifurcation with
the Casiquiare was Mount Duida. Humboldt was in ecstasy:

"Here soars high above the clouds the mighty peak of the Yeonnamari
or *Duida,* a mountain that presents one of the grandest spectacles in the
natural scenery of the tropical world. Its altitude, according to my trigo-
nometrical observation, is 8,800 feet. . . . Its southern slope is a treeless,
grassy plain, redolent with the odor of pineapples, whose fragrance scents
the humid evening air. Among lowly meadow plants rise the juicy stems
of the anona, whose golden-yellow fruits gleam from the midst of a
bluish-green diadem of leaves. Where the mountain springs break forth
beneath the grassy covering, rise isolated groups of lofty fan palms. . . ."

As he left this almost fabulous Cerro Duida, whose sides glittered like silver when the setting sun fell full upon it, Humboldt
declared that no person would ever reach its summit, but in this

he was wrong, for American scientists * a hundred years later scaled it.

In a matter of days they had entered the Orinoco. Now as they moved with the current they were quickly wafted to the Río Atabapo, whose "white waters," in Humboldt's words, "brought us by degrees a more serene sky, stars, alligators, and mosquitoes."

Aimé Bonpland had fallen into a lethargy ever since they had left the Mission of San Fernando de Atabapo. It seemed to be the prelude to something far more serious than melancholia. He had been bitten by the anopheles. In his system the germs of malaria were beginning to grow. First there were persistent pains in the back, then terrific headaches, then melancholia and listlessness. His state grew steadily worse as the boat whirled past the Mission of San Fernando, past the rapids of Maipures, and down to Auyacoa. They arranged the lancha to give him as wide a space as possible to rest, but the boat bearing the explorers and Padre Zea, and now quite a zoo, was greatly overcrowded. Padre Zea had begun to "whisper some complaints at the daily augmentation of this ambulatory collection." The floating zoo consisted of two manikin birds, a motmot, and two guans, besides eight monkeys. There were spider monkeys, marmosets, two night-loving monkeys of the genus Nyctipithecus, and a very woolly monkey of good simian humor and a strong prehensile tail of which Humboldt became the discoverer.† This was his favorite, with the "skin of the face black and wrinkled, the forehead low, with projecting eyebrows that resemble strikingly those of an old Negro." There were toucans, too, trained from egghood by the Indians from whom they had purchased them. They hopped about, complete masters of the boat. With their long beaks and mischievous manners they kept the small floating lancha in an uproar. Padre Zea insisted that they made the sign of the cross with their heads before drinking, and that it was for this gesture rather than their cry that they were called *Diostedé* — "God gives it to thee." Added to these were 16,000 pressed-plant specimens in triplicate, animal skins, bird skins, bark specimens, and geological specimens which had now reached such proportions that the explorers were forced to sit in the rain while their collections were protected by the overhanging *barroza*.

* G. H. H. Tate and C. B. Hitchcock scrambled over the last precipice of Cerro Duida in 1928. Its height was found to be 7,960 feet. Humboldt was off a thousand feet. Many birds and plants new to science were found atop Duida.

† The woolly monkey, genus Lagothrix, was described by Geoffrey from specimens brought back by Humboldt. It is known as "Humboldt's woolly monkey."

[125]

Actually they were usually unmindful of these discomforts. Had they not laid open a section of the New World which had been closed for three hundred years? Had they not traveled eighteen hundred miles on its rivers? They had located the exact position of the Orinoco-Negro canal; they had dispelled the legends of the fabulous Lake of Manoa; they had discovered numerous medicinal plants; they had laid the groundwork of the botany of South America. Manatees, electric eels, howling monkeys, cow trees, alligators — it had all been well worth while. They had been in the Americas a little less than a year, and in that short space of time they had made known more than had been unearthed in centuries. The discomfort they could stand, provided they pushed back the frontiers of the unknown. Then, too, they would soon be out of this insect inferno of the Orinoco. The five-knot current of the tawny-colored river was whisking them over uncounted miles. They passed numerous rivers, and came to the confluence with the Apure, a river that they had descended only two months ago. The helmsman turned their lancha eastward to follow the Lower Orinoco — and at that spot Aimé Bonpland was suddenly stricken unconscious with a raging fever.

There was now no doubt that Bonpland was deathly ill. He was alternately racked with chills and fever. His eyes rolled in his head. He vomited his food, and his great tousled head seemed unable to hold itself erect on his powerful neck. Humboldt was beside himself. He gave him an infusion of quinine bark, but Bonpland was unable to hold it down. By the time they reached Angostura they despaired of his life.

They carried poor Bonpland to the house of Dr. Félix Fafreras, who gave him all his care. He administered infusions of honey and the bark extolled by the Capuchin missionaries, the *corteza angostura*. Quinine also was given in quantities that made the patient gag. All the while Humboldt was agitated by sad presages. He could not forget that they were at the place where Löfling, the favorite pupil of Linnæus and the first modern botanist to visit South America, had died of fever. "I cannot describe the anxiety I endured during the illness," Humboldt wrote to his brother. "I could never hope to meet a friend again so faithful, courageous, and active. Throughout the journey he evinced many astonishing proofs of courage and resolution. . . ."

Humboldt had already made a will, "to be opened in the event of my death," which contained a bequest to Bonpland of 80,000 francs. There are few instances in the history of science of such intimate contact between two men. The friendship not only outlived their American experiences, but continued for more than a half a century, with deep personal attachment. Humboldt spent some anxious weeks on the Lower Orinoco while Bonpland hovered between life and death. Then, whether it was the administrations of Don Félix, the curative powers of the angostura bitters, the potency of the febrifuge, quinine, or just the splendid recuperative powers of Bonpland, the patient recovered. He took on new life and within the space of a month was his old self.

As soon as they were able to travel they left Angostura, and once more crossed the llanos to the port of Nueva Barcelona in the north, a few miles southwest of Cumaná.

The malarial fever having left Bonpland, he was promptly infected with another fever, and one that he could not throw off, one for which there was no medicine. It was love fever. For days he was tantalized by a *samba,* an Indian girl with some white blood in her veins, whose errands took her by their house. She aroused in him such flesh-tearing desires that he laid siege to her, even proposing marriage. The brown-skinned girl consented, her every movement breathing voluptuousness. But a few days before they would have embarked on what was the equivalent of a honeymoon, she disappeared — gone, it was rumored, with a handsome, taciturn Indian. Bonpland set out after her; for some weeks Humboldt heard nothing from him.

Through all this Humboldt had patiently waited for the sexual fire to extinguish itself. He was much upset by the train of events; he would never find such another companion as Bonpland. Time was pressing, too. More lands waited to be discovered. In his mind he weighed the various itineraries that were open to him. He thought ceaselessly of the voyage around the world on which he had been invited by Captain Nicolas Baudin. Bonpland and Humboldt were, officially, still members of that party. He made a plan to sail to Mexico, cross to the Pacific port of Acapulco, catch a galleon sailing for Manila, and join Baudin. But in America one did not always go where one wanted; one went where the vessels touched. There was a ship sailing in a fortnight for Cuba; perhaps from that ancient isle he could get a small vessel to take him to Mexico. A few days before he was to sail, on the 24th of November 1800, Bonpland rolled in from the back country, weighed down with specimens. In the flight after his samba he had come across a wonderful collecting area, and in his search for butterflies and plants his love was forgotten. Humboldt was overjoyed.

Together once more, they set sail on a long and difficult journey,

[127]

during which they were fired on by a pirate vessel, captured by an English man-of-war, and menaced by a fire that swept the vessel. Forty-four days later, on December 18, they landed at Havana.

They did not know it then, but Cuba was only a roundabout stop on the return to South America.

CHAPTER XIII
The Kingdom of New Granada

CARTAGENA HAD CHANGED little since the time it had been visited by La Condamine and the Academicians. The gigantic terraced fortress still stood golden gray and silent in the sun and as immovable as the continent. The ramparts were more pock-marked, scarred by fire from the siege guns of Admiral Vernon in 1741. But the narrow, cobblestone streets were the same. Here were the same rose-pink houses that La Condamine had seen, houses with their deep eaves and overhanging balconies; the same massive doors studded with iron nails; the same grated windows, out of which flower-bedecked señoritas looked with liquid eyes upon their dark-haired lovers.

To Humboldt Cartagena brought the look of Seville, but a sad Seville without the air of mingled joyousness and paganism. It had a different air, too, from the Cuba he had just left. He had been much taken with Cuba. There he and Bonpland had arranged for their botanical specimens to be sent off. The extreme humidity of the tropics, the termites, ants, fungus, dry rot, the milliards of insects large and small that took refuge in their pressed plants, all seemed undeterred by the camphor, the turpentine, the tarred boards, and the other preservatives then in use in European herbariums. Out of eight collected specimens, five had to be thrown away. They decided to split the collection into three triplicate parts. One would go to Germany by way of England, another to France by way of Cadiz; the third was to remain at Havana. They had good reason to congratulate themselves on their foresight. One collection did not arrive safely. Padre Juan Gonzales, who was their companion on the Lower Orinoco and who had helped to nurse Bonpland to life again, was to carry the plants to Paris by way of Cadiz. His ship was wrecked on the coast of Africa and he was lost as well as the plants he guarded and all the insects that Bonpland had collected on the Negro and Orinoco.

Humboldt and Bonpland had gone to Cuba hoping to join the expedition of Captain Baudin; but there they had received a letter from Paris informing them that the expedition had just started for Cape Horn. This intelligence came in time to prevent their leaving for Mexico and the Philippines. For the moment Humboldt was uncertain about his next movements. He had acquired

[129]

Bonpland's late sickness. A pair of luminous dark eyes, belonging to Ignacia Rodríguez, had captivated the young Baron. For some days he was completely befuddled. He thought of going to Mexico, then to explore the Isthmus of Panama to look into the "possibilities of a connection between the oceans." He next thought of going to Texas and sailing up the Mississippi. Never had he known such indecision in all his young life. Whether Humboldt felt this relationship growing complicated and taking him from his wonted task, or whether he learned definitely that Captain Baudin would not come to Cuba, or — as might well be as true as anything else — he was seized with wanderlust and a vessel was on its way to South America, we do not know. We only know that he left Cuba in April 1801 and returned to the South America that he thought he had left forever. The first thing that he did on his arrival in Cartagena de Indias was to address a letter to Baudin:

CARTAGENA, April 12, 1801

CITIZEN!

When I embraced you for the last time in the rue Helvétius in Paris, on the eve of my departure for Africa and the East Indies, I had but a feeble hope of seeing you again and of sailing under your orders. . . . Just as we were starting from Havana for Mexico and the Philippines, the gratifying news reached us that your perseverance had overcome every obstacle. After making our calculations, we felt sure that you would touch at Valparaiso, at Lima or Guayaquil. We changed our plans at once, and in spite of the stormy gales of this shore, we started in a little pilot boat to look for you in the South Sea, to try whether by reviving our old plans we could join our labors with yours and sail with you on the South Sea. A long passage of twenty-one days from Havana to Cartagena unforunately hindered us from taking the route of Panama and Guayaquil. We fear that the wind has ceased blowing in the South Sea, and we have decided to continue our journey on land by the way of the River Magdalena, Santa Fé, Popayan, Quito. . . .

I hope we shall arrive in June or early July at the city of Quito, where I will wait for the news of your arrival at Lima. . . .

Greetings and unchangeable friendship,
Alexander Humboldt

Accordingly, Humboldt made his way, with the ever faithful Bonpland, along the trail that led around La Popa and across the swampy delta lands to the banks of the Magdalena. Here was the fluvial highway to the high interior points of the viceroyalty of Nueva Granada. It was by all odds the best way to reach the capital, Santa Fé de Bogotá.

Now, the Magdalena is *the* river of Colombia. It is not the longest — both the Putamayo and the Caquetá are longer — but for four centuries its muddy, incalculable stream has been the main artery of trade and communication. To a large degree the course of the Magdalena, cutting the country from south to north for nearly a thousand miles, is the course of Colombian history.

It had played its part in 1538 when the conquistador Gonzalo Jiménez de Quesada made his way, painfully and heroically, up the rivers, over the fissured cordilleras, to the tablelands of this undiscovered country. There Quesada founded Santa Fé de Bogotá, City of the Holy Faith. But the natives did not permit him to establish his realm without bloodshed: the opposition was spirited and sanguinary. Those who opposed Quesada, that redoubtable lawyer with the aspirations of a conqueror, were no lowly Indians, but a confederation of tribes called *Chibcha,* who effectively ruled and occupied the Colombian cordilleras from Quito, the outpost of the Inca empire, to the savannas of Cundinamarca. They were mountain people. Their agricultural economy centered on the potato, the bean, and oca tubers. They had neither domesticated animals — the llama did not come that far north — nor any mechanical device to assist their agriculture, yet these mountains became as thickly populated as some regions in Europe.

The Chibchas were excellent goldsmiths and competent farmers. Of their social structure history knows little; all was destroyed in the holocaust of conquest, destroyed by a legend that kept the South Americans in a dither for centuries, for an ancient custom of the Chibchas inspired the legend of El Dorado.

On the summit of a peak in the Colombian Andes is the Lake of Guatavita. This was the lake of El Dorado, part of a Chibcha legend. The legend told, as all legends must, of a Princess involved in some tangled domestic altercation. She threw herself into the lake. The Prince remained by it in anguish for some months; then, after consulting a sorcerer, he dove into the lake, remaining under for some time. When he bobbed to the surface, he spread the glad tidings: "The Princess is alive! She sits in a palace more beautiful than ours. . . . She will not return. She is happier there."

So the lake became a place of pilgrimage. Twice a year there were sacrificial ceremonies. A chieftain (El Dorado) had his body besmeared with a sticky, resinous balsam, and on it the Indian pilgrims blew gold dust. The gilded man, thus accoutred, was poled out into the center of the lake on a raft loaded down, so the fable insists, with gold and emeralds. The chieftain tossed the gold, the emeralds, and the platinum images into the lake and then he followed them, immersing himself until free of the gold dust. The throngs on the shore then tossed in their own offerings to the holy ones, and the ceremony was complete.

[131]

When Sebastián de Belalcázar sacked Quito in 1534, he heard of the Lake of Guatavita, as did Quesada, and still another conquistador, Federmann. With their condottieri (overwhelmed with that malady for which gold was the only specific) all three expeditions advanced upon the regions of Lake Guatavita. The Chibchas were slaughtered without respite, and the Spanish conquest, splendid and incredible, settled down to the casual exploitation of the lands. The Indians that survived the butchery were eclipsed in the "yoke of peace." Peace, yes, but a troubled peace! For the myth of the Lake of El Dorado galvanized the actions of men for centuries. From the charming folkway of the Chibchas, performed in a small Andean lake, the fable of El Dorado grew and swept the whole of South America, luring men on to the search.

Humboldt followed his own El Dorado — the dream of a passage around the world with Captain Baudin. And for this South America may be grateful, for in his search for a port in which to meet the elusive captain and his vessels, he traveled far and wide.

Now, in April 1801, Humboldt and Bonpland stood on the shores of the Río Magdalena. The river begins in the marshy deltas of the Caribbean, where palm trees whisper. There the main channel is lost in a wide expanse, scrawled with watercourses like a child's drawing-board, the whole woven with jungles, lakes, morasses, and meadows, patched with poisonous scum. There cattle wander up to their distended bellies in water, feeding on blue water-hyacinths. White ibises dot the mangroves, white egrets, blown by the Caribbean wind, make noiseless passage from island to island of tropical vegetation. Here there are no trade winds to waft one up the river as on the Orinoco; from the very beginning one must secure polers to propel a vessel up the turgid, tawny waters.

Fortunately for the explorers, they joined with Dr. de Rieux, an old French physician who had been long enough in the Spanish colonies to grow immune to all the plagues and discomforts. They secured a *bongo,* a large dugout extended on both sides by addition of boards, with the traditional *toldo* or covering above. In this Humboldt and Bonpland and their French guest were poled up the Magdalena past El Banco, where the Río Cauca joins the main stream, then up past the sprawling, wretched town of Tamalameque, which was named after a "powerful Lord feared by his neighbors in war and peace." Here Quesada, the conqueror, had forced the narrow causeway that guarded the village, decimated the Indians and fallen on the food that the Indians had left in their flight.

This was historical ground which Humboldt and Bonpland passed and the Frenchman never let them forget it. There was

Gamarra, a village like all the rest of the leaf-hut clusters, littered with sucking pigs, hens with attendant broods, and naked, dark children playing on the mud banks. But Gamarra had some distinction: a conquistador was struck here with a poison arrow and a captain was garroted by his men. So items of history were included as they went on up past Puerto Wilches, Barranca-Bermeja, and numerous other villages that Humboldt neglected to put into his notebook.

The days were all the same — morning with the raucous call of parrots, the chatter of monkeys, the ghostly parade of white-plumed egrets; then breakfast on the river's edge; a few hours of plant-collecting; then noon as the bongo was pushed up the river; note-taking and anecdote-trading. In the late afternoon the rain fell in torrents; the evening was spent under mosquito nets which successfully held off the assault of myriads of insects. So up they went past the similar villages, and at the end of fifty-five days of leisurely passage they came to rest at Honda. They had reached the end of river travel; henceforth the Magdalena broke up into cataracts and waterfalls like the Upper Orinoco.

They had only to display the King's seal to be given the best rooms in the King's way-house, erected and maintained for travelers. While the innkeeper looked for sufficient horses and mules to carry their excellencies six thousand feet up into the cordilleras, Bonpland collected and Humboldt finished his astronomical calculations. On their ascent of the Magdalena he had taken numerous geographical positions and angles, he had determined the velocity of the flow of the river, the temperature of the water, and its widths at various points; from all this data he was fashioning a map of the Magdalena. In time the mules and horses were found and, mounted as befitted gentlemen, they climbed the sides of the Andes and so arrived, days later, at Bogotá.

Santa Fé de Bogotá had been a fabulous city, founded on the accursed gold of the Americas. But it had now, with the dispersal of the Chibchas, become a small, easy-going colonial city. With the gold's disappearance the Santafernos were forced into stock-raising and agriculture. But the money poured into their churches raised them to presumptuous piles, with twisted baroque columns and fantastic over-adorned façades hung with grape clusters and meaningless arabesques.

Yet Humboldt and Bonpland did not come to see the white towers of the Cathedral or the massive-towered monasteries of Monserrate or Guadalupe, or the hundred-odd churches, all monuments to colonial piety, that ornamented the streets of the vice-royalty; nor did they come to see the strange dress of the Bogoteños

[133]

— the *roanas,* the broad-brimmed hats, or the women of Santa Fé dressed in their blue flannel petticoats and cloth mantles. They had come to pay homage to a man — Dr. José Celestino Mutis, the celebrated botanist, the discoverer of nocturnal variation in the barometer, the co-author of a grammar (written to satisfy the regal request of Catherine of Russia to Charles III) of Colombian Indian languages. Doctor, priest, teacher of natural science, director of the Expedición Botánica, metallurgist, and creator of a Colombian renaissance, Dr. Mutis was the last of the retinue of scientists that the late Carlos III had sent to the Americas.

The fame of Mutis had leaped far beyond the borders of sky-scraping Bogotá. Humboldt had seen his plant collections in Madrid. The learned of Europe knew of him through the accolade that Linnæus had bestowed upon him: *"Nomen immortale, quod nulla ætas numquam delebit."* And to see this man of "immortal name" Humboldt and Bonpland had journeyed up the jungle-bound Río Magdalena.

Mutis received them in his library, which served also as a herbarium for 20,000 collected plants. Tall and heavy-set, he was majestic in figure, with dark, piercing eyes, gray hair, and his face endowed with a series of chins that cascaded down over his clerical bands. He was delighted to make the acquaintance of Humboldt and Bonpland. Word of their collecting and good works had already been brought to him by that mysterious bush-telegraph by which most things in the New World were revealed. For their part, the explorers looked upon the most important figure of the many expeditions that had been sent out from Spain by Carlos III.

Humboldt and Bonpland were lodged near his house in Bogotá, and as a gesture of friendship Mutis presented Humboldt with a hundred of his finest drawings. On their return to Europe, years later, Humboldt and Bonpland inserted in a section of their *Plantes equinoctiales* an account of their journey to New Granada as well as a portrait of Mutis, with a grateful inscription.

Yet more than scientific research came from behind the study walls. Revolution was sweeping the Colombian soil. Nariño, who had lit the uncertain flame of rebellion with his publication of a Spanish translation of the *Rights of Man,* was languishing in prison. And there were others. There was Zea, a brilliant young botanist, who was too imbued with revolutionary zeal to dissemble it. He was bundled up one night by the King's guards and sent to Madrid to make acquaintance with the executioner, but he emerged instead the director of Madrid's Jardín Botánico. And there were many more. Humboldt was amazed at the critical acumen and the philosophical audacity of the Creoles. These men were intellectuals as the result of long educational discipline. It is impossible to estimate the stimulation the presence of modern, liberty-spawned men such as Humboldt and Bonpland gave them. Their discourse on Paris, the Paris of the Revolution, of Danton, of Robespierre, awakened in their audience all the latent ideas of political freedom. Here, sitting before them, were savants from the very lap of freedom. They were not vulgar sans-culottes, but men who had looked upon the goddess of liberty. This Bonpland, for example, was not the one to discourse of liberty, yet he admitted over a glass of fiery wine that he believed in "revolutionary palingenesis" — and that phrase ran its length through the scientific and revolutionary front of Bogotá.

Mutis, sensing what the contact with Humboldt would mean to his collaborators, asked if his most promising pupil, Francisco José de Caldas, might accompany them to Quito. Humboldt was delighted to have the young Caldas with him. A scientist who had discovered the method of determining the altitude by the temperature at which water boils, Caldas was also a revolutionist. His future was to be brilliant, but short. In 1816, when Spain began to suppress the revolution in earnest, José de Caldas fell before a firing squad. The Spanish General Morillo, in refusing clemency, had the same answer as the Revolutionary Tribunal in Paris passing on the decapitation of Lavoisier: "Spain has no need of savants." When Humboldt heard of this execution, he made great protest, but only after a hundred years was a tablet to Caldas unveiled in Madrid: "In perpetual atonement to the memory of the immortal Colombian, José de Caldas."

In September 1801 the expedition was on its way to Quito. Down they went into Ibague, and then along the famed and ancient valley of Cauca to Popayán and Almaguer. Then they climbed over the wind-swept paramo to Pasto, heaven-high in the hail-pelted Andes. The trip from there to Quito was filled with horrible experiences — wind-swept days, shelterless nights, lack of food, and dizzying twelve-inch paths with frowning abysses on both sides. There were days when they had to rest while their feet recovered from the attacks of niguas. As this point the usual good nature of Humboldt broke its bounds when he was offered a place on an Indian's back until his feet recovered. The mountain Indians, called *caballitos* — little horses — were employed at a pittance as bearers over mountains which even mules could not negotiate. Humboldt refused outright, with no attempt at ceremony: "It really makes one's blood boil to hear the qualities of a human being described in the same terms as one would employ in speaking of a horse or mule."

They could now congratulate themselves on sending their fine heavy instruments by sea while they took the Andean trail. There was rain and yet more rain. High up, above 10,000 feet, the world was naked and sterile, and the air as cold as on the glaciers of Switzerland. "It would hardly be possible," Humboldt remembered, "to picture a more horrible road. Here we spent Christmas, 1801, and although they had nothing, we were welcomed by the inhabitants with touching hospitality."

Beyond this high paramo they passed from the Kingdom of New Granada into the Audiencia de Quito. Almost at once they were met by smiling skies and fertile valleys.

This was sacred scientific ground. La Condamine had worked here.

They reached Quito in January 1802.

CHAPTER XIV
The Realm of the Quitus

Quito had changed since the great earthquake of 1797, which had killed forty thousand people at one violent stroke. It had completely altered the climate. Whereas Pierre Bouguer had found the mean temperature to be 67 degrees, which accounted for the feeling that Quito was the land of "eternal spring," Humboldt now found it autumnal, for it stood at a mean 42 degrees.

Quito still was gay. The people were, as always, hospitable and amiable — notwithstanding the continual shocks to which the town was subject. "The town breathes," Humboldt wrote, "only an atmosphere of luxury and voluptuousness . . . and perhaps nowhere is there a population so much given up to the pursuit of pleasure. . . ." The enjoyments were simple, the spectacles of the church pretentious. Fiestas of all kinds filled the calendar; the narrow, cobblestoned streets were alive with music and fireworks and dancing, creating the impression of a continuous round of festivity.

"I spent a very pleasant time in Quito," Humboldt wrote. "Indeed, for the last three years I have never had cause on any occasion to complain of the agents of the Spanish government." They had been offered the house of the Marquis de Selva Alegre, and Humboldt had reason to thank him for comforts after the four months of privation through which they passed on the way down from Bogotá.

Humboldt at once interested himself in the ancient history of Quito. He found it had already been a metropolis when the Incas conquered it in 1450 and made it a part of their expanding empire. Pre-Inca Quito was a rich and varied mosaic of indigenous culture, ruled by a tribe called the Caras-Scyris. Whatever their differences, the mountain tribes had much in common, their civilizations rooted in the rock-hard Andes.

There was no want. There was no poverty. There was no monetary standard. There was only barter, handicraft culture revolved about the feeling of function. They produced all they needed, but only for specific wants; there was a pooling of interests, held within a profoundly communistic agricultural system. It was not a speculative or theoretical communism, but a system of natural growth. Life was organic here; there was a correlation between all its parts. The sea, the mountains, and the jungle were knit as one. Through their Inca the Indians had fused a coastal and mountain culture into a practical synthesis. They built their economy solidly upon the substance which most deeply formed their world — the earth. They developed corn, cassava tubers, calabash, potatoes, *mishna,* and *legena.* The four-footed ruminants of the paramos, the llama, the alpaca, the guanaco, were tamed, and from them were obtained wool, meat, and beasts of burden. Needs were few and the leaders possessed a positive genius in preventing these wants from growing. The dispenser of land, the source of the highest good, was the Inca, who ruled the land as a benevolent despot.

This Incaic civilization, nestling in the Andes, with its far-flung empire, was as close as man would ever get to Utopia. But its cycle was complete; its apogee had been reached. Even before the coming of white men there were signs of spiritual backsliding. As in ancient Rome, distance had become the fatal factor of dissolution. Geography, which the Incas had conquered for so long, now conquered the Incas. There were dissensions and internecine quarrels. Like Rome, the empire cracked from within. An age-old system with scarcely a historical prelude crashed about their heads. Pizarro beheaded their Inca.

The city of the Quitus was conquered in 1534 by Belalcázar and the last organized native resistance to Christian knight-errantry fell. Administrative necessity demanded the establishment of a city, so from the ruins of an ancient citadel a new one arose. Mayor, alderman, and secretaries were chosen from among the motley group of conquistadores; and those who disdained such civil and bourgeois positions were permitted to follow their leader, Sebastián de Belalcázar, northward to Colombia, where the image of El Dorado began to haunt their souls.

Those conquistadores who remained fixed upon a name for the city. Its charter, later inscribed, called it San Francisco de Quito, and the date, March 28, 1534, was in the very dawn of American history. Then Jacques Cartier was only sailing up the St. Lawrence River; it was eighty-five years before the Pilgrim Fathers were to land at Plymouth; modern Quito had already been founded.

The collapse of the Indian civilization in the Andean countries ushered in the colonial period of South America. The knights-errant grew restive under this change. Colonists began to come to the New World; and between those who conquered and those who settled, there was friction. This turned into open quarrels.

A decade passed. Colonial life had grown in strength with each new shipload of immigrants. Of all hues and professions, they filed into the new city of Quito. The age of the conquistador had reached its total eclipse. Hispanic America was conquered by adventurers, knights-errant, crusaders, and men of God, but colonists settled the country. Ten years had passed since the fall of Quitu, and yet no white women had been permitted to come to the New World. Conquistador and colonist mated with the Indian women. At first they only followed their healthy biological urge; gradually the kind, loyal, patient Quechua women won their respect. The Spaniard believed that marriage would sanctify his spouse, that it would make her a Christian. He believed that from the issue of his marriage would also come Christian subjects of the King of Spain. This tragic misunderstanding eventually shaped much of Spanish colonial history. For the fruit of this union was the *cholo* — the half-caste. And the fusion of these two bloods took place everywhere in the Andean regions.

While this racial tragedy was brewing, the Indians who had fled into hiding at the time of the conquest began to return. And they found no great revolution. Since the Spanish colony had to be predicated on earth, people were needed to work the earth. And the only people who could endure daily toil in these rarefied regions were the Indians who had been acclimated to the high Andes for centuries.

The Indian shunned the Spaniard, but he had to pay for this "inner avoidance" of his conqueror. Neither his defense nor his "scorched earth" policy had been of avail to him in his fight to maintain his realm. On his return he still refused to recognize the presence of the Spaniard, doing so only when a show of force compelled him. His will was unbent. Since his will was that of the clan and community, for the Quechua had always depended on group thinking, he moved in the spirit of the clan. A stoic precept: "You are part of a social whole, a factor necessary to complete the sum," was as much an Indian as a Grecian maxim. The Andean land was not naturally fertile. It had become fecund through centuries of communal work which had been accomplished only by clan activity. Now that group power had been changed. Now, for the first time in history, the Indian experienced actual want. The vast engineering feats of aqueducts, roads, terracing, had broken down — mostly from neglect. The llamas, which he had so carefully tended through the centuries, had been thoughtlessly slaughtered. The Indian went back to his life and carried on his functions like an automaton. Neither conqueror nor conquered understood the other. They lived and were actuated by different things. The Spaniard had an individual soul, the Indian a collective one, and this conditioned all their functions.

Deprived of earthly dignity, the spirit of the Indian resisted, became recalcitrant and degraded. More and more he turned to his fermented corn *chicha*. He chewed more and more coca leaves — the narcotics of the cocaine alkaloids helped to deaden his pain. To the colonist this was merely a confirmation of his base animal nature. The Spaniard did not see this man as he originally was in his heyday — proud, happy, content. They saw him only in a condition wrought by conquest. They saw only the sullen, treacherous creature whose brain had been befogged with cocaine; "in low animal terms they judged him — in low animal manner they treated him."

Three hundred years failed to change this attitude. Humboldt saw that, in 1800, the problem of the Indian, although somewhat modified where racial fusion had taken place, was as it had been in the past. The Andean Indian still remained an exile in his own land.

In the years immediately following the conquest Spain took gold, silver, and raw products from the New World, but she forbade her colonists to create industries in her possessions. All manufactured goods, all finished products, Spain furnished to the New World. South America became a storehouse — nothing more. Even bordering viceroyalties were not permitted to exchange their products direct; all must go through Spain, even though months and years be spent in the exchange. Spain exported to her colonies, even though she had to buy the manufactured products at higher prices from England or Germany. No economic mutuality was permitted between the colonial city and its land — and in Humboldt's time this morbid economic status was the inherited curse of the colonial epoch.

Then trouble came to the colonies. Dissatisfaction, like an unchecked fire whipped by the high winds of frustration, ran through the people. The Indians, virtually enslaved by the acts known as the *encomienda,* were given new laws to protect them. Church as church, King as king, did not condone a policy of enslavement. Rumors of the "New Laws" already began to sift through colonial circles with irritating effect.

The "New Laws" threatened to undermine the whole system of latifundia. Was this, the colonists asked, their reward for coming to these lofty heights, enduring cold, misery, isolation, and danger? Was this their recompense for sending regularly the "royal fifth" of the Incas' treasures to the King of Spain? Was it, then, they asked, for all this insecurity of person, income, and future that the sons of Castile had braved the dangers of the Andes and helped to knit these inhospitable lands to the crown? How else

could the land, the mines, be forced to yield revenues except
through the bodies and toil of the Indians?

To his credit, the King of Spain, although harassed by lobby-
ists, was adamant. The Indians, it was ruled, were the wards of
the crown, and the wrongs of the conquest must be righted. One
night the town crier announced along the narrow stone streets of
Quito, Bogotá, Lima, over the verdure-splashed villas of Caracas,
the *Nuevas Leyes de las Indias* — "eight hours and no longer shall
the Indian labor; there shall be a weekly day of rest; women and
children shall labor half as long as the men. . . . Authorized
guilds through the medium of the Indian's *ayllus* or clans will
again come into being to assist in carrying out these provisions.
The Indians shall not be bound by serfdom to the hacienda — the
encomienda shall be supplanted with a more humane system."

These laws were of historical and humanistic importance. Not
until the nineteenth century did Humboldt find in any state in
Christendom such benevolent and farseeing safeguards of labor
as those which the Spanish crown embodied in the Laws of the
Indies and tried to enforce for the protection of the natives.

The spirit that promulgated them was good. But laws are abstract things; there is always a regrettable hiatus between dictum
and deed, and these new Laws of the Indies were more honored
by the colonists in the breach than in the observance.

So the pattern of colonial life in the high Andes was set, as in
a crucible; throughout the colonial period there was only slight
variation in it. The Indians, with some slight relief, due mostly
to the Laws of the Indies, passed into permanent serfdom. Great
estates were founded; the church expanded and became also a
landlord.

At first Catholicism essayed the impossible. She attempted to
uproot the ancient Indian religions that, on the surface, the conquest had destroyed. But when this proved impossible, the church
modified her external ritual enough to mesh with the ancient cultural patterns of the Andean people. Thus the Indian accepted
the church, but only on his own terms. Nor, Humboldt found,
was the attitude of the church toward her Indian "wards" merely
negative. Through the Indian's love for color and his infinite patience in working stone, metal, or wood, the church was able to
usher in a renaissance of the arts. Fabulous stone churches with
minutely carved rococo exteriors were erected, all fashioned by
the Indians under the direction of the priest architects. They
were taught the use of modern tools, metal saws, adzes, and hand
lathes, and this, combined with their own native dexterity, was
reflected in the production of great inlaid chests, tables, tooled

leather chairs, and churchly monuments. As goldsmiths they were unexcelled; many of the exports to Spain included the delicately wrought filigrees of native Andean craftsmen. In addition they supplied the church with beautifully woven vestments, and so a lively trade was set up in these ecclesiastical artifacts.

For two centuries and a half the colonist had been held within the stone seraglio of the cordilleras. All the arable land was held in immense latifundia, by either church or colonist or crown — great landholding corporations which would prove themselves to be South America's curse. The spirit of exploration, with a few notable exceptions, had died within the colonies after the seventeenth century; the colonist clung to his cities. Although the Spaniard traced the hemisphere from one end to the other within fifty years after the great Admiral of the Ocean Sea discovered it (it took the Anglo-Saxon two hundred years to reach the Pacific), the Spanish conquest never was completed. Great gaps appeared in the maps of regions to which he laid claim.

Spain was afraid of the Renaissance, the Reformation, and the rising tide of republicanism. For centuries she succeeded all too well in barring new ideas from her colonies. The will of Spain was to make the New World her body, the heart and the brain she would maintain three thousand miles across the ocean sea. "The shot heard round the world" in the first American Revolution was scarcely heard in Quito or in Bogotá, or in Lima or La Paz. Faint cries of revolution came to them, but revolution was not new. Revolution was the political ataxia of the Andes. Only recently, in 1780, Tupac Amaru, the last of the Incas, had revolted in Peru and brought his Indians down to seek justice, only to be slaughtered. No, revolt was not new to the Andes. But hold! They did not understand that the revolution that had occurred among the Anglo-Saxons in North America was a *new* type of revolution. It freed man of old forms and old fetters. The Andean colonists heard this, but remained unmoved.

Then came the Reign of Terror in Paris. Louis XVI lost his head. The French guillotine rose and fell. This was *the* Revolution. The days were changed, the names of the months were changed. Even the years were revolutionized. The "shot heard round the world" at last reached the Andes. The cholo heard it and grew restless; the Creole heard it and wondered how this would affect his income; the Indian heard it, juggled it in his obtuse brain, and then went back to his serfdom. The viceroys heard it, too, and reinforced their garrisons. The printing press, sponsored by the intellectual cholo, began to pick up the refrain: "Liberty, equality, fraternity"; and tracts of revolt — Rousseau, Voltaire, *The Rights of Man* — began to flutter down. Now all could see this was not "just another revolution"; this was *the* Revolution.

In the threat of this new danger to the status quo in the world, Spain began to liberalize her colonial possessions. The Creoles, who for years had demanded more part in the administration of their own viceroyalties, were given such power. Printing was no longer so rigidly supervised. The crown enforced the expulsion of Jesuits, their property was seized, and the church was removed from its position as banker to the state. All these belated reforms were made to meet the criticisms of the colonists, as well as to cushion them against the shocks that the new Napoleonic order would bring in Europe. But it was too late. This, Humboldt discovered during his first weeks in Quito. For the very residence in which he was a guest, the palatial home of the Marquis de Selva Alegre, was a distribution point of revolutionary literature.

CHAPTER XV
The Ascent of Chimborazo

IN THE SECRET CHEMISTRY of the emotions, man is attracted without cease by that which is least attainable. So it was inevitable that Alexander von Humboldt should have essayed to climb Mount Chimborazo.

Out of the inter-Andean valley, near the town of Riobamba, Chimborazo rises 22,000 feet above sea-level. Its grandeur is overwhelming; its vast hulk, snow-topped for the last seven thousand feet, is an epic of creative nature. Chimborazo is the most magnificent spectacle of the Andes. Of the earth's wonders one's expectations are sometimes wrought to such a pitch of expectancy that seeing them brings disenchantment; Rousseau confessed to disappointment when he first saw the sea. But Chimborazo does not disenchant, it fulfills the hopes its strange name arouses. In Humboldt's youth Chimborazo had a fame as of some celestial legend as the highest, the greatest mountain in the world.

> . . . I learnt the royal genealogies
> Of Oviedo, the internal laws
> Of the Burmese empire . . . and . . . by how many feet
> Mount Chimborazo outsoars Himmeleh. . . .

Wherever Humboldt and Bonpland went in the Audiencia of Quito there was the frigid snow-covered hulk of Chimborazo beckoning, urging them on. No one had ever climbed to its top. To the Indians it was inviolable, to the Creoles it was inaccessible. That made it all the more tantalizing to the explorers. The first part of their eight months in Quito was only, in fact, preparation for the assault on Chimborazo. They began their work by climbing Pichincha, the smallest of the volcanoes in the Valley of Añaquito. There they experimented with the electrical, magnetic, and hydraulic properties of the air. They studied the altitudes and their relation to temperature, and there Humboldt determined the relations between latitudinal and altitudinal climates, which he used so effectively in the development of plant geography.[*]

There, too, on the ground made classic by the geodetic researches of La Condamine, Humboldt began to lay down the base by which points on the earth's surface are joined by isothermal lines. He discovered that, in general, as we proceed from the equa-

[*] *De distributione geographica plantarum.*

The volcano of Chimborazo, which in Humboldt's time was thought to be the greatest mountain in the world. Humboldt attempted to reach its 21,000-foot height with Bonpland, but failed by 3,000 feet. The original plate is a magnificent hand-washed lithograph.

The ruins of the palace of the Inca Huyana Capac at Ingapirca in the Ecuadorian Andes. Humboldt was greatly interested in the archæology of South America and devoted much research to it. Humboldt and Bonpland may be seen at the right of the picture with their native guide.

tor toward the poles, the mean temperature decreases one degree Fahrenheit with each degree of latitude. But as they ascended Pichincha the mean temperature decreased with each 300 feet of altitude. Thus he found that 300,000 feet of latitude equal 300 feet of altitude. In all this he was the pioneer.

"The ultimate aim of physical geography," he wrote, "is . . . to recognize unity in the vast diversity of phenomena. . . . I have conceived the mad notion of representing in a graphic and attractive manner the whole of the physical aspect of the universe in one work, which is to include all that is at present known of celestial and terrestrial phenomena, from the nature of the nebula down to the geography of the mosses clinging to a granite rock. . . ."

Humboldt was inspired by the Quitonian air, the magnificent scenery, and, if the clacking tongues of the gossips may be trusted, by the company of Rosita, the charming and heretofore inaccessible daughter of Juan Pio Montúfar, Marquis de Selva Alegre.

Humboldt found the Marquis a most remarkable man. His view of government, which he expounded often during the months when he entertained Humboldt, was that all society is an organized system held together in part voluntarily, in part by a combination of moral pressure and coercion. He dwelt long on the coercion thesis. He denounced the lack of a free press; he scoffed at the educational system which the government had forced on the colonies. He launched, with one Francisco Espejo, a revolutionary curriculum — "Escuela de Concordia" — which aroused the monarchical authorities. This Espejo, an intelligent cholo of Quito, had lauded the rebellion of Tupac Amaru, declaring that his cause was just and he was but seeking to recover the ancient and legitimate rights of the Indians. Because of his association with this man, the Marquis was most suspect. In essence Espejo's pamphlet was no less than an attack on the King, his ministers, and the royal inspectors. The authorities denounced the book as "bloodthirsty and seditious satire," with the conclusion that "any tribunal of Europe would consider it sufficient grounds for imprisoning the author for life," as they eventually did, for Espejo died on the eve of his release from prison.

Such was one of the confreres of the Marquis de Selva Alegre. Democratic ideas, revolutionary plans, flowed through his villa like new-pressed wine, and as heady; these his children inherited. To hear the charming Rosita Montúfar discourse on freedom, while her whole person aroused the sense of desire, was an added attraction to the susceptible young Humboldt. Only rumor suggests how far the romance — if there was one — developed. But whatever it was, it held him on and on in Quito.

At the villa at Chillo, Humboldt and Bonpland gained another recruit to their expedition, the young, intense Carlos Montúfar, the eldest son of the Marquis. He felt at home in their company. He was eager to learn the intricacies of astronomy and geodesy. Humboldt used him in making his plan of Quito, the best since Pedro Maldonado laid down his cartographic survey. Carlos Montúfar followed Humboldt when he climbed the volcano of Cotopaxi, up to the snow line. He went with them when they tramped the plains of Yarqui. He stood with bowed head as Humboldt picked up the fragments of the pyramids that La Condamine had so painstakingly erected to mark his base line.

The contact with Humboldt and Bonpland galvanized the feelings of Carlos Montúfar. With these modern Europeans before him, he realized how profound had been the isolation of the kingdoms of the New World. He was destined to go everywhere with Humboldt — to Chimborazo, to the Amazon, to Lima, Mexico, Paris, London; and all these journeys were but preparations for the second American revolution. But, as the young will, Carlos Montúfar jumped the revolutionary gun. In 1810, after three months' delirium of revolutionary rule, he was shot, with many others, and his heart burnt in the plaza of Quito. But in June 1803 he was preparing himself, along with Humboldt and Bonpland, for the ascent of the great snow-covered volcano of Chimborazo.

On June 9 they left Quito, riding down the long inter-Andean valley, through the heaven-scraping cities of Latacunga and Ambato, over the dry desert-like paramo to the base of Chimborazo. The night of June 22 they slept in the little straw-thatched hut of the Alcalde of the village of Calpi. At daybreak the next morning, with Indian guides, they began their historic ascent. The first 6,000 feet were gradual and easy, but then the path became more and more precipitous. They had just reached the snow line when their Indians, deaf to entreaties and threats alike, deserted them, scrambling down the slope, leaving the expedition without carriers and with 7,000 feet more to be scaled. "We were left alone," Humboldt relates, "Bonpland, our estimable friend Carlos Montúfar, a half-caste Indian from the neighboring village of San Juan — and myself."

Slowly they inched themselves upward over the icy crevices of mighty Chimborazo. In places the ridge that they followed, covered with snow and ice, was no wider than eight to ten inches. On each side were fearful abysses from whose sides projected huge masses of naked rock. Enveloped in mist, they looked down into a vast void of nothingness.

The Ascent of Chimborazo

As they climbed, the rock became more friable, the ascent increasingly difficult and dangerous. "We advanced," Humboldt recalled, "all the more slowly, as every place that seemed insecure had first to be tested. . . . Fortunately, the attempt to reach the summit of Chimborazo had been reserved for our last great enterprise. . . ."

At 17,000 feet they could no longer see the summit. They opened the tube barometer at a spot where the ridge was wide enough to permit two persons to stand together, and finding themselves still not much higher than the smaller peak of Antisana, they shut up their barometer and began again the ascent into the mist-filled heavens of Chimborazo. Now there were further difficulties. One after another, depending on his own metabolism, the explorers began to grow nauseated and vertiginous. Blood exuded from their lips and gums. Small veins in their eyes broke, rained blood, and left them partly blinded. Carlos Montúfar bled profusely from the ears and mouth, but he refused to give up. A few more hundred feet upward and they saw again the dome-shaped summit. "It was a grand and solemn spectacle, and the hope of attaining the object of all our efforts animated us with renewed strength." Then, just at the moment when they thought they would be able to make that summit, they came upon a deep chasm, so wide there was no way to span it. Chimborazo had successfully defied the efforts even of a Humboldt. It was then afternoon. The temperature stood below freezing. Don Carlos was visibly ill. They took out their barometers for the last time and found that the mercury stood at $\frac{2}{1110}$ inches, which showed, according to the barometric formula of the day, that they had reached an elevation of 19,286 feet. This was the highest that man had ever reached until the Alpinist Webb climbed the Himalayas. "I had all my life," Humboldt wrote when an old man, "imagined that of all mortals I was the one who had risen highest in all the world. . . ."

Toward the end of his life, at an age when men do not speak lightly, he declared that he still considered Chimborazo the grandest mountain in the world. And when he sat in 1859 for his last portrait, a venerable titan with hair as white as Chimborazo's glaciers, his figure bent with age, his face as serene as that of Zeus, he insisted that he be painted with none of his decorations. Instead he suggested that great Mount Chimborazo be placed in the background; of all that he had accomplished in his ninety years of life, he regarded "this as the greatest."

On the wind-swept, hail-pelted glacier of Chimborazo they delayed no longer. They were weak from loss of blood and deeply sensible to the cold. Icy blasts of hail whipped by them. Humboldt stopped only long enough to stuff some chips of rock of Chimborazo into his pocket, for he foresaw, this most human man, that "in Europe we should be asked for a fragment from Chimborazo."

The explorers rested in the village of Calpi to recover from their assault on the "highest mountain in the world" and there a packet of letters reached them. In it was a communication from Captain Baudin. At last the exploratory ships had left France, but they had not shaped their course for South America; instead they began their world-encircling cruise by rounding the Cape of Good Hope. Humboldt had focused his hopes on that voyage, and even though he was opening a new world in South America, he still had dreamed of going with the expedition of Captain Baudin. Now that dream had come to an end.

So they decided to leave Quito. With new wonders still to be unveiled, they mounted their horses and began the thousand-mile journey down the Andes to Lima, ostensibly to observe there, in the City of Kings, the passage of the planet Mercury across the sun's disk.

Now the Andean world offered new things for their attention. At Cañar, the ancient seat of the Cañari nation, they sought out the ruins of the fortress, high on the wind-swept barren paramo. In writing of the structures of the Incas, Humboldt became the first archæologist of South America.* The ruins had been mentioned before, but always in hyperbole with bizarre interpretations and curiously drawn illustrations. Humboldt's interpretations were modern, scientific, and exact, and his illustrations the best that had ever appeared.

South of Cañar was Cuenca. The city welcomed them with its usual magnificent, overwhelming hospitality and the explorers were its guests for ten days. A bullfight was arranged in their honor, and they could not help recalling that in this same *torreo,* fifty years before, Dr. Senièrgues had been set upon and killed by a Cuencan mob. Then once more they were riding down the Andes on their way to Loja, the most southern of the cities of the Audiencia de Quito.

Aimé Bonpland wished to collect in Loja. He found no resistance in Humboldt, for Loja had a special significance. Here on the slopes beyond the little Andean city of stone walls and red tile roofs lay the forests from which first came the important medicinal plant, cinchona, the bark of which yielded the valued

---

* These archæological observations are contained in a sumptuous folio volume with a multitude of colored plates under the title of *Vues des Cordillères et monuments des peuples indigènes de l'Amérique.*

quinine. While Bonpland collected its reddish leaves and flowers, Humboldt watched the "febrifuge-bark hunters" as they left Loja and returned days later loaded down with the coarse bark. He heard from the natives the legends of the manner in which the Viceroy's wife, in 1638, was cured of malaria by the use of quinine. The legend had it that Don Gerónimo Fernández de Cabrera, Bobadilla y Mendoza, Conde de Chinchón, on a visit to Loja with his wife, was thrown into paroxysms of grief when she was struck down suddenly with a recurrence of the *paludismo* fever. The Alcalde of Loja suggested quinine powder, and this, administered as a last hope, brought the immediate return of her health. Quinine had been known centuries before, so Humboldt learned, and extensively used by the Incas under the name of quinquina. There was a legend, which he dismissed as "monkish superstition," that the Indians learned of the tree's efficacy by observing "lions who cured themselves of the intermittent fever by gnawing the bark." At first, after the dramatic cure of the Countess of Chinchón (a tale since discounted), quinine was known as *pulvia comtissæ* — the Countess's powder; later Jesuit's bark, because Cardinal de Lugo, Procurator General of the Society of Jesus, recommended it to Cardinal Mazarin.

Humboldt believed that the quinine trade would soon come to an unseasonable end, if trees were not planted elsewhere or if the Spanish government did not undertake a program of conservation. "If the governments in America do not attend to the preservation of the quina, either by prohibiting the felling of the trees or by obliging the territorial magistrates to enforce the cutters to guard them from destruction, the highly esteemed product of the New World will be swept from the country." And indeed it was, a half-century later, when Richard Spruce sent plants to India.

Humboldt was busy, too, as a cartographer. That is what determined him to journey to the Upper Amazon village of Jaen. From there Charles-Marie de La Condamine had started his celebrated journey down the Amazon. Humboldt, armed with a new chronometer and bent on improving the map of La Condamine, decided to make the journey down the Andean slopes, drenched in rain, festooned with unnamed trees, deluged by rising rivers, to "improve a map."

In August they descended from mountain-girt Loja south-southeast into the hot valley of the Amazon. It was a new world, different from the bare, treeless paramo and from the flat llanos and giant forests of the Orinoco. Here all was water: water dripped, tumbled, and splashed. Every inch of soil was covered with tree, bush, or climbing vine, and the trees, parasite-laden, hung by slender root threads over the endless number of cascading streams. The explorers were forced to cross the Río de Guancabamba twenty-seven times, so capricious was the road. On the twenty mules that formed their caravan were their instruments, their manuscripts, and the dried plants which they had spent a whole year collecting. They stood on the nether side in animated suspense while the mules, time after time, negotiated the rapids of the Guancabamba. As they made their way down to Jaen de Bracamoros, the highest point of canoe navigation on the Upper Marañón, they could look back and see the cordilleras, like an untamed herd charging with glorious vigor behind them.

They came upon the Río Chamaya, a tributary of the Marañón, on whose banks, like mushrooms in the forest, stood the little village of Jaen. Like Charles-Marie de La Condamine before them, they found balsas at the edge of the river, and these, poled by Indians, conveyed them to the town. At last Humboldt stood on the Amazon. Another desire of his youth had been fulfilled — to see the waters down which Orellana had sailed when he had deserted Pizarro in the jungle; to see the genesis of the great waters that connected with the Orinoco.

They remained seventeen days in the Amazon. When Humboldt had observed Jupiter's satellites and the lunar distances and when he had corrected La Condamine's map, he was ready to return once more to the high cordilleras. They proceeded to climb the Andes and cross the magnetic equator to the city of Cajamarca. In this ancient citadel of the Incas they rode past the quiet baked-earth houses, through flocks of graceful, tawny-colored llamas. They passed harvest festivals of the Indians and watched the ceremonies of the dance, with Panpipe accompaniment, until the monotonous and depressive character of the performance was enough to make them howl. For the Indian dance had neither the eroticism of the Arab nor the rhythm of the Negro; it was repeated in a formula whose monotony itself was like a symbol of the dusk of their departed vigor.

Cajamarca was a place of evil omen. Here the Inca Atahualpa, unwilling to allow himself to be baptized by Vicente de Valverde, was, much to the anguish of his people, garroted publicly in the plaza. At this Andean city, higher than either Quito or Bogotá, the slaughter of the Inca people began. So it was with great curiosity that Humboldt found the descendants of the Inca still living in Cajamarca within the vicious circle of oppression. Reduced to a poverty out of which there was no escape, they lived in a state of complete resignation. There was nothing left them save the despair of a people whom time had forgotten.

Humboldt, who had expressed himself so strongly on Negro slavery, was deeply touched by the pitiful state of the Indians of Cajamarca — indeed, of the whole cordillera — who more than three hundred years before had known a golden age of civilization. The son of the Cacique Astorpilca became the explorers' cicerone and led them over the ruins of the buildings. He spoke of the great treasure that lay beneath them, of palanquins of gold, of golden birds exquisitely fashioned; and Humboldt felt the most profound melancholy when he understood that these dreams and fancies were founded on recollections and traditions from remote times. These illusions of great fortune lying under the ruins of the ancient fortresses doubtless assuaged the Indians' great privation.

Humboldt asked the young descendant of the Inca: "Since you and your parents so firmly believe in the existence of these treasures that lie so near you, do you not in your poverty sometimes feel a wish to dig for them?"

The young Indian boy juggled this pertinent question for a while in his brain and then answered simply and humbly: "Such a desire never comes to us, Your Grace. My father says it would be sinful. If we found the golden branches of the garden beneath this ancient *castillo,* our white neighbors would hate us, injure us, perhaps kill us. We have," he said with a resignation as pitiful as it was explanatory, "we have a little field — and good wheat."

The explorers remained only five days in the ancient capital of the Incas. Since the transit of Mercury across the sun's disk would not wait as they collected, looked into ancient mines, and critically examined the thoughts of a descendant of a people whom time had ground to dust, they had to move on. They were now in the mountain fastness of the cordilleras, two miles above sea-level. The only way to get to Lima, the City of Kings, was to cut through the Ceja de la Montaña, wind down to the ancient town of Trujillo on the coast, and thence make their way along the arid coastline six hundred miles. For eighteen months they had traveled in the cordilleras, from Bogotá to Cajamarca, and they had yet to see the ocean. To be so long in the New World, to have climbed its highest peaks, without a glimpse of the Pacific! The descent to the coast held even brighter prospects. They would see the walled cities of Chimu kings, they would at last escape from the mountains to the sea and take their course along the open shores.

The desire to behold certain objects is not excited solely by their grandeur or their importance, or even by their beauty. In each individual this desire is interwoven with the pleasing impressions of youth and with early predilections for particular pursuits. In proportion as the fulfillment of a wish may have appeared improbable its realization affords the greater pleasure. Here was Humboldt, who had pushed back the frontiers of America as no man had before or would after him; who had seen kings and ministers, unknown rivers, and giant Chimborazo. . . . Now he wished only to see the Pacific. It was this rare, high, and finely directed enthusiasm of Humboldt's that bespoke the great explorer. He enjoyed the anticipation of the happy moment when he would first behold the constellation of the Southern Cross, when he would come in sight of snow-topped Chimborazo, or when he would gaze on a forest of tree-ferns. Humboldt knew that the days on which such wishes are fulfilled mark epochs in one's life and create indelible impressions for which reason alone may not account. "The longing wish I felt to behold the Pacific from the lofty ridges of the Andes," Humboldt remembered, "was mingled with recollections of the interest with which, as a boy, I had dwelt on the narrative of the adventurous expedition of Vasco Nuñez de Balboa. . . ."

They had rounded a tall cactus-studded hill. The sky which had been so long obscured now suddenly brightened, a sharp breeze dispersed the last ribbon of mist, and the dark-blue canopy of the sky was seen between narrow lines of the highest feathery cumulus. And there was the Pacific! Humboldt saw it with tears in his eyes. He felt like one who had traveled to Mecca, like some Andean Indian who before the shrine of the Inca at Cuzco had doffed his woven headgear and remained silent for a space of minutes. The Pacific lay far below, a line of the deepest blue, with the feathered edges of its giant surf quietly reflecting an immense mass of light, rising in immeasurable expanse until it was bounded by the clearly defined horizon. Humboldt, who had infected his companions with the lure of the Pacific, dismounted and the three stood quietly gazing on the panorama of the great South Sea. He was so befuddled that he even forgot to open his barometer and take the altitude of the Alto de Guangamarca! This, like nothing else, explains the effect of "the first view of the Pacific Ocean."

The mule road corkscrewed down the last mountain ridge and led to Trujillo, founded by Pizarro and named by him after his birthplace in Spain. It was set close to the ancient walled city of Chanchan, now a ruin buried in the vast aridities of the Peruvian coastal desert, but once a great metropolis, the key city of the ancient Chimus, raised in the dim centuries of antiquity to Pachacamac, the Creator God. They walked through the maze of ruins, thickly studded with pyramids, streets, open squares, reservoirs, sunken gardens, and tastefully laid-out watercourses that supplied moisture to the once verdant gardens. From here they set their course due southward, following the undulating Pacific shore.

They had traveled for some days when Humboldt began to be tormented by a persistent question: Why was this great coast an absolute desert? Why did this desert, beginning at the narrow waist of Chile, continue for thousands of miles northward to Ecuador, where it abruptly ended and changed into thick jungle? What caused this phenomenon?

The state of the ancient Chimu ruins on the coast showed that it had not rained there for centuries. In fact, the edifices were built of adobe and unprotected by cement. Had it rained over a period of time, they would have been washed away. Yet these ruins were a thousand years old at the very least! In Ecuador, on the same coast, rain fell at a rate of a hundred inches a year. Here not a drop fell. Why?

He looked at the bare, dead, cloud-topped Andes and then upon an ocean that was no longer blue, but instead a dull leaden gray. There was a succession of parched mountain and parched deserts, of blistering coastal terraces broken only by forbidding cliffs. Everything seemed to be swallowed up by the illimitable aridity. The ocean, although practically stormless, was rolled up by steadfast southerly winds. Here and there a native fisherman in his small reed craft would come in on a breaker, the frail craft awash as much because of the mountainous piles of fish in the boat as because of the heavy breakers. Sea lions could be heard barking, sea otters swam in small groups, and birds, streams of birds like long black ribbons drawn across the heavens, moved in ceaseless flight along the littoral. These were the only signs of life on the desert-bound Pacific. One of Humboldt's greatest interests was geophysics and the effect of the temperature upon the earth. Here he was presented with the greatest puzzle. Why was this a desert when the air was so humid? Why were the sunsets so striking when so many of the days were marked by dull skies? Only the afternoons were filled with sunshine. In spite of the threat of rain, it never rained; and though the vegetation appeared to be dried and burned up, like one of Bonpland's collected and dried plants, still the air was humid. Now Humboldt knew what a man in Quito meant by the remark: "When you see no more trees — it is Peru."

So he weighed the air and took the temperature numerous times during the day. He dipped his thermometers in the water and exposed himself to the fury of the breakers to take further oceanic temperatures. Now he began to see one answer to the puzzle: the entire length of coast was bathed by a cool ocean current, a cur-

rent that seemed to move northward. Humboldt questioned sea-
captains who had sailed from Chile northward; he cross-examined
the native fishermen; he put his sharpened deductive powers to
work; he carefully weighed the natural phenomena of the air and
the water. Aimé Bonpland complained about the scarcity of plants,
yet Humboldt felt that the plants themselves would contribute to
the unraveling of this phenomenon.

At Huacho, a small Indian village on the promontory of a bar-
ranca, Humboldt and Bonpland looked into the ancient salt
works that lay close to the shore. As they stood watching the seals
disporting themselves, they were suddenly struck with a smell
something like that of the abattoirs of Paris. It produced a nausea
more overwhelming than the *soroche* of the mountains. Suddenly
they remembered, the smell came from guano, the most concentrated stench of putrescence in the world. Humboldt climbed
over the island of Mazorca, which lay a mile or so off shore. The
small three-hundred-foot island was filled with the nesting-places
of terns, gulls, pelicans, and cormorants; close to the sea were colonies of sea lions. Humboldt collected a sizable quantity of guano,
over the protestations of Bonpland, who thought that they were
exposed to the stench of the odors of mankind in sufficient doses
without dragging with them this highly concentrated bird-dung.
But Humboldt had been stimulated more by the idea of the dung
than by the effect on his olfactory senses. Guano, he knew, was extensively used by the ancient people of the Andes. Most of their
land had been a barren desert except for a few narrow valleys that
were traversed by inconstant streams. Guano was the answer to
their agricultural system. With incredible feats of labor they built
giant terraces along the whole of the Andes. Into these terraces
they carried the earth they gathered in the valleys. They developed
canals and irrigation ditches. Yet all this work would have been
meaningless without some sort of fertilizer. So the Peruvians began to use guano. The inhabitants of Mazorca even showed Humboldt some of the ancient workings of the Incas where with copper instruments they cut through the age-old walls of guano, which
they carried to the top of the Andes to fertilize their corn and
potatoes.

It was the Peruvian Indians who had discovered the efficacy of
guano, but it was Humboldt who rediscovered it, introduced it to
Europe, and thus stimulated a trade that brought to Peru a new
industry and a trade involving millions of dollars. Humboldt
caught a cormorant and noted that its daily passage of excrement
was five ounces. He was shown plants that had been fertilized with
guano, and those that had been fertilized with ordinary manure.

Soon his experiments, as they were begun here on the shores of Peru and then carried on in the laboratories of Europe, confirmed what he had deduced: guano exceeded in strength the ordinary barnyard manure thirty-five times! It owed its value to the peculiar manner in which foods are united by the alchemy of the birds' intestinal tract and made into a compound easily absorbed by plants. Guano lay hundreds of feet thick on some of the islands. This meant little or no rain had fallen on the coast over a period of centuries. On one island, Chincha, there was an estimated bird population of five million; that meant it would take a thousand tons of fish daily to fill the stomachs of these insatiable dung-producers. The cool stream that flowed along the coast brought a vast abundance of marine plants, fish and animals; the cormorants and pelicans lived off the fish and dropped their dung over the small islands where they nested; and this dung enabled the ancient Peruvians to expand from primitive protohistory into a people who produced a social and economic Utopia in the Andes, the like of which the world had never seen and will never see again. The answer lay in the origin of the Pacific current and all its related phenomena.

All these activities of the small gray-eyed man were remembered by the natives. One Don Simón, who had acted as Humboldt's guide to the salt works on the coast, recalled Humboldt's visit to the learned von Tschudi thirty years later:

"Don Alejandro de Humboldt? Of course I remember him," said Simón, "a short man with eyes as gray as the ocean." He related with enthusiastic pleasure his recollections of the youthful and indefatigable traveler. And when he had learned years later that Humboldt had written a book, he got hold of the Spanish edition of it. But at that point he said: *"Ahí perdido los estribos"* — "At that point, señor, I lost my stirrups" — meaning that he did not understand it.

On the last lap of their journey along the arid coastline of Peru the explorers crossed brackish streams filled with fish, passed sun-dried algarrobo trees alive with hummingbirds. Moving inland where their mules might have a better footing than on the friable sand, they saw horses wading in the marsh sloughs, munching succulent water plants. Occasionally they would burst into a lagoon, hidden by growths of rushes, and flush a nesting-place of the long-legged roseate flamingoes. Only such occasions as this broke the monotony of a six-hundred-mile desert journey during the months of September and October.

It was at the gateway of Lima, in the ancient port of Callao, that Humboldt at last obtained his answer to the problem: Why is

there no rainfall on the Peruvian and Chilean coast? * At Callao
he made elaborate barometric studies and was struck by the fact
that the temperature of the water was 60 degrees, while inland the
air temperature was 73 degrees. The relation between temperatures of the sea and land was reversed. Thus, when the air from
over the ocean rolled onto the land, its temperature was raised
instead of being lowered, and so its moisture-carrying capacity
was increased. So in place of condensation, absorption took place,
and so long as these conditions prevailed, rain could not fall.
Early in his Andean travels Humboldt had made observations
which indicated that as we proceed from the equator toward the
poles, the mean temperature decreases one degree Fahrenheit with
each degree of latitude. Here at Callao there was an exception to
this law. The mean annual temperature was far below the theoretical temperature for its latitude, a fact due to the cold current. It was a partial answer to the phenomenon that had puzzled
him. He did no more than this, but in so doing he called the attention of the scientific world to the problem, and that brought
numerous well-equipped expeditions to study the phenomenon of
the cold stream, now called the Humboldt Current. Later investigation explained how "the entire length of the coast is bathed by
a cool ocean current, more uniform in character and more profound in its influence upon climate and living things than any
other in the world. The current is not only directly responsible
for the existence of the guano birds and for all the other spectacu-
lar evidences of prolific life, but moreover, in its relation with the
configuration of the coast and islands on one hand and with the
outlying heated water of the tropical Pacific on the other, it
produces areas of distinct ocean temperature which appear
to be hardly less significant in their effect upon the ranges of
animals than the famous climatic lifezones of the adjoining continent." †

The current owes its origin chiefly to the prevailing westerly
winds of the southern latitudes and the meteorological whirl of
the eastern South Pacific. Moving in a stream 150 miles wide, the
current lowers the temperature of the air that moves across it.
Since its capacity for heat exceeds that of air, "it absorbs heat from
the latter. And the absorption of sufficient warmth from the air
to raise the temperature of a given mass of water one degree will

---

* The first written exposition of this coastal phenomena was given in Alexander von Humboldt's *Mémoire sur les lignes isothermes* (1817) and *Ansichten der Natur* (*Aspects of Nature*), Bohn edition, p. 97.

† Robert Cushman Murphy: *Bird Islands of Peru,* pp. 28–9.

result in a mass of air 3,000 times as great in cubic content being lowered one degree of temperature." *

Humboldt and Bonpland were quite an attraction in Lima when they unpacked their instruments — telescopes, theodolites, and sextants — and made ready to observe the transit of the planet Mercury across the sun's disk. They were anxious to complete all this work since a vessel was leaving on January 3, 1803 from Callao for Guayaquil and Acapulco, Mexico. Meanwhile they enjoyed Lima as they had enjoyed Quito and Bogotá. For Lima was, as it had been for centuries, the seat of the viceregal power in South America. Its affairs were handled with an opulence that befitted its station. In his palace on the Plaza Mayor the Viceroy and his family lived aloof in state, superior to the proudest of colonial aristocracy.

There were formal receptions — *besa mano* affairs — at which, in respect to the King's regent, hands were kissed. Nobility was received in the plaza; Indians, Negroes, and the mixed races flocked into the plaza to watch the arrival of this glittering spectacle — men in knee-breeches and powdered periwigs, slender women with small feet, dressed in the latest European fashion, with the velvet fitting close to the body in order to show the delicate figure better. The onlookers received only the backwash of the strains of music, just as they received only the backwash of the riches of the Peruvian realm. As he watched the great of Lima bow before the Viceroy, kiss his hand, and then step through the stately measures of Spanish court dances, Humboldt smiled ironically and said: "These people have not yet heard of the French Revolution."

This Peru of the Viceroy the explorers left on January 2. Aimé Bonpland, Carlos Montúfar, and Alexander von Humboldt took passage on the frigate *Orué* for Acapulco and set off on the cold current. South America gave the departing explorers a resounding *despedida*. As the royal corvette pushed its way through the channel of Jambelí to enter the mouth of the Río Guayas, which debouches its hyacinth-festooned water into the open sea, Cotopaxi was in eruption. Humboldt had heard the rumbling far out to sea. Cotopaxi, which raises its Fujiyama-like cone forty-three miles south of the equator, had for centuries been the spokesman for the South American volcanoes. It was the ideal volcano. It comported itself in a regular and well-behaved manner. It was not one of the provoking sort, exploding in paroxysms and going to sleep afterward; it was in a state of perpetual activity. At night, far out to

* Ibid., p. 30.

sea, Humboldt could see its top glowing like the end of a lighted cigar. The rumblings kept up all through the days as the corvette edged up the great Río Guayas. In the darkness there was a moaning noise that rose into a roar, and then a deluge of water, blocks of ice, mud, and rock tore down from its sloping side, with all the violence of an avalanche. Humboldt was getting more than a royal salute. The great Cotopaxi was in eruption, Bonpland jokingly remarked, so that Humboldt could see the inner workings of nature.

To this volcanic accompaniment the vessel went up with the tide of the Guayas and pressed by the tangled forest. Behind them was the blue brilliant waste of sea, and before them the naked Andes. Humboldt was seeing trees again after the dreary wastes of Peru, and amid this flaming green that surrounded pallid Guayaquil he conceived the idea of breaching the Andes yet once more to look into the yawning, lava-emitting Cotopaxi. They had exactly six weeks on this hot coast before the vessel would sail for Acapulco, and Humboldt managed to paddle as far up as Babahoyo, a small cluster of huts and houses on one of the myriad branches of the Río Guayas. But there he finally capitulated in favor of the more somber realism of Bonpland, who urged that they not continue. Vessels leaving South America were too great a rarity, and there would not soon be another *Orué*.

Cotopaxi was still booming when they finally lifted anchor and drifted down the Guayas to the open sea. It was February 15, 1803, and the years had swept by as if borne on the fringes of a hurricane. The vessel set its course for Acapulco, and for the first time Humboldt and Bonpland could rest themselves comfortably on the quarter-deck. Carlos Montúfar was still with them. He would follow to Mexico, to North America, and to England. What were his thoughts, this son of a Creole Marquis, as he looked upon his land from far out at sea? Did he know what contact with Humboldt would bring? In the presence of this man of ideas, the innate strivings of Carlos Montúfar would germinate. With O'Higgins, Nariño, José de San Martín, he would form the *Gran Unión Americana* in London, but he would not see the liberty that he would help to forge.

Aimé Bonpland was not agitated by ideas of this sort. He was the scientist *par excellence*, a hedonist of nature, satisfied with the here and now. Surrounded by the piles of plants he had collected, he was delighted to bask in the sun like a chameleon and to give his great malaria-racked body new energy for the next step. In his quiet way he had been able to direct and give content to the energies of Humboldt and fill up, as it were, the lacunæ in this man's zoological and botanical background. Of the three, Bonpland was the most satisfied.

Humboldt spent many hours leaning over the gunwales and looking at the receding coastline of South America and those gigantic hulks of rock over which he had scrambled. He had spent three years in South America. With Bonpland he had explored the land that forms the present states of Venezuela, Colombia, Ecuador, and Peru. He had crossed the mountains of Paría as far as Esmeralda on the Upper Orinoco and San Carlos del Río Negro on the frontiers of Brazil. He had cruised the Caribbean, spent some weeks in Cuba, doubled back across the turbulent Mar Cáribo and after weeks at Río Sinu and the great port of Cartagena had ascended the Magdalena to Bogotá and followed the path along the Andes to Quito. From the Amazon to the glacier heights of Chimborazo, from the Inca's Palace at Cajamarca to the glistening, stinking guano hills of the bird islands of Peru, the most civilized European of his epoch had traveled, 1,300 leagues by land, 650 leagues by water. There was reason why this great man could say later that all this travel "furnished me with a pretty accurate knowledge of local circumstances." Here was the man who three years hence would meet the ardent young Simón Bolívar in Paris. He would use his great authority to canalize the immense energy of that remarkable man. It was with reason that Bolívar said of him: "Baron de Humboldt did more for the Americas than all of the conquistadores."

CHAPTER XVI
The Rediscovery of America

HENCEFORTH THE LIFE OF Alexander von Humboldt was an uninterrupted course of triumphs. Mexico (which was then, in 1803, the Virreinato de Nueva España) afforded him honors reserved usually for officers of the crown. In company with Aimé Bonpland and Carlos Montúfar he debarked at Acapulco, collected in the regions about that port, and then took the long ride to Mexico City. He passed through Taxco and examined its silver mines; he traveled on to Cuernavaca and spent the night in the ancient palace of Hernán Cortés; and in Mexico City he was welcomed by no less than the august Viceroy, el Conde Iturrigaray. The mountains of the Nevada de Toluca received his attention, and the ancient ruins of Tula. The great estates of Querétaro were examined and yielded information out of which he fashioned his famed book: *Essai politique sur le royaume de la Nouvelle-Espagne*. While Bonpland collected plants and Montúfar tested the republican sentiments of the Mexican liberals, Humboldt was indefatigable in his research into all the varied cultures that made Nueva España the richest of the King's possessions. After he had climbed its mountains, collected its ancient Mexican codices, studied its people, drawn and worked among the ruins of its civilization, Humboldt's eleven-month exploration of Mexico reached a fitting climax in his being invited to ride in state with the Viceroy to visit and pass upon the work on the canals at Desagüe. Anything else would have been anticlimactic. On the 7th of March 1804 he left with Bonpland and Montúfar for Vera Cruz to take ship to Cuba, and so left Hispanic America, never to return.

After a short stay in Havana, where he picked up his collections from the Orinoco that he had left there in 1801, he directed his itinerary to the United States. For in Cuba he had received, through the hands of the United States Consul, a letter from Thomas Jefferson inviting him to come to North America:

Congratulations on your arrival . . . in good health after a tour in the course of which you have been exposed to so many hardships and hazards. The countries you have visited are those of the least known and most interesting; and lively desire will be felt generally to receive the information you will be able to give. Accept, I pray you, my respectful salutations and assurances of great respect and consideration. . . .

May 28, 1804   Jefferson

The meeting between Jefferson and Humboldt must have been a memorable moment. Each was, in his own way, the supreme representative of his age. Humanists and scientists both, and both profoundly interested in the curiosities of the world, they found an immediate sphere of interest in South America. Of the eight weeks that Humboldt spent in the United States, three were spent at Monticello. There Jefferson communicated to Humboldt an extraordinary project for the future division of the continent of America into three great republics in which were to be incorporated the Spanish possessions of Mexico and South America. These two titans gave the lie to the saying that philosophers do not know how to act, while politicians do not know how to think. But there was a great loyalty in Humboldt toward the King of Spain, who had made his great expedition to the Americas possible. Humboldt inspired, but he did not incite; he took no political advantage of his *carta blanca* to move through the King's possessions. What he contributed to Jefferson's political project for South America was never disclosed. The days passed quickly, all too quickly. In July 1804, after visits at Washington, Monticello, Baltimore, and Philadelphia, Humboldt, with, as always, Montúfar and Bonpland, sailed down the Delaware on the frigate *Favorita* bound for France.

For half a century Humboldt was an American favorite. His *Essai Politique* on Cuba, like the one on Mexico, was eagerly translated and read in North America. His views on slavery were widely quoted. They were even used in the political campaign between Frémont and James Buchanan. Frémont, the explorer who scattered Humboldt's name on counties, cities, rivers, and mountains throughout the Northwest, was able to write later to his idol: "In the history of your life and opinions we find abundant reason for believing that in the struggle in which the friends of liberal progress in this country find themselves engaged, we shall have the strength of your name." Nor was Frémont the only American to express himself so strongly. In 1858, a year before Humboldt's death, the U. S. Secretary of War, John B. Floyd, wrote to him: "Never can we forget the services you have rendered, not only to us, but to all the world. The name of Humboldt is a household word through our immense country, from the shores of the Atlantic to the waters of the Pacific. We have honored ourselves by its use in many parts of our territory, so that posterity will find it everywhere linked with the names of Washington, Jefferson and Franklin." Floyd did not speak in hyperbole; Humboldt's name is given to valleys and rivers in Nevada, bays and forests in California, cities in Iowa, Kansas, and Tennessee;

counties in California, Iowa, and Nevada. And he has been honored similarly in Mexico and South America. Animals, trees, plants, rivers, cities, streets, and currents bear his name; six countries in Latin America simultaneously and spontaneously, two years before his death declared him *benemérito*.

His return to Europe in August 1804 was regarded with universal joy. Here Humboldt, who had yet to write a single word for public consumption, was nevertheless idolized throughout the continent. The ordinary citizen knew nothing of the 40,000 miles that he had traveled, or the 60,000 plants he had helped to collect (thousands of which were new to science) or the great piles of notes he had taken on geology, astronomy, volcanology, and archæology, or of the thirty immense chests of specimens, the 1,500 measurements, and the sections of the Andes. They knew only the man who had made known so much that was unknown of South America, through his celebrated letters to the great of Europe. This was the same Humboldt whose complete works on the Americas would number twenty-nine volumes of immense folios, quartos, and octavos, illustrated with upward of 1,426 maps and plates, the man who would directly inspire other scientists — Darwin, Schomburgk, Linden, Funck-Brentano, Moritz, Wagner, and Carl Sachs among them — to embark on a continuation of his investigations. To the people, Alexander von Humboldt was a man of prodigious energy and of great simplicity and noble character. They knew that he had spent most of his personal fortune. The 85,000 thalers that had been his in 1798 were now reduced to 38,500 thalers, the interest from which was scarcely enough for him to live on. In Paris he signed a contract to pay the publisher Candolle 180,000 francs for the printing costs of his giant folios on America, and that about ended his fortune. To compensate him for this, the King of Prussia made him his Court Chamberlain (even though he remained in Paris for fifteen years) and arranged a generous sinecure for him, so that his writings could go on uninterrupted. He was even offered the title of Prince of the realm, but this was an honor Humboldt refused to accept.

It was hard for him to settle down at once. He went to Rome to visit his brother; he met the young Simón Bolívar and with him ascended Mount Vesuvius. Humboldt knew that South America was ripe for freedom. He had met, talked, and walked with most of the precursors of the revolution to be. But the people needed a leader. Humboldt doubted that a man of the needed stature could be found to undertake the herculean task. He spoke to young Bolívar of his great country, its illimitable possibilities — Humboldt the savant became Humboldt the inspirer. Bolívar vowed that he would be the man that Humboldt said was needed — and yet Humboldt did not dishonor his patron, the King. There was never direct sedition or unworthiness attached to his inspiration. He spoke of freedom with the same detachment with which he spoke of the temperature. Dedicating his book on Mexico, *Essai politique sur le royaume de la Nouvelle-Espagne,* to the King of Spain, he wrote:

To His Catholic Majesty, Charles IV, King
of Spain and the Indies
Sire,

Having enjoyed your protection and your great benevolence during the many years that I have traveled in the distant lands subject to your sovereignty, I am doing no more than performing a sacred duty in placing at the foot of your throne my most profound and respectful acknowledgment of these favors.

In the year 1799 in Aranjuéz I had the good fortune of being received personally by Your Majesty, who condescended to applaud the enthusiasm of one whom the love of science would carry up the banks of the Río Orinoco and the peaks of the Andes.

Due to the confidence inspired by the favors of Your Majesty, I dare to place your august name in front of this work which traces a picture of a vast empire, whose prosperity, Sire, pleases your heart.

None of the monarchs who have occupied the Spanish throne have more freely than yourself distributed the knowledge of this magnificent part of the globe, which is subject to the law of Spain. The coasts of America have been delineated by able astronomers with the munificence due to a great sovereign. There have been published at the expense of Your Majesty exact maps of the same coasts and also detailed plans of the various strategic ports. You also ordered that Lima issue annually a *Mercurio Peruana*, a factual and statistical progress-sheet of the inhabitants, the commerce, and the finances.

But there was still missing a statistical report on the Kingdom of Nueva España. To overcome this omission, I collected much of my own material, the first outline of which I brought to the attention of the Viceroy of Mexico who held office in 1804. I should be very happy if I could presume that this very humble work, in a newly edited edition, were not unworthy of being dedicated to Your Majesty.

In my work are reflected the sentiments of gratitude which I owe to the government that has protected me and to this nation, noble and faithful, which has received me not as a traveler, but as one of its citizens. Could a work like this displease a good king, who himself refers to national interest, to the perfection of social institutions, and to the eternal principles on which rest the prosperity of the people?

I am, with all respect, Sire, Your Catholic Majesty's very humble and obedient servant.

Baron A. von Humboldt

Paris, March 8, 1808

In Paris after the Italian interlude, Humboldt began the preparation of eleven stupendous books on his explorations and researches in the Americas. He wrote the first volume of his explorations in Venezuela under the title of *Voyage aux régions équinoxiales du Noveau Continent.* Then followed in collaboration with Aimé Bonpland, *Plantæ æquinoctiales; Nova genera et species plantarum; Essai sur la géographie des plantes; Relation abrégée de l'expédition; Observations astronomiques et mesures géodesiques; Observations magnetiques; Pasigraphie géologique; Atlas géologique; Voyage aux Tropiques.* . . . The effect of this stupendous literary activity on the intellectual circles of Europe can be understood only if one recalls the absolute poverty of information existing in Europe about America. Humboldt's discourses before the Académie des Sciences (which promptly made him a member), his writings, his scientific activities, the ceaseless flow of the great of Europe who came to his study, gave him a fame only eclipsed by that of the Emperor of the French. So long did Humboldt live in Paris, so well was he known, that when a stranger wished to visit him and did not know his precise address, almost any Parisian coachman could say: "Ah yes, the house of Baron de Humboldt!"

Napoleon, with whom he was compared in greatness, made a point of open resentment. When Humboldt was presented to him, the Emperor remarked coldly:

"M. de Humboldt . . . I understand you are interested in botany. My wife also studies it."

Which Humboldt well knew, for as soon as he could, he had pulled the political strings that made Aimé Bonpland Superintendent of the Royal Botanical Gardens at Malmaison. Those ten years between 1805 and 1814 were Bonpland's happiest. Humboldt had insisted that the second collection of plants — 60,000 dried specimens — be presented in Bonpland's name to the Jardin des Plantes. Then with the aid of Jussieu and Lamarck he prevailed upon Napoleon to grant Bonpland an annual pension of 3,000 francs. The grant signed by Napoleon read: "As an expression of our esteem for this donation, and in conformity with the desires of M. de Humboldt, we concede to M. Bonpland in recognition of his travels and his researches an annual pension of 3,000 francs."

It can be seen that Humboldt never permitted anyone to forget that Aimé Bonpland was his faithful coadjutor in his explorations of the Americas. Still Aimé Bonpland did not take well to writing up his botanical material; more and more it was neglected; he gave himself over to his duties with the Empress. Josephine was an understanding patroness, the gardens at Malmaison flourished

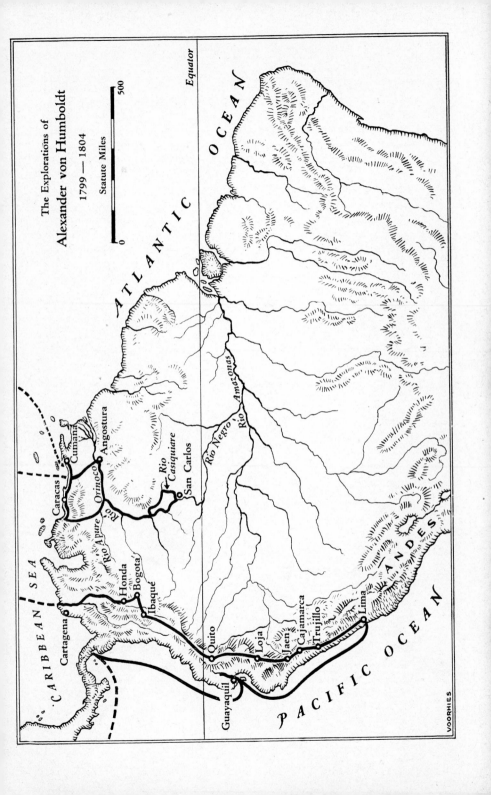

The Explorations of
Alexander von Humboldt
1799 — 1804

Statute Miles

500

0

ATLANTIC OCEAN

Equator

CARIBBEAN SEA

Cumaná

Caracas

Angostura

Orinoco

Rio Apure

Río Casiquiare

San Carlos

Río Negro

Río Amazonas

Cartagena

Honda

Bogotá

Ibaqué

Quito

Guayaquil

Loja

Jaen

Cajamarca

Trujillo

Lima

ANDES

PACIFIC OCEAN

VOORHIES

and Bonpland was in a botanist's heaven. But it did not last long. Napoleon, under the urge of his desire for an heir, divorced Josephine. With her decline Bonpland's star began to set. He stayed until she died. Then, bewildered by the turn of events, he turned his back on France, accepted the post of Director of the Museum at Buenos Aires, and in 1816 left for South America to continue the labors of the eighteenth-century French botanist Feuillée.

The South America of 1816 was not the South America of 1799. Freedom had come, but freedom had brought chaos. Dictators reigned. Wild and unmanageable *cimarrones* roamed the pampas. The states that had won their freedom by fighting together now fought each other. Poor Bonpland, who knew nothing of politics or the struggles of men, was only collecting the leaves of the maté in Paraguay when down swooped the gaucho cavalry of Dr. Francia. Bonpland's servants were killed before his eyes and in the mêlée he received a saber gash across the head that laid bare the bone. Francia — Dr. José Gaspar Rodríguez Francia, the spoiled child of South America, the *caudillo* of Paraguay — then made Aimé Bonpland his personal prisoner. When Bonpland nursed himself back to health, he found himself a captive, unshackled, but involuntary physician to the garrison at Ascunción. Later he became Director of Agriculture: still he remained a captive. Rumor of Bonpland's contretemps seeped out across the Atlantic and reached the ears of Humboldt. His anger and anxiety knew no bounds. He put into motion the connections and power which he had gathered over half a century. He wrote to Lord Canning, who he knew was interested in the American republics, and begged his intervention. The French traveler Grandsire was dispatched to Buenos Aires with letters from Chauteaubriand to demand Bonpland's release. When Simón Bolívar heard of the imprisonment, he threatened to march over the Andes and lay siege to Paraguay unless Bonpland was released. Although assailed from all sides, Dr. Francia remained adamant. He kept his prisoner for nine more years in the confines of Paraguay. And thus the story of Bonpland, like some stirring serial, filled the salons of Europe. Then one day the world's journals carried the news: "Aimé Bonpland is released by Dr. Francia."

In Europe there were celebrations and speeches. People who did not know the difference between a petiole and a peduncle, or Dioscorides from Linnæus, joined in the celebrations. Such are the effects of publicity. Honors were showered on Bonpland. Humboldt had him decorated with the Order of the Red Eagle. He became a chevalier of the Legion of Honor. France raised his annual pension. Monarchs praised him. The Imperial Academy of Vienna, in order to give him real and lasting honor, called their official botanical organ *Bonplandia* after him.

Aimé Bonpland accepted all this, as he had most things in his life, passively. He had no desire to return to Europe. The world had passed him by. He was afraid of it. "What compensation," he wrote to Humboldt, "could I find in the noise and bustle of Paris? Should I labor in some garret there for any bookseller who might undertake to print my books?"

Everything was lost for him now but botany. Bonpland continued to collect, for he found his small pension large enough to support his meager wants. In the Banda Oriental of Uruguay he built a small grass-thatched adobe house that he called Sansouci. There, despite his age, he became the patriarch of an endless procession of coffee-colored children, and among them he botanized until he was eighty-three years of age. Toward the last, the ex-director of Malmaison, one-time physician to the Empress of France, bent, white-thatched, and toothless, said to a visitor sent by Humboldt:

"Come — come and see me again — and remember me to Humboldt."

While Europe, between 1806 and 1814 became one great suppurating wound and bled under the eagles of Napoleon, Humboldt, the "good European," kept to his writings. With stopped Ulysses-ears, deaf to the enticements of all the metaphysical rat-catchers who would have had him turn politician, Humboldt ignored the transient glory of politics and guided his vast publishing projects through the press. Though war ravaged Europe for a decade, Humboldt managed to see most of his work published. When the last giant item was sent through the binder's, the Humboldtian galaxy was the brightest in the European heavens, for Napoleon's star had set with his disastrous Russian campaign. He had been exiled to Elba.

Humboldt could now no longer disregard the entreaties of his King to help at Vienna in the reconstruction of Europe. They had need of his encyclopedic intelligence. Moreover he knew personally all the men who would decide Europe's fate. Talleyrand, that enigmatical man, Bishop of the old regime, member of the revolutionary States General, Foreign Minister of the Republic, and a power himself during the power-mad days of Napoleon — Talleyrand was now the man of the hour, for he had helped to dethrone Napoleon. Humboldt was in Paris when Talleyrand and Czar Alexander met there and were proclaimed the liberators of mankind. Then he went to the conference of Vienna with Prince Hardenberg as the representative of Prussia. His old schoolfellow Metternich was now Prime Minister of Austria. All these great men hoped to settle Napoleon's Europe, to bring liberty and universal happiness, initiate invigorating reforms, and create the palingenesis of mankind. Then, in the midst of the discussions, Napoleon escaped from Elba and roused his Old Guard; and for one hundred days — until the defeat at Waterloo — all the rare ideals with which the conference began were suspended. After that the reaction set in, the Holy Alliance came into being, legitimacy of governments became the issue, the joyful and chimerical hopes of the "palingenesis of mankind" disappeared in the specious and equivocal arguments of the delegates at the Congress of Vienna.

Humboldt was not pleased with his role as politician. A man used to cold, precise, scientific delineation of a problem, he could not stomach the inanities of little-traveled statesmen. He was happy to return to his writing and he never actively entered the political arena again, though from 1827 on he was attached to the court in Berlin. Previously he had even refused to assist in the conferences that would lead to a treaty between Mexico and Central America: "It would be wholly inconsistent with my character and my intimate horror of the mysteries of diplomacy were I to renounce a position of independence which I have so long preserved."

Meanwhile, through all these years, a great book was in preparation, different from all the others which had dealt with America. It was called *Kosmos*. Humboldt knew that it "savored of affectation," yet he believed it had the advantage of including in one term the heavens and the earth — and so it did.

In 1829 he journeyed across Russia and Siberia to the Yenisei River. It was so rapid a trip that it could not, even by a single discovery, touch his American odyssey, which remained his career. But it did give the stimulus to *Kosmos*.

Never had any natural scientist conceived a plan of such grandeur. He began it in 1845, at the age of seventy-six, and continued the work until his death. The last volume of it was published posthumously. Fragmentary and defective as it is, it contains a tremendous encyclopedic explanation of the physical universe. This book is now seldom read, though it did great service in emphasizing the relations between the forms and habits of plants, and characters of soil. It was Humboldt's style that aroused interest. Never had nature been described before in such grandeur. He himself complained that he wrote sentences like a "Warsaw dressing-gown with forty pockets of parentheses." For while contemporary Goethe regarded the verb as the thing, the verb which was the life-giving, controlling, and directing power, Humboldt's medium was the adjective.

All this activity went on until his ninetieth year. He was beset by so many people in his closing years that he sought to limit them to save his strength. He corresponded with the great of the world: prince, scholar, explorer, and revolutionist. Stephens, discoverer of the Mayas of Yucatán, whose *Incidents of Travel* provoked the renaissance of archæology, came to see him. And Prescott, author of *The Conquest of Mexico,* wrote him. So venerable an aspect did this man have that Bayard Taylor, who went to see him in 1857, began an essay thus: "I came to Berlin not to visit its museums and galleries, its operas, its theatres, nor to mingle in the gay life — but for the sake of seeing and speaking with the world's greatest living man — Alexander von Humboldt. . . ."

As he pressed the hand of the small stooped man with the face of a cherub and the white thatch of Jove, he could well say that he pressed the hand that had touched those of Frederick the Great, Schiller, Goethe, Bolívar, Napoleon, the Marshals of France, Jefferson, Franklin, Laplace, Cuvier, Herder, Guy-Lussac, Hamilton, Beethoven, Walter Scott — in short, every great man Europe and America had produced in three quarters of a century. He could look into the eyes of a man who had seen the meeting-place of the waters of the Orinoco and the Amazon; who had climbed Chimborazo, Popocatepetl, the Alps; the gray eyes that had seen the Caspian, the Urals, Siberia, and the Tatar steppes. These were the hands and the eyes of a man who had rediscovered the Americas and who was, in the words of his greatest spiritual protégé, Charles Darwin, "the greatest scientific traveler who ever lived."

By 1858 Humboldt prepared for the inevitable: "The dead and the aged," he said, "ride fast. I have lived so long," he confided to Taylor, "that I have almost lost the consciousness of time. I belong to the age of Jefferson and Gallatin. . . . Why, I heard of Washington's death while traveling in South America."

In 1859, at the age of ninety, Friedrich Heinrich Alexander, Baron von Humboldt, crying a thousand thanks in his failing voice "for all those who had the patience to cleanse my Augean stables," breathed his last. And with him the whole of romantic natural philosophy was buried. The uniform conception of nature received in his *Kosmos* its most glorious memorial. It seems now almost symbolical that the creator of this synthesis of heaven and earth should have died the same year that the *Origin of Species* was published. But long before Humboldt died, Charles Darwin had taken up the work in South America.

PART III

◇◆◇◆◇◆◇◆◇◆◇◆◇◆◇◆◇◆◇◆◇◆◇◆◇◆◇◆◇

CHAPTER XVII
Erasmus Darwin's Grandson

"FEBRUARY 29TH, 1832." Young Charles Darwin wrote that
date in his diary with a scrawling flourish. It was a day long to
remember. He sat for a moment dreaming, staring out of the port-
hole; then he disentangled his long legs, jumped up, ran halfway
to the door, remembered something, and ran back to his diary. In
a scribble so bad that only he could read it, he wrote:

"About 9 o'clock we were near to the coast of Brazil."

The whole ship was astir. Seamen raced up the rigging to reef
the sails, the leadsman hung over the bow. Orders were being
barked about the *Beagle,* making Darwin feel, now more than
ever, his uselessness on a ship. H.M.S. *Beagle* began to roll in the
ground-swell, listing at such an angle that he was forced to hold
onto the rigging to prevent his tall body from rolling clumsily to
the other side. Through it all, however, his handsome young face
was abeam with the pleasure of expectancy.

At twenty-two Charles Robert Darwin was over six feet in
height, with shoulders large and legs long and thin for his frame.
He had an ample mop of brown hair which swept over his rounded
forehead, cascading into romantic sideburns. Only in the gray
eyes, the long, thick-knobbed nose, and the heavy beetle-brows was
there any resemblance to the future "philosopher of Down," whose
Pan-like countenance would be reproduced far and wide as that of
the notorious author of *The Origin of Species.*

Captain Robert FitzRoy came on deck now to bring the *Beagle*
into the harbor of Todos Santos. FitzRoy, four years Darwin's
senior, was in command of this surveying voyage around South
America. Young Charles was wholly awed by FitzRoy, and in the
first days of the voyage was moved by hero-worship for the Captain, whom he found "silent, darkly handsome, well-bred, of almost excessively aristocratic temper and bearing." Now there was
a caress in the eyes of FitzRoy as he glanced at the masts and at

[169]

the line of wake that the *Beagle* left on the rolling turquoise seas, for the *Beagle* was his creation. Built as a ten-gun brig, he had had her altered, rebuilt, entirely refitted as a bristling six-gun barque, made over, not to insure the supremacy of Britannia on the seven seas, but to carry a chain of measurements and soundings around South America.

The nearer the land loomed, the more feverish the activities of the sailors. Commands were being flung from every part of the quarter-deck. Men who had lazed for days on the deck were now stung into fervid activity. Lieutenant Sullivan raced by, issuing orders with the cut of a snapped bull-whip. He was responsible for the smartness of the ship. Many was the time he had wanted to throw Darwin and his "damned beastly devilments" over the side. "If I were the skipper," he said with grinning seriousness, "I would soon have you and all your damned mess out of the place." Even now, in the act of bringing in the ship, Sullivan had a few cutting words to say.

The *Beagle* was rolling into the harbor of Bahia. There, hanging on the rigging, was young Covington, who was delegated to act as Darwin's servant ashore, eagerly watching the landfall, obsessed with the idea of eating the fruit people called a *"bananer."* And Mellerish, the grinning Mellerish, was beside him shouting at the dolphins which were cutting through the spindrift in gentle arcs like harbor-masters bringing the ship into port. Who would have believed that this young Midshipman Mellerish would some day be an Admiral in the Queen's Navy? At the moment he was only famous for his own introduction: "I am Mellerish of Midhurst, I have read Byron and I don't care a damn for anyone." George Rowlett, the purser, stood by Darwin, drinking in the scenery of Brazil and sharing young Charles's unquenchable enthusiasm. He was to be Darwin's most intimate companion in his four years in South America. And there was Harris — Old Thunder-and-Lightning Harris, as he was called by all — racing along the deck, upbraiding a seaman for knocking off one of his lightning conductors. Captain FitzRoy had allowed this eccentric to put his apparatus all over his ship, even though its installation met with such great prejudice in England. Still, the Russian Navy adopted his invention, and later England; he would end his long life as Sir William Snow Harris.

Darwin's first landfall in South America, at Bahia, put him in a "chaos of delight." As soon as he landed he made his way into the forest on the edge of town, fully equipped with entomologist's net and botanical vasculum. He was so overcome with emotion at being in a real jungle that he could scarcely find words to describe

his feelings: ". . . delight is however a weak term for such transports of pleasure. . . . The land is one great wild, untidy, luxu-
riant hothouse, made by nature for herself, but taken possession of
by man, who studded it with gay and formal gardens. The form of
the orange-tree, the coco-nut tree, the palm, the mango, the tree
fern, the banana, remains clear and separate, but the thousand
beauties which unite these into one perfect scene must fade away;
yet they have, like a tale heard in childhood, a picture full of
indistinct, but most beautiful figures. . . ." Young Darwin collected spiders and beetles. Large Morpho butterflies idly flew by,
followed by others of shimmering blue, like freshly fired enamel.
He felt that no human palette could do justice to the chromatic
splendor of the Brazilian butterflies as they floated through the
flower-bedecked forest. He lost all sense of time. The morning
passed, the afternoon came on, and with it rain. Caught in a
tropical downpour, he took refuge under enormous roots which
supported lofty trunks. So protected in the dripping forest, he
was "transported" to the visions contained in the *Arabian Nights*.
Whereas Charles had formerly admired Humboldt and his descriptions of tropical scenery, "now I almost adore him; he alone
gives any notion of the feelings which are raised in the mind on
first entering the tropics." When the rain had ceased and he made
his way back to the ship, the delirium of delight still possessed
him.

The night was still, the barque shifted gently on the ground-
swell. The smells of the rich earth blew off shore; the wind of the
night wafted in the scent of pineapple and banana. Young Charles
sat down to his improvised desk on top of the chart table and tried
to find his first words about South America. ". . . I believe from
what I have seen, Humboldt's glorious descriptions are & will
for ever be unparalleled: but even he with his dark blue skies &
the rare union of poetry with science which he so strongly dis-
plays when writing on tropical scenery, with all this falls short of
the truth. The delight one experiences in such times bewilders
the mind; if the eye attempts to follow the flight of a gaudy but-
ter-fly, it is arrested by some strange tree or fruit; in watching an
insect one forgets it in the strange flower it is crawling over; if
turning to admire the splendour of the scenery, the individual
character of the foreground fixes the attention. The mind is a
chaos of delight out of which a world of future & more quiet
pleasure will arise. I am at present fit only to read Humboldt. . . ."

He closed his diary, eased himself into his hammock, picked up
Humboldt's *Personal Narrative*. Hardly had he put his eyes to the

title-page of this "magical book" when his mind raced over all the events that had changed him from theological student to naturalist on H.M.S. *Beagle,* lying off the shore of Brazil.

It was on August 29, 1831, a day he would never forget, that the great change had come about. He had been tramping over the hills and moors beyond Shrewsbury, dreading the time he would have to return to Christ's at Cambridge. When he returned home, a letter was waiting for him. It was from Henslow of Cambridge, the botany professor to whom he was deeply attached. Its contents were astounding — incredible: "A Captain FitzRoy is to command a vessel going to Tierra del Fuego . . . the voyage is to last two years . . . he wishes a Naturalist as companion . . . you may consider the situation at your disposal. I have the greatest anxiety that you should go."

To go to South America — to see the lands that Humboldt had so wonderfully described! He went through the letter again. He read it aloud to his sisters. They thought it dreadful. They spoke of two years as being an eternity. He laid the idea before his father, but Dr. Robert Darwin promptly put his foot down. What sort of business was this, to go wandering about the world in a stinking ship? He reminded Charles that he had studied medicine at Edinburgh, to become a doctor like his father and his grandfather before him — and had failed. At that time his father had upbraided him with "You care for nothing but shooting, dogs, and rat-catching — you will be a disgrace to yourself and all your family." And now after his past failures he wanted to go away on a sailing cruise for two years, tossing up his studies just like that. Had he no thought for the future? Had he no idea who he was? At this rebuke Charles had to remember who he really was — the grandson of the renowned Erasmus Darwin.

Erasmus Darwin had already taken his departure from this earth when his descendant, Charles Robert Darwin, uttered his first cry on February 12, 1809, the same day and hour that one Nancy Hanks in Kentucky was giving birth to Abraham Lincoln. All in all, the year 1809 was not a bad year for incipient geniuses. Gladstone and Braille were born in that year, and Tennyson, Fitzgerald of the *Rubáiyát,* Edgar Allan Poe, Mendelssohn, and Holmes also.

Shrewsbury at the time of Darwin's birth was a bustling town of 14,000, lying within a considerable rural area, near the main loop of the deep, swift-flowing Severn River. Erasmus Darwin, its late leading physician, had been able to bequeath the sum of £25,000 to each of his children. One of these was Robert Waring Darwin, destined to become Charles Darwin's father. He took his inheritance, studied medicine in Leiden, and then settled down in Shrewsbury as, by inheritance, its leading physician. Such was the genealogy of the author of the theory of evolution.

During Charles Darwin's childhood, sufficiently commonplace in itself, all Europe was astir over the last desperate struggle with Napoleon. Young Charles could remember all his life that day in July 1815 when the ancient towers of Shrewsbury rang their bells and people fired skyrockets to celebrate the final defeat of Napoleon. The night was filled far beyond his bedtime with the flashes and bangings of the celebration.

Charles Darwin was not a *Wunderkind*. He did not, like Mozart, compose sonatas at the age of nine. He did not make pronouncements on natural history that stirred men to their depths. He was a child of his age and of his time, neither more brilliant nor less intelligent than any English child of his class or station. He went to the grammar school of Shrewsbury, and passed many happy hours sitting with his physician-father as he made his professional rounds in the family chaise. He watched butterflies and beetles go their appointed ways, he picked up bright-colored shells and pebbles. Unlike Humboldt, his youthful interests were not directed. His formal education began under the Reverend Samuel Butler (grandfather of the author of *The Way of All Flesh*) and his studies, which were pre-eminently classical, neither engaged nor interested him. He passed his grades only by his master's judicious use of cajolery and the birch rod, and "merit money" from home. He was weak at spelling, he was atrocious at foreign languages (a lack which his travels never fully overcame) , he cribbed his classical verses, he hummed in the classroom, and fell afoul of the sharp-tongued dominie, who unhesitatingly pronounced him a "fool." These years Darwin recalled as an unfilled void. "The school as a means of education to me was simply a blank"; but other interests were taking hold. His collections of insects became a bit more systematic; he picked up grandfather Erasmus's *Loves of the Plants* and read it with wonderment, and this turned him to botany. Outside classes, and even in them, he read Byron, Thomson, and Shakespeare. Then one day from a schoolfellow he snatched a book entitled *Wonders of the World*. "Those entrancing pages he and his classmates read over and over, disputing among themselves whether these astounding things could possibly be true, and wishing that they might travel to most of the distant countries to see for themselves." *

At the age of sixteen collecting had become a passion — shells, minerals, insects, birds' eggs, and then the skins of birds and rats.

---

* *Charles Darwin,* by Geoffrey West (New Haven, 1939) , p. 54.

Darwin always thought of himself as a "born naturalist." But Dr. Dorsey insists that he was no more a "born naturalist than he was a born liar." Natural history, in his youth, had a social value. Most of the gentry collected one thing or another. But with the youthful Charles Darwin, the collecting went beyond idle curiosity. If the Reverend Dr. Samuel Butler could have composed a single line to describe him on the diploma that permitted Charles's entry into the University of Edinburgh for the study of materia medica, he might have put: "rat-catcher and pococurante."

Darwin's foibles were a small matter to the Chancellor of Edinburgh University. He was only too happy to welcome the grandson of Erasmus Darwin to the student body. And there Charles gave himself over to his collecting. He went to the lectures of the Natural History Society, he heard Audubon (buckskins and all) lecture about North American birds, he walked on the beaches with Dr. Grant and collected marine animals and shore birds. From a Negro who had been with Waterton in South America he learned to remove and prepare bird skins. But the anatomical-medical garden was left uncultivated. The Dean of the medical faculty broke the news gently to Dr. Robert Darwin. He thought that Charles was not destined, so to speak, for the medical profession. Much as the Dean would have liked to have had the grandson of the illustrious Erasmus in his classes, still . . . Dr. Darwin took the hint. Charles was withdrawn from Edinburgh and put into Christ's College, Cambridge. In one jump his mental horizon changed from the natural to the supernatural. But do not believe that this changed young Charles's instincts. He kept up his collecting, and added to it a passion for shooting, hunting, and riding over the countryside.

Now two other influences entered his life, influences that were to change not only Darwin, but the whole world as well. These were a man and a book. The man was the Reverend John Stevens Henslow, Professor of Botany; and the book Alexander von Humboldt's *Personal Narrative of Travels to the Equinoxial Regions of America during the Years 1799–1804.* Henslow taught him the botany of pistils, of calyx, and of corollas. He learned the reproduction of plants and something of the system by which they are arranged. He also put his head and hand into geology and found it intensely interesting. Henceforth his collections took on order. Henslow kept him to the ground, but Humboldt transported him to the clouds. From the reading of Humboldt, he said, stemmed the whole subsequent course of his life. It released him from the local and gave him a desire to travel. He fell under the spell of those great descriptions of tropical nature, and never recovered.

Until the end of his life, for Charles Darwin, Humboldt remained "the greatest scientific traveler who ever lived."

There are for each one of us, according to our turn of mind, certain books that open up horizons hitherto undreamed of and mark an epoch in our mental life. They fling open the gates of a new world, they are the spark without which the fire will not blaze. Such was Humboldt's *Personal Narrative* to Darwin. When he should have been studying the *Evidences of Christianity,* he was following Humboldt up the Orinoco; when he should have been learning the common doxology, he sat down and copied Humboldt's account of his ascent to the top of Tenerife. And on a botanical excursion with Professor Henslow and his pupils, he read the most thrilling passages aloud to them with an infectious enthusiasm. They all sat about staring misty-eyed as they listened: "We anchored at several soundings, for the mist was so thick we could scarcely distinguish objects . . . but the moment in which we began to salute the place the fog was instantly dispelled. The peak appeared in a break above the clouds, and the first rays of the sun, which had not risen, illumined the summit of the volcano. . . . We can easily conceive now how the inhabitants, even of the beautiful climates of Greece and Italy, might have recognized one of the Fortunate Isles in the western part of Tenerife."

"Ah, but to see it with my own eyes!" exclaimed Darwin, laying down the book. He was all for leaving at once. He even went to London with an introduction to a merchant who might possess information of vessels sailing thither. All through the spring and summer of 1831 he could think, talk, dream of nothing else. He studied Spanish, which he owned that he found "immensely stupid." He read and re-read Humboldt, and continued to do so even after he earned his B.A. at Cambridge. He knew it not, but South America was calling. Then came that day of days when he rode in and found Henslow's letter, which told him of the chance to accompany the *Beagle.*

Dr. Darwin put his foot down, this time emphatically. It was a wild scheme on every ground. Charles protested; he was not abandoning the church, it was only an interim between his studies and his settling down in some quiet parish. "All the more reason for not going," was the father's retort. Charles persisted in his arguments, but his father was adamant, and so with a heavy heart Darwin wrote to Henslow thanking him, but bowing to his father's objections — he would have to refuse.

Then Uncle Joe interceded. Uncle Joe was Joseph Wedgwood of the famous family of potters. He wrote to Charles's father. He stressed that Charles's theological study was not in any sense profound, that his leading interests were more naturalistic than supernaturalistic; as for the danger of the sea, the small ship, the discomforts, and the rest of the objections, it would be the making of Charles. Gradually Dr. Darwin gave way and at last reluctantly consented. Charles dispatched a new letter to Professor Henslow revoking his refusal. Then he took a chaise and went post-haste to see Captain FitzRoy, saying: "I trust the place is not given away."

Captain FitzRoy was a striking character. Descended from Charles II and Barbara Villiers through the Dukes of Grafton, he had entered the Navy at fourteen, and was a Lieutenant before he was twenty. He had seen service in the Mediterranean and in 1826, with the ships *Adventure* and *Beagle*, had begun the coastal survey of South America. In 1828 Captain Stokes of the *Beagle* committed suicide. As his first officer, FitzRoy took his place and continued the survey. Impressed, the Admiralty gave him command of the *Beagle*, and the work continued under FitzRoy's direction. FitzRoy had lamented the lack of some qualified person aboard who could ferret out the mysteries of the zoological and geological phenomena that passed in an undeciphered tableau before their eyes. He returned to England in 1828, "inwardly resolving that if ever I left England again on a similar expedition, I would endeavour to carry a person qualified to examine the land." His resolution had been carried out; he had such a person, and it was Charles Darwin, aged twenty-one.

Now came the final preparations.

Into his carpetbag Charles put twelve shirts, slippers, Spanish textbooks, a new microscope; he bought a brace of pistols and a rifle for fifty pounds; he set out for Plymouth to take his place aboard H.M.S. *Beagle*. Space being limited, his library had to be select. Along went Milton's *Paradise Lost* and all the volumes of his beloved Humboldt, and before he left, Professor Charles Lyell pressed into his hands the first volume of his *Principles of Geology, Being an Inquiry on How Far the Former Changes of the Earth's Surface are Referable to Causes Now in Operation*. This was about the sum of Charles Darwin's material equipment; the rest would be forged by living nature in South America.

Lyell's *Principles* was to play an important part in his South American odyssey, for the geological approach was, in a sense, revolutionary, and Lyell's theories parted company forever with the ecclesiastically authorized date of October 4, 4404 B.C. as that of the Creation. This date had already been questioned by Hutton, an early English geologist. He had suggested, much to the horror of the clergy, that the earth possessed greater antiquity, millions of years in fact. The next geological thesis was that all the foundation of the world was continuous and to explain it there was the catastrophic theory of Werner (Humboldt's old geology teacher, who held court in Freiburg). Werner believed that all existing rocks had been deposited from primeval water, a chaotic fluid — that the whole earth was dissolved in the all-embracing ocean, after which layers of inorganic material were deposited from this chaotic fluid as the water evaporated or receded. Then came the great Cuvier, the celebrated anatomist and courtier, who, having fossils pouring in on him until his workshop looked like a catacomb, and finding them assuredly the remains of animals that once peopled the earth, had to find a geological reason for their present non-existence. During each geological epoch, he argued, these earth-inhabitants were overwhelmed, completely obliterated by catastrophes, and the animals buried in the rocks. God, not at all discouraged by this destruction of his handiwork, began all over again to create another whole series of animal species, each time, if you please, making them better. Lyell demolished all this. As Darwin read, he saw clearly how Lyell's concept of purely normal agencies — without the inception of God or catastrophe — explained geological evolution. Now all the geological world was presented to him logically and in an ordered fashion, organized and expounded in clear dispassionate prose. The Lyell book came to Darwin's attention at precisely the right moment, at the crucial time when he approached the shores of South America. This was the beginning; and Charles, not sensing anything of the future, sent a letter to his father in which he wrote with charming naïveté: "I think, if I can so soon judge, I shall be able to do some original work in Natural History."

March 4 was Carnival time in Bahia. Wickham, First Lieutenant on the *Beagle,* "a glorious fellow," and young Sullivan, the Second "Lieut," accompanied by Charles Darwin, were determined to face its "dangers."

The streets were alive with people, costumed and uncostumed. The women — black, maroon, ebony, white, yellow — were all in a gay mood. The *caboclos,* of Indian blood mixed with Negro, wore crude shawls wrapped about them, the fringed ends hanging down over their left shoulder. The men's shirts were bright with checks and flower patterns. People passed by with baskets balanced one atop another, only to have them knocked off by the surging crowd. The party from the *Beagle* was pelted unmercifully with wax balls full of water which broke like exploding balloons and wet everyone within a yard's radius. Under the awnings of some ramshackle penthouses that were ranged along a strip near the jetty, they were wetted with water from large tin squirts. "We found it very difficult," Charles wrote, "to maintain our dignity whilst walking through the streets. Charles the V said that he was a brave man who could snuff a candle with his fingers without flinching. I say it is he who can walk at a steady pace, when buckets of water on each side are ready to be dashed over him."

Charles Darwin, six foot two, towering above all the others, pale of skin and blue of eye, of course was a natural mark for the carnival-makers of Bahia. Before they had passed through the whole of the town they were wet to the skin. Not willing to face a return, they waited until dark and then stumbled along the cobblestoned streets filled with the uncollected filth of the carnival. "It was the first time," Darwin wrote, "Wickham had been on shore and he vowed if he was here for six months, it should be the only one."

The *Beagle* completed its survey within two weeks and was ready to lift anchor by the 15th of March. During that time Charles had gone ashore again and again. He had gone often to the forests of Bahia, collecting spiders, flies, and moths with such avidity that the crew called him "fly-catcher." The natives, who called him *"El Diablo,"* grew warmly fond of this tall young man who trod their forests with botanical satchel and entomologist's net. Even Fitz-Roy approved of Charles, describing him as "a very sensible, hard-working man and a pleasant mess-mate," and Charles in turn thought FitzRoy a "very extraordinary person — his greatest fault as a companion is his austere silence produced from excessive thinking."

This "austere silence" was broken at Bahia. Charles and Fitz-Roy had a violent quarrel, an altercation of such seriousness that it almost sent Charles packing home to England. Charles, who had traditionally hated slavery, and who had been aroused by Humboldt's expressed detestation of it, gave out at dinner with some heat that he thought the whole system of slavery atrocious and barbarous. Darwin had found the Brazilian Negro gentle and reasonably industrious. He felt deeply for these black people torn from their own lands. FitzRoy, assuming the correct Tory attitude, defended slavery. He denied inhuman treatment of slaves and to top it off asserted the rights of property by which they were held. Charles opposed FitzRoy's arguments. The Captain exploded. "Did Mr. Darwin presume to question his word? Then the devil take Mr. Darwin. He would not sleep under the same deck with him." Charles was bewildered by this, he was deeply hurt, but his sense of the moral issue none the less remained steadfast. He was for going ashore that very night, but Sullivan and Rowlett begged him to have his mess with them. FitzRoy, still exploding, vented the residue of his spleen on the unfortunate Wickham, whom he encountered on deck. Later he came to Charles and apologized in so complete a manner that Darwin again took his place in the cabin. The wound of argument healed.

The night of March 17 Darwin took a "farewell stroll" ashore. The next morning the *Beagle* sailed for Rio de Janeiro.

CHAPTER XVIII
The Naturalists Open Brazil

Rio de Janeiro seemed to be a pause between earth and water. The upward thrust of its mountains completely dominated by an immense cone of granite — the Pão de Açucar — which shot up a thousand or more feet out of the Bay of Guanabara, up into the cloudless sky of Brazil. Eagerly the young naturalist, with Augustus Earle, draftsman to the *Beagle,* leapt ashore to see this wonder land. They were caught up and lost in the bewildering maze of tropical plants that festooned the city. From the depths of the jungles that surrounded the capital city a peculiar pungent odor — indescribably warm and heavy — drifted in, leaving the impressionable senses of Charles drugged as if by some century-old wine. They rubbed shoulders with well-dressed fildalgos, Negro fruit-sellers, sailors from the ships that spotted the harbor, mulatto women, and then fat priests, fiercely perspiring under their dark habits. Darwin confided this to his diary in the most exuberant manner: "We wandered through the streets, admiring their gay & crowded appearance. The plan of the town is very regular, the lines, like those in Edinburgh, running parallel & others crossing them at right angles. The principal streets leading from the squares are straight & broad; from the gay colours of the houses, ornamented by balconys, from the numerous Churches & Convents & from the numbers hurrying along the streets the city has an appearance which bespeaks the commercial capital of South America. The morning has been for me very fertile in plans: most probably I shall make an expedition of some miles into the interior. . . . [After a long walk at Botofago] we returned to Rio in great spirits & dined at a Table d'Hote where we met several English officers serving under the Brazilian colours."

Darwin soon found that a continent steeped in chaos was not the easiest place in which to conduct excursions in natural history, although admittedly he found fewer difficulties in Brazil than in the rest of South America. Brazil, unlike Spanish America, had not been swept by a bloody revolution. Not that it did not have its troubles. When Napoleon, in the heyday of his power, decided to seize Portugal in order to get at its overseas possessions, Portugal found herself in a desperate position. Should she permit Napoleon to occupy the country, England would blockade her. That would mean the loss of Brazil, for England ruled the sea.

The gaudy, thriving port of Rio de Janeiro visited by Darwin in 1832. Brazil at this time was still a monarchy and ruled by the House of Braganza.

Montevideo, the port of Uruguay, as pictured in 1832 by the artist of H.M.S. *Beagle*.

So when Napoleon gave his final ultimatum and General Junot by forced marches had reached the gates of Lisbon, the whole house of Braganza, its municipal council, its leading officers, its clergy, its generals, and most of the nobility (not failing to mention its treasury of 200,000,000 cruzados) fled the country and crossed the Atlantic under protection of the British fleet — and King João IV became Emperor of Brazil.

The Brazilian revolution, when it came, was like the Brazilians themselves, casual, legal, and practically bloodless. The colonists, even though unready for self-government, demanded complete independence like their Spanish neighbors, and the son of João IV declared Brazil an independent empire and assumed rule as Pedro I of Brazil. But the revolutionary caldron had not boiled away. Just a few months before the arrival of H.M.S. *Beagle,* Pedro I was forced to abdicate in favor of his five-year-old son, with the sagacious remark that he would have a better chance to rule Brazil without so many prejudices attached to his person because "My son has the advantage over me of being a Brazilian."

England had always had friendly relations with Brazil. This sprang from her centuries-old alliance with Portugal. Now that chaos ruled the continent, England, more than any other nation, had a dominance over trade. It was only natural that Darwin should have found Englishmen serving under the colors of Brazil.

It was all very casual in the Brazil of 1832, a casualness that did not entirely please a young naturalist eager to explore the hinterland beyond Sugar Loaf peak. Yet revolutions and abdications created vigilance, a vigilance that passed, as all governmental red tape is bound to do, beyond the bounds of common sense. Charles Darwin bumped right into it. With anger he made an entry in his diary:

"*April 6*th. . . . The day has been frittered away in obtaining the passports for my expedition into the interior. It is never pleasant to submit to the insolence of men in office; but to the Brazilians, who are as contemptible in their minds as their persons are miserable, it is nearly intolerable. But the prospect of wild forest, tenanted by beautiful birds, Monkeys & Sloths & lakes by Cavies & Alligators, will make any Naturalist lick the dust even from the foot of a Brazilian."

At last Darwin had his passport visaed by a dark-eyed, liquid-mannered Brazilian. He could then continue his preparations for a fortnight's journey into the interior, back of the coastal mountains of Rio de Janeiro to the Rio Macahé.

"*April 8*th. At 9 o'clock I joined my party at Praia Grande, a village on the opposite side of the Bay. We were six in number & consisted of Mr Patrick Lennon, a regular Irishman, who when the Brazils were first opened up to the English, made a large fortune by selling spectacles, Thermoms., etc., etc. About eight years since he purchased a tract of forest country on the [Rio] Macae & put an English agent over it. Communication is so difficult that from that time to the present he has been unable to obtain any remittances. After many delays Mr Patrick resolved in person to visit his estate. It was easily arranged that I should be a companion & certainly in many respects it has been an excellent opportunity for seeing the country & its inhabitants. Mr Lennon had resided in Rio 20 years & was in consequence well qualified to obtain information — in his disposition very shrewd & intelligent. He was accompanied by his nephew, a sharp youngster, following the steps of his Uncle & making money. Thirdly came Mr Laurie, a well informed, clever Scotchman, *selfish, unprincipled* man, by trade partly Slave-merchant, partly swindler. He brought a friend, a Mr Gosling, an apprentice to a Druggist. . . . A black boy as guide & myself completed the party, & the wilds of Brazils have seldom seen a more extraordinary & quixotic set of adventurers."

Charles was simply overcome with his view of a jungle, and such a forestscape is best viewed on horseback, where one's whole attention can be given to drinking in its beauty. He thought that the "grandeur of all its parts could not be exceeded. . . . As the gleams of sunshine penetrated the entangled mass, I was forcibly reminded of the two French engravings — of Maurice Rugendas & Le Compte de Clavac. . . . I was at an utter loss how sufficiently to admire this scene. . . ."

Darkness claimed the day; still they rode through the forest. The scene, by the dim light of the moon, was gloomily romantic. A few fireflies spotted the night; a solitary snipe, disturbed by the horsemen, rose from a marsh lagoon and gave a plaintive cry, the only sound that broke the dull beat of the horses' hoofs. On their second day, after a miserable night spent in a pig-scented hovel, they took their morning meal at a *venda,* which, young Charles was anxious to mention in his journal, was Portuguese for an "inn." Here in the courtyard of mud and horse-dung they dismounted and unsaddled the horses. The innkeeper approached them and with a grand salaam begged the senhores to suggest how this unworthy person might serve the renowned gentlemen. Food? Anything you choose, senhor. But "anything you choose" ended up with fowl, rice, and *farinha* — what they were always served. Darwin was being introduced to the methods and manners of the sons of Iberia.

So, besieged by parrots and toucans, spiders, parasol ants, and vampire bats, Charles was in, "essentially, an educative period." He was trying his wings, as a fledgling does; he was looking into the natural history of animals and essaying a hypothesis here and there, a truism here, a guess there. This first trip in from Rio de Janeiro to the fazenda at Sôcego gave him not only opportunity of collecting along a jungle route of a hundred miles, but a quiet, deep mental strengthening, a constant increase in his intellectual capacity. Geoffrey West writes: "He was busy with observations on the sky, the temperature, the earth, the rocks, animals, birds, people, clouds, climate . . . the initial interest in butterflies and insects was growing and becoming all-enveloping . . . even the initial Humboldtian impulse was as fresh, as keen, as free as ever."

All was grist for Darwin in this Brazilian mill. South America called and Darwin had answered. To be sure, he was not, as were La Condamine and Humboldt, a geographical discoverer, for knowledge of South America had increased greatly since Humboldt left there in 1803. Inspired by his publications, German explorers had gone to Brazil in droves. As soon as the Continental blockade was lifted by Britain, as soon as Napoleon was safely ensconced at St. Helena, the seas were filled with ships bound for South America, stuffed with traders and factors — but bearing explorers too. Humboldt had released a flood-tide. South America was now better known to a few, but it was still, to the world at large, a vast and uncharted terra incognita. And Charles Darwin, collecting in the month of April 1832 at the Fazenda de Sôcego, was unknowingly laying the base of a new science. South America was in need of a new impetus, and it was this young naturalist who gave it to her.

The *Beagle* sailed from Rio de Janeiro on July 5 to make its way southward for the continuation of the survey. Darwin, writing in the small cabin that he shared with Captain FitzRoy, set the theme of the next phase of the trip: "The moon is now shining brightly on the glassy water; everyone is in high spirits at again being at sea & a little more wind is all that is wanted. . . ."

The days flew by in the best sailing weather that Darwin had yet experienced. The frightful seasickness to which he was constantly subjected as soon as he set foot on a vessel had, for the moment, been forgotten.

"Everybody," the diary goes on, "is full of expectation & interest about the undescribed coast of Patagonia. Endless plans are forming for catching Ostriches, Guanaco, Foxes, etc. Already in our day dreams have we returned heavily loaded with Cavies, Partridges, Snipes, etc. I believe the unexplored course of the río Negro [in Patagonia] will be investigated. What can be imagined more exciting than following a great river through a totally unknown country?"

On the 21st of July the *Beagle* was surrounded by penguins and sea lions, ". . . which made such odd noises that in the middle watch Mr Chaffers went below to report to Mr Wickham that he heard cattle lowing on the shore." And now, as the *Beagle* was moving into the great La Plata estuary, they began to feel a "true specimen of the Plata weather." There were heavy gusts of wind and rain, the day was cold and raw, the nights "an extraordinary spectacle; — the darkness of the sky is interrupted by the most vivid lightning, the tops of our masts & higher yards shone with electric fluid [St. Elmo's fire] playing about them; . . . the sea was so highly luminous that the penguins might be traced by the stream of light in their wake."

On the morning of the 25th he found that the *Beagle* was anchored in the broad, muddy expanse of Río de la Plata. To the left was Argentina, as flat as the river itself, stretching out for thousands of miles of rolling pampas; to the right was "La Banda Oriental" — the east bank and the little Republic of Uruguay. It, too, had a pampas that resembled that of Argentina, but in the distance there were mountains, the same mountains which must have been seen in 1515 by Juan Díaz de Solís, who exclaimed: *"Monte video"* — "I see a mountain" — which exclamation was retained as the name of Uruguay's chief city and capital. And to the city of *"I see a mountain"* Charles Darwin went for a brief visit.

The city was chaotic. The Military Governor came to FitzRoy to beg his assistance in putting down a rebellion of armed Negro troops. FitzRoy, not wishing to be involved in the imbroglio, wanted to ascertain if the revolution was merely a party affair, or if the inhabitants were, in fact, in danger of their lives. Darwin confessed that the "politicks of the place are quite unintelligible." FitzRoy armed his men and landed some of them, but later withdrew without participating in the conflict. All through the next night Charles could hear the sound of muskets being fired in the city. By August 12 Darwin noted that the situation in Uruguay had grown better, "the unsettled politicks and weather permitting us to walk in the country." There on the pampas he saw large flocks of rheas, which he invariably called ostriches. He came across herds of capybaras and killed one that weighed ninety-eight pounds. This gargantuan among rodents, large as it is, none the less is a mite alongside its fossilized Miocene ancestors which Darwin was later to dig out of the Patagonian shales.

In Uruguay, Darwin became acquainted with the bola. This is simply a well-plaited rope of rawhide, eight feet long, which terminates in two round leather-covered stones, or *bolas*. One of the bolas is held, the other whirled overhead and let go; the momentum pulls the first from the hand, and the whole contrivance flies toward its object with the speed of an arrow. As soon as it strikes an object — horse, ostrich, lion, or man — it winds about until it has caught the victim as in the tentacles of an octopus. Charles amused himself with the bolas, much to the quiet, polite merriment of the bearded gauchos who stood on the sidelines picking their teeth with their knives. While he was swinging it, one bola caught on a bush, jerking the other out of his hand. It fell to the ground and caught one leg of his horse. The animal stopped dead. It was only through sheer strength that Darwin kept his saddle. The gauchos roared at this clumsiness. "We have seen many things, señor, but never a man who has caught himself with his own bola."

Darwin was thoroughly impressed by the virile, rude, although pleasant gauchos. Tall and handsome, proud and dissolute, with black curling mustachios, clanking spurs, daggers hung in wide metal-studded belts, they inspired him with a curiosity which was both cautious and friendly. Their politeness he found excessive. They never drank in his presence without asking him first to taste, bowing gracefully the while. To Darwin they seemed quite ready, "if occasion offered, to cut your throat." He surprised them one day by his use of promethean matches, which he had to ignite by biting. He even caused a tremendous sensation by "washing his face every morning." He was closely questioned by a tradesman, of a superior sort, who had got about in his time. He was very suspicious of anyone who washed his face every morning! He had heard of the ablutions of the Mohammedan religion, and knowing Darwin to be a "heretick" — that is, a Protestant — he and the poor people of Las Minas "thought themselves in the presence of the devil incarnate."

Darwin had six weeks in the Banda Oriental. He collected birds, animals, snakes, and a great variety of flowering plants. He wrote many letters, he sent back his first consignment of plants to Professor Henslow at Cambridge. He also dispatched the first hundred pages of his diary — which was to become the *Journal of the Voyage of the* Beagle — for the amusement of his family. His geological notes grew; so did the botanical notes and the small biological histories. He had time, too, for "frivolities," as he called them. He crossed over to Buenos Aires and visited English and Spanish homes; he attended a Presidential ball, a bullfight. He saw a production of Rossini's opera *La Cenerentola,* which had been produced at Covent Garden in 1830. He admired the women — ah, those languorous Spanish women! In a letter to his sister Caroline he became as enthusiastic about the señoritas as he did about the fossils and the insects: ". . . our chief amusement was riding about and admiring the Spanish ladies. After watching one of these angels gliding down the street, involuntarily we groaned out, 'How foolish English women are, they can neither walk nor dress.' And then how ugly Miss sounds after Signorita. I am sorry for you all. It would do the whole tribe of you a great deal of good to come to Buenos Ayres."

And the gauchos of the Banda Oriental believed this too. While visiting among them one day, he came face to face with a wild-looking gaucho, who faced him with arms akimbo, his fierce mustachios and wild eyes belying his urbane manner. He stated that he had a question that he wanted Darwin to answer with all truth. Charles trembled as to how deeply scientific it would be.

"Answer me the truth, Don Carlos. Are not the ladies of Buenos Ayres the handsomest in the world?"

Charles swallowed hard and said: "Sí, señor, charmingly so."

The gaucho was all smiles. He showed his strong white teeth, buried in that frenzied mat called a mustache. He nodded. "I have yet another question. Do ladies in any other part of the world wear such large combs?"

With great solemnity Charles assured him and those gathered about him that no others in all the world have such large combs. The gauchos were overcome with delight. They poured their *trago* down a bit faster. The gaucho who had asked the questions was utterly delirious with all this confirmation. "Look here, señores. Look! Here is a man who has seen half the world, who confirms this. We always thought so, but now we know it."

Not long after this memorable conversation the *Beagle* dropped anchor in the river, and after a short stay for revictualing was ready to sail back to Patagonia.*

* Actually Darwin had sailed with the *Beagle* to Patagonia and to Tierra del Fuego on its first voyage there between December and April 1832, but as the *Beagle* moved over the same ground again, it has been thought wise, in order to preserve the continuity of the narrative and to avoid repetition, to join both of Darwin's excursions to Patagonia and Tierra del Fuego into one. For the record, however, he remained in the La Plata region from July 28 to August 17, 1832. Then the *Beagle* sailed for Bahía Blanca, a port in Patagonia, some 400 miles south, which they reached on September 6. On October 3 the *Beagle* was back again at the Río de la Plata and Darwin in Buenos Aires. Then by December 16 they were at Tierra del Fuego, at the end of South America. In April 1833, they were again in Bahía Blanca. Here Darwin disembarked, deciding to take the land route northward from Bahía Blanca to Buenos Aires so as to study, collect natural history specimens, and avoid the tediousness of another sea voyage. It is at this point, in August 1833, in the flat, treeless land of the pampas of Patagonia, that the stream of the narrative is resumed.

CHAPTER XIX
Dictators and Fossils

DARWIN WAS in a state which might have been analyzed as complete delirium. His eyes stared wildly, his hands trembled and shook so violently he could hardly control them. All because he had just discovered "a perfect catacomb for monsters of extinct races."

In a reddish clay bank of the great pampean formation on Punta Alta, in Patagonia, near Bahía Blanca, Darwin had fallen upon an ossuary of lost-world mammals. Here were bones of Megatheriums and Scelidotheriums, virtually intact. He found an animal with a neck like a camel, and a Toxodon, "perhaps one of the strangest animals ever discovered, seeming a cross somewhere between a sloth and an elephant." Then he unearthed an animal certainly the same in structure as the present-day manatee. He found the fossils of animals that were very much like the armadillos which ran around the pampas; he found skeletons of giant sloths that in many respects resembled the sloth that painfully crawled from tree to tree in the South American jungles. All these lay embedded on the beach not 220 yards apart.

The gaucho who had led him to the spot in order to show him the bones of the monsters "created by the devil" was astonished at the names that Darwin applied to each new skull that he unearthed.

"I do not think it strange, señor, that these animals are here, since the devil does strange things. But I do not understand how you should know all their names."

The gaucho's belief was not much different from that of Europeans of the Middle Ages. They thought that the fossil fish that were dug up now and then by miners, as well as the fossil plants that were found in slate, were the work of a most spiteful demiurge. *Lusus naturæ*, "nature's sports," they called them — shapes which nature had playfully molded from the inorganic to resemble living things. But the Greeks two thousand years before had known better. Fossils were definitely regarded by them as remains of plants and animals. But then the Greeks knew, too, that the world was round and moved in infinite space. In Darwin's time fossils had begun to take on a new significance. Professor Lyell, whose second volume had reached Charles just before he sailed for Patagonia, gave considerable significance to fossils, which he had begun to use as time-indicators in determining the age of geological progression. Lyell saw but one logical explanation of the phenomena of fossils: they were the remains of extinct animals. As for the similarity of fossils to existing animals, that was the step to evolution, and one that Lyell had not taken.

When Darwin left England in 1831 nothing seemed to his youthful mind more immutable than the belief in the immutability of the species. Then the voyage to South America, his own curiosity, the *Principles* of Lyell explaining that geological changes were gradual and uniform, began to work a change. Out of the pages, Lyell spoke to Darwin; that ended for him the cataclysmal nightmares of Cuvier. Now the raw pampean earth of Patagonia spoke to him from the ossuary of prehistoric periods. The Toxodons, the Megatheriums, the fossil sloths and armadillos intoned like a Greek chorus: "Lend me your ear, you of the incipient English parish — we are the bones of the past, the past that also contains the future."

As Darwin handled these bones of "extinct monsters," he saw that existing animals have a close relation in form with extinct species. As the cold pampero whipped across the grass-tufted plains and he packed his "bones" on the backs of mules he had hired, his whole being was assailed by nascent doubts of the fixity of species. Here before him was the earth and its creation-story. On the other side there were the voices of hallowed literati such as Milton. Had he not read, just the night before in his hammock aboard the *Beagle,* from the pages of *Paradise Lost:*

> The Earth obey'd and straight,
> Op'ning her fertile womb, teem'd at a birth
> Innumerous living creatures, perfect forms,
> Limb'd and full grown. . . .

But what did John Milton know about zoology? Now the earth says . . . but away with thoughts and speculations! . . .

The *Beagle* had laid down a line of soundings from Río de la Plata southward, dumping Darwin off in Patagonia so that he could "botanize and geologize" while the survey went on. To push the work more rapidly, FitzRoy hired two small schooners and left them to carry on about Tierra del Fuego, while the *Beagle* put north to pick up Charles and complete the shore-soundings. Darwin had remained at Bahía Blanca, at the mouth of the Río Negro, where "the town is indifferently called El Carmen or Patagones — built on the face of a cliff which fronts the river." He had been left there in July 1833, a "convinced creationist." When he was picked up a month later, with his "extinct monsters," he had himself undergone an evolution; hence forward he would look into South America in a wholly different manner.

Charles was eager to get on board with his bones, but he did not make the mistake of entertaining FitzRoy with his speculations on their origin, for the Captain was a fundamentalist, a creationist with strong religious feelings. Besides, the Captain was severely irritated at a dispatch from the Admiralty disapproving of his action in hiring the schooners. They refused to authorize this added expense; Captain FitzRoy was informed that he must assume this himself. In addition, the Admiralty had not yet accepted the idea of changing the term "larboard" to "port," a suggestion for maritime parlance out of FitzRoy's South American experience. FitzRoy was not in a good mood.

The days ahead would be dull and monotonous with the ceaseless sounding operations, so Charles asked and received permission to travel the 400-mile distance to Buenos Aires by land. With a gaucho as guide, he put his tall, sun-tanned body, wind-tossed hair, beetle-brows, and all, on a horse, and set off across the pampas of Patagonia in September 1833.

They rode for some leagues across the vast limitless plain, the horizon encircling them in a ring as faultless as that made by a pebble dropped into smooth water. Above them was the clear September sky, wintry and pale, tinged in the west with saffron hues. In the shadows of the pampean night they came across a square of low straw huts, lying near a lone stunted ombu tree. This was the encampment of General Rosas. Their next movement depended on him, and Rosas at the moment was out on an Indian-hunting expedition. "I believe," Darwin wrote in his diary, "such a villainous Banditti-like army was never before collected together. The greater number of men are of a mixed race." It was on these "Banditti" that Rosas depended in his expeditions of extermination against the Indians of the pampas. As in North America, Indians with horses, rifles, and lances made the expansion of the white man a dreadfully slow and horror-strewn process. The Guaranis held the north of Argentina, the Tehuelches — the large-footed Patagonians — the south. Most of Argentine's thirteen million acres were involved in the sanguinary battle.

This great country of Argentina extended from the tropical forest of the Chaco to the icy cliffs of Tierra del Fuego, a total length of 2,300 miles. It was so large that Darwin had to use pencil and paper to figure out that it was ten times the area of the British Isles. Yet it had been much larger under the viceroys. Then the *Virreinato del Río de la Plata* controlled all of what is now Argentina, in addition to what is now Uruguay, Paraguay, and most of

Bolivia, including Lake Titicaca. It even had an outlet into the Pacific. Revolutionary movements and the institution of new republics had cut off Bolivia, Paraguay, and even Uruguay. Argentina had become first a junta, then a dictatorship, then a republic, and then chaos. And Juan Manuel Rosas had come out of this anarchy with the title of Governor of Buenos Aires, which he held from 1829 to 1832. This son of a trader in hides, without even the rudiments of a formal education, rose from gaucho to President of the Governing Junta, then, by a well-known South American formula, to autocratic dictator. An orgy of violence and bloodshed ushered in his regime. The strain of conspiracies provoked Rosas into a savagery that made his heraldic symbol, *mazorca* (an ear of corn), into an ironic pun, *más horca* (more gallows). Yet when his three-year rule had ended, he refused re-election and used the next years trying to exterminate the Indians and make more room for the settlers now pouring in from Europe. He wanted to give substance to his countrymen's proverbial dictum *"Gobernar es poblar"* — "To govern is to populate." And so it came to be that Charles Darwin met the famed *caudillo* of the pampas on one of his Indian-hunting expeditions.

Darwin believed Rosas a man of "extraordinary character." He found the *caudillo's* conversation sensible, enthusiastic, yet held within bounds by a certain gravity which the Spanish term *dignidad*. Although the Río de la Plata ran red with blood from the executions that Rosas's rule imposed, he lived hard, he rode hard, and was, as Darwin noted, beloved by his men and possessed of an unbounded popularity. In 1833 Darwin believed that these qualities "would have a predominant influence in the country," and would presumably be used to its "prosperity and advancement." But in the 1845 edition of his *Journal* Darwin adds a footnote: "This prophecy has turned out entirely and miserably wrong." After Rosas's uncontrollable despotic whims put him at odds with all his neighbors, he was finally so beset with enemies that he sought exile in England, where he died in 1877. Darwin saw him once more in Southampton, a most reserved, mild Gargantua, a South American taking his ease in England's peace.

Darwin was highly elated at the chance to see the notorious General Rosas. But he was glad, too, to leave the hovel that he had shared for two days with a scar-marked Spaniard who had served with Napoleon, and on September 8, with the gaucho he had hired as a guide, he set out on the road to Buenos Aires.

It took no little courage to ride over the pampas. These sweeping treeless savannas were in actuality war-fields almost deserted of people and human habitation. Here and there, along a path where the horizon and the endless pampas met as one, they would come across the smoldering remains of a house. There would be the bones of horses, or the half-eaten carcass of a steer attended by vultures. Then a grave marked with a rude cross would bear mute testimony that the war between the Indian and the white man had taken another victim. "The warfare," Darwin wrote, "is too bloody to last; the Christians killing every Indian & the Indians doing the same by the Christians." The gaucho guide was frightened half to death most of the time. At the sight of an "ostrich" miles away, he would throw himself to the ground, shouting for Charles to do likewise in abject fear that it might be marauding Indians returning to scorch the earth. What fear Charles had was transmitted into excitement. He had the unalloyed pleasure of being able to study the animals and the birds of the pampas without interruption by man. Deer, guanacos, rheas (ostriches), viscachas, skunks, armadillos passed in review. The rhea, the greatest and most unbirdlike bird of two continents, interested him most, for it could not fly; with its long neck and ungainly wingless body, it seemed to make a perfect target for man, especially when he had lasso-like bolas and fleet-footed horses. Yet the rhea was more than a match for man. When being chased, it could outrun most horses, and when cornered, it could swing about and sidestep the bullet speed of a thrown bola. Rheas roamed the entire length of Argentina, even extending into the pampas of Brazil and into the environs of Buenos Aires itself. Charles was told that its crude, hollow nests were filled, during the months of September, October, and November, with twenty or more eggs, of such size that each was by weight equivalent to twelve hen's eggs. Throughout July the pampas were filled with the mating-call of the male rhea, a booming sound like a foghorn, which brought on male and female alike; and while the females looked on, the male rheas would struggle over the sphere of influence. A singular performance, as W. H. Hudson verified later, in which the "combatants twist their necks together like a couple of serpents and while so entwined viciously bite at each other's heads with their beaks, while they waltz about in a circle." After fighting came the mating, and after mating gestation. Egg-laying, Darwin discovered, was a communal project. Nests were scooped out of the soil; the females flocked to the spot and dropped their eggs. The male bird then plopped his five-foot length down on the brood and incubated the entire cache.

All this engaged the young naturalist, and his observations were made with uncommon accuracy. Learning that there was another species of rhea, he gathered together the neck, the large feathers, and a piece of the skin cast aside by a hunter who had shot one. He preserved them and sent them back to England, where it proved to be a new species. Gould, who described it, named it Darwin's rhea, *Rhea darwini*. Charles was making progress!

He was also interesting himself in the puma that hunted on the pampas. He heard the gauchos tell of this two-hundred-pound, fawn-colored cat that climbs to the top of stunted ombu trees to scout the plains for any moving thing; and of how, when it springs, it jumps on the back of its quarry, sinks its long, retractable claws into the back, and then raises a paw and brings it down on the neck of its prey, dislocating the cervical vertebræ. Darwin was careful to check this story. He had seen pumas, although only in the distance. He made it a point to examine the skeletons of dead guanacos lying stiff on the pampas, and there he saw the confirmation — their necks had been dislocated.

Charles was upset at seeing so many guanaco carcasses spotting the treeless pampas, for to him the guanaco was "an elegant animal — with its long slender neck and fine legs," in æsthetic contradiction to a Mr. Musters, who had lived in Patagonia, and who characterized the guanaco as having the "head of a camel, the body of a deer, the wool of a sheep, and the neigh of a horse." As Charles rode on beside his gloomy gaucho guide, he loved to see the guanacos run alongside of the rheas, just as in Africa the zebras ran with the ostriches. A very near relative of the llama, the guanaco was found from Bolivia to the tip of Tierra del Fuego. Herds of them, as many as five hundred in a single body, could be seen grazing on the stunted pampean grass. The young guanaco has a dainty coat of soft, russet-colored fleece, which increases in thickness as it grows older. The ancient Andean people used this fleece to make their famed woolens. But the guanaco, despite its seven-foot length, five-foot height, and weight of two hundred pounds, never became a beast of burden as did the llama.

These days of observation and of speculation over the long pampean countryside were broken by their arrival each evening at military posts. These had been set up by General Rosas at intervals of a day's ride, or *jornada*. Each one was simply an encampment of a lieutenant and a few soldiers with their horses, sleeping in pampas-grass huts. By the time they had passed the ninth *posta* they had come into the purple land. More and more *estancias* appeared on the rolling pampas — flat ranchos with tile roofs shaded by a single ombu tree.

It was raining hard the night of September 19 when Charles saw his first ombu, the branches shaking wildly in the teeth of an ice-cold pampero that swept down the plains. At the post-house the owner would not allow them entry unless they had a regular passport. There were so many robbers about the country, he could trust no one. When he read Charles's passport, saying: *El Naturalista Carlos Darwin,* his suspicions rolled away. Where he was hesitant before, he now was lavish with respect and civility. Poor man, as he had not the slightest idea what a *naturalista* was, he thought Charles some great *ilustre.* So, praising God on his threshold, Darwin and his gaucho passed within the portals of El Ombu. For the first time since he left the *Beagle,* weeks before, he slept in a bed.

In two more *postas* they reached Buenos Aires. To Darwin, after riding over the anemic-appearing plains, "Buenos Ayres looked quite pretty; with its Agave hedges, its groves of Olives, peaches & Willows; all just throwing out their fresh green leaves. I rode to the house of Mr Lumb, an English merchant, who gave me a most hospitable reception; I soon enjoyed all the comforts of an English house."

A few days of rest; then, on the 27th of September, he started on another expedition of 300 miles up the banks of the Río de la Plata to the point where it joins and becomes the Río Paraná. But it was not a very profitable journey; the roads were bad, political conditions in the interior provinces chaotic. "I have been forewarned that nearly all the good people in this province [of Santa Fé] are most dexterous thieves; they soon proved it by stealing my pistol." By the time he reached the city of Santa Fé, he was very ill. "Unwell & feverish" appeared quite often in his notes. Still, he stuck to his original plan to scour the countryside for those items of natural history that remained to be discovered. On the road to the Río Paraná, where rumor had it he would find "giant's bones imbedded in the river's banks," he passed houses recently burnt and plundered by the pampas Indians, and "there was a spectacle which my guide looked at with great satisfaction, viz. the skeleton with the dried skin hanging to the bones, an Indian suspended to a tree." By the 4th of October he was again "unwell in bed." He managed, however, to make more entries in his diary: "St. Fé is a nice straggling town, with many gardens. It is kept clean & in good order. The governor of the province, López, is a tyrant; which perhaps is the best form of government for the inhabitants. He was a common soldier at the great revolution & now has been 17 years in power. His chief occupation is killing Indians: a short time since he slaughtered 48 of them. The children are sold for between 3 & 4 pounds sterling."

A few days later he was up again and at last reached the Paraná. There he found his fossils, but could not extract them because they

had become so friable. After that he threw up the sponge and decided to return down the river to Buenos Aires.

The trip down the muddy Plata on a slow-sailing balandra
found his mind very active. The indolence brought about much
contemplation and his mind wavered between accepting and re-
jecting the fossil evidence of the rocks. It was refreshing to rest
one's back on the sacks of maté and prepared hides and watch the
panorama of the river. The kingfishers attracted him, the snowy-
white egrets bestirred his naturalist soul, and he could always
count on seeing during the day a phalanx of roseate flamingos
crossing the bow of the rat-infested balandra.

The closer they came to Buenos Aires, the more chaotic became
the country. Open rebellion had broken out, and Darwin was in
the midst of it. "I found to my utter astonishment that I was a sort
of prisoner. About a week before, a violent revolution had broken
out; all the ports were under an embargo. . . . The General told
me that the city was in a state of closed blockade; that he could
only give me a passport to the General-in-chief of the rebels. . . .
I soon began to talk about the General's [Rosas's] civility to me at
the Río Colorado. Magic could not have altered circumstances
quicker than this conversation did. . . . I was exceedingly glad
when I found myself safe on the stones of Buenos Aires."

After all this confusion Darwin was happy to cross the water and
step into the orderly routine of H.M.S. *Beagle*. Never had the word
"order" seemed so important to him. There were still a few more
weeks in the flat lands of the Banda Oriental, which he used to
augment his collections. Then, at long last, the *Beagle* weighed
anchor on the 7th day of December 1833. Real adventure lay
ahead: they were returning to the Land of Fire.

The Indian gauchos of the pampas. These were the companions of Darwin on his rides across the pampas. They stand before a store in Buenos Aires where are exhibited fans from ostrich plumes, and jaguar skins, with stirrups hanging from the ceiling.

ZAPALLO MAN.

HUEMUL WOMAN.

HUEMUL BOY.

YAPOO MAN.

YACANA MAN.

PECHERAY MAN.

Fuegian Indians of Tierra del Fuego. Darwin lived among these people for a year while the *Beagle* picked its way among the ice floes of Cape Horn. These are the first pictures of a people discovered as early as 1519 by Magellan.

CHAPTER XX
The Land of Fire

H.M.S. *Beagle* met the wide, foaming regiment of combers head on. The spindrift covered the deck from bow to stern. The vessel had doubled the Cape of San Diego and was now moving through the strait that separated the rugged ice-bound hills of Tierra del Fuego from Staaten Island. They were coming to the Land of Fire with but one purpose; to bring back to their native lands three Fuegian savages whom Captain FitzRoy had taken as hostages on a previous survey of Cape Horn.

The desolation of this land was overwhelming: the hills fissured, torn by earthquakes and whipped by winds; the shores buffeted by tremendous waves; the sky dull and sullen. The ship pitched horribly, Darwin was deathly ill.

It is at this time that Darwin introduces the Fuegians, three of the strangest passengers ever carried by an English man-of-war. Jemmy Button, a young man of twenty-two, was short, thick, and fat and a great favorite with the sailors. His copper-colored skin, black horsehair thatch, the Mongolic slant of eye could not be eliminated despite the embroidery of civilization which he affected. Charles observed that Jemmy "used to wear gloves, his hair neatly cut, and was distressed if his well-polished shoes were dirtied." He was indeed a Narcissus, and he carried a mirror into which he looked every moment of the day. Next there was Fuegia Basket: "a nice modest, reserved young girl with a rather pleasing but sometimes sullen expression, but very quick in learning anything, especially language." Fuegia, who was eleven years old, was FitzRoy's favorite. York Minster, named after a rugged islet off Cape Horn, was a powerful, taciturn savage with strong, handsomely white teeth, a frown-wreathed face, and jet-black eyes. He was the last of FitzRoy's trinity.

In the year 1826 two ships, H.M.S. *Adventure*, a stout, strongly-stayed brig captained by Parker King, R.N., and the *Beagle* commanded by Captain Stokes, had been sent by the British Admiralty into the waters of Cape Horn to make a thorough exploration of the passage to the Pacific for the benefit of whaling ships. Until 1828 these ships worked, taking myriad bearings and soundings about this stygian, tumultuous ocean. The task of maintaining a vessel and a crew in these turgid waters for two years, and the desolation of the land, so affected Captain Stokes that he developed a fit of melancholia which ended in suicide. As soon as their winter haven off the coast of Chile had been reached, he fired a bullet into his brain, giving his second-in-command his place in the not too frequent Fuegian sun. Robert FitzRoy took over command of the *Beagle*. A stern taskmaster, and a man of probity, this Captain FitzRoy. He took up the tasks set by the Admiralty with all the agonized energy of Prometheus bound.

The sounding of the bays and the inlets around Tierra del Fuego was done in whaleboats, and this allowed the Fuegians to enter the picture. For while First Mate Murray and his men were busy on the shore, a band of naked natives filched the whaleboat. Murray was forced to a makeshift. He floated back to the *Beagle* ensconced in a basket. "Yes, sir!" Murray raged, "a bloody basket made of reeds and caulked with clay."

Murray hastened to FitzRoy and reported: "I regret to report, sir, that the Fuegians have stole our whaleboat."

Now, many deeds of violence, done in the heat of passion, may be condoned. But not the theft of a whaleboat from His Majesty's Navy.

"Arm the men," was FitzRoy's reaction. "Lower the other whaleboat."

So the search began. It was far more difficult than looking for a needle in a haystack, for in the Land of Fire there were thousands upon thousands of ice-choked fjords, inlets, coves, harbors, and swamps where a boat might hide. The search went on for weeks. It began to jangle the nerves of FitzRoy; months were spent chasing clues about the desolate peaks and glaciers of Tierra del Fuego. Yet even this paid geographical dividends, for FitzRoy put his men to work sounding, and as they entered places where they would not otherwise have gone, their survey became the more complete. Still there was no boat.

FitzRoy then thought of the hostage technique. They surprised a small tribe of Indians. There was a struggle. A Fuegian bounced a large rock on the skull of a sailor. Mr. Murray shot at one of them. The sailors seized two men, three women, and six children and returned to the *Beagle* with their captives.

They were not long detained. When they had filled their ravenous stomachs at the ship's mess, the adults and two of the oldest children made a dash for the side of the ship and dived into the icy waters. The *Beagle* was left with three young babies and an eight-year-old girl, who was promptly dubbed Fuegia. Murray, remembering that he had traveled in the subarctic waters in a clay-lined basket, added "Basket" to her name, and so she became Fuegia Basket.

Three brown bellowing babies on the *Beagle* added an unwanted complication. FitzRoy therefore ordered the long suffering Murray to take the three howling brats and deposit them with any Fuegians they might encounter. He was not to return with them. He did, however, keep Fuegia Basket, who by now, dressed in a sailor's uniform, chatted merrily with all the unconcern of a healthy young animal.

With FitzRoy on the rampage, alarm broke out all over the Fuegian country. The crew could see fires burning, smoke signals spotting the sky, as the Indians told one another of the hostage raids being carried on by the *Beagle*. One curious native, dressed in a guanaco skin, came out to the ship to see what all the rumpus was about. He was invited to come aboard. "He did so," someone remembered, "quite unconcernedly, sat down and was contented and at his ease." A pair of pants to hide his nakedness, a cropping of his black horse-like hair, a tar soap bath to remove the black and red paint with which he had bedaubed himself, and this sullen, bronze-skinned giant became York Minster.

Captain FitzRoy gave up the search for the whaleboat now. The ship's carpenter set about making another, and the survey went on. Near Horn Island they picked up more Fuegians, guanaco skins, paint, bellowing voices, and all. One intelligent-appearing boy of fourteen, seeing York Minster and Fuegia Basket sitting so content on the gunwales eating, signaled his willingness to come aboard also. The sailor paid his father "a nice shiny mother-of-pearl button" for the boy. And so he became Jemmy Button.

They picked up one more native, whom they called Boat Memory; then the *Adventure* and *Beagle* sailed for home in 1828. In England their commission pennant was run down, the men were paid off, and reports were sent to the Admiralty. There was also a note from Captain FitzRoy: "I have the honour of reporting that there now is on board His Majesty's Ship *Beagle,* under my command, four natives of Tierra del Fuego. Should not His Majesty's Government direct otherwise, I shall procure for these people a suitable education and after three years shall send them back with as large a stock as I can collect of those articles most useful to them and most likely to improve the condition of their countrymen who are scarcely superior to the brute creation."

As soon as they descended the gangplank, smallpox fell on the Fuegians. Boat Memory, aged twenty, died at once from the pox. Doctors vaccinated the others. These survived and were placed in

the Church Missionary Society, where they imbibed such education as one can pour into an indifferent student. "We plan to take
them back to Cape Horn in a couple of years," said one of the
Beagle's sailors, "to teach the savages an' cannibals Christian ways
an' to lead up their heathen people to the light an' to teach 'em
English manners."

Strangely enough, this noble experiment played its part in the
opening of South America. Interest in these natives was great, for
no one in all England, save those salts who roamed the earth, had
ever seen a " savage." So the fame of the savages spread. King
William and Queen Adelaide gave them royal audience. They
talked to the Fuegians for a while, asking about their country,
the animals, their customs. Queen Adelaide even took little Fuegia
Basket on her knee, kissed her, and gave her a pretty new blue
bonnet and a few five-pound notes to buy clothes for her return
trip.

That return came on the wings of passion.

Coxswain Bennett, wandering unexpectedly into the mission
school one day in the year of disgrace 1830, surprised York Minster and little eleven-year-old Fuegia Basket in sexual embrace.
Bennett knew his duty. He turned Fuegia's brown bottom over
his knee and beat it soundly, while all the time she cried: "It no
me. No! York — only York!"

FitzRoy's honest soul was profoundly shocked. All the gentle
ways of England for naught — and only eleven years old! He was
not consoled by Coxswain Bennett's proffering that "them heathen
women ripens rapid, sir." He decided (for he felt his responsibility
deeply) to hire a vessel to take them back to the Land of Fire — in
fact, accompany them part way himself before any event, such as a
child born to an eleven-year-old girl, could shock the English countryside. The Admiralty, advised of his plans, suggested the recom-
missioning of H.M.S. *Beagle* to survey more of the regions of Tierra
del Fuego. And FitzRoy, who knew how much they had missed by
not having on their first voyage "some man of science" to collect
the things of nature in its own turbulent theater, sought for a
naturalist and fished up Charles Darwin.

The *Beagle* gained the Strait of LeMaire and then beat its way
through the white lines of hail and the jutting icebergs to come to
anchor December 17, 1832 (for this was during the first trip to
Cape Horn) in the Bay of Good Success. Indians of the Huash
tribe crowded the shores as the *Beagle* dropped its whaleboats and
the men pulled into the bay. Darwin writes: "A party of Fuegians
. . . perched on a wild peak overhanging the sea . . . sprang up

& waving their cloaks of [guanaco] skins sent forth a loud sonorous shout. . . ."

As soon as the crew landed, the women and children ran into the wild, heavy woods, leaving the tall, guanaco-skinned Huash men to face the white intruders. The Indians, when they sensed that the *Beagle's* crew intended to build a shelter, advanced toward the party shouting vehemently. The echo of their voices sounded like a foghorn in the silent reaches of the Fuegian forests.

Darwin was deeply impressed by the meeting of the brown and white men. He had heard of this wild wind-swept country of penguins and albatrosses, of icebergs and subarctic weather, of tall, fierce, cannibalistic Indians. Now he actually saw it.

"It was without exception the most curious & interesting spectacle I ever beheld. I would not have believed how entire the difference between savage & civilized man is. It is greater than between a wild & domesticated animal, in as much as in man there is great power of improvement."

Four of the Fuegians approached. An old man was seemingly the leader, with the powerful young men beside him. All were about six feet tall. They were dressed in guanaco skins, and wore fur caps. Their cascading horsehair was as entangled as a fouled fish-line. Their eyes were circled with white paint, their lips painted a deep ocher. One of them was daubed black with pine soot. "From their dress, etc. etc. . . ." Darwin wrote, "they resembled the representations of Devils on the Stage in Der Freischutz. The old man had a white feather cap, from under which black hair hung around his face. The skin is a dirty copper colour. The only garment was a large guanaco skin . . . merely thrown over the shoulder, one arm & leg being bare."

Darwin, who outranged them slightly in height, gave the chief a piece of red cloth, which the Indian at once unrolled and threw about his neck like a scarf. Instantly Darwin and the old man became good friends. He patted Darwin's chest in what he regarded as a friendly manner — even though the strength of the blow about tore Darwin's heart from its moorings — "clucking all the while," Darwin wrote, "with the same noise people do when feeding chickens. . . ." The breast-pounding went on for some time. The old man was doing his best to give him the friendly greeting of his country. Finally he gave Darwin three tremendous wallops, fore and aft, simultaneously. Then Old Man stood back and bared his copper-colored chest and invited Charles to do the same. Emboldened, Darwin let Old Man have three terrific slaps on the chest, not knowing what to expect after that. When he looked up, Old Man was grinning broadly.

Jemmy Button, Fuegia Basket, and York Minster were brought ashore for the purpose of translating — and the first trial of the noble experiment proved an utter dud. They pretended they did not know the language, although it was apparent that the dialects of the Huash people at Good Success Bay and the language of the Yahgan, of which tribe they were, were similar. Jemmy Button, who had slicked down his hair for the occasion and put on a stiff collar and gloves, affected an air of scorn and snobbishness. But this did not get by Old Man. Behind that façade of London airs Old Man smelled a Fuegian. He began a long harangue, shouting, beating his chest, gesticulating wildly, the purport being that he wanted Jemmy to stay with them. Jemmy grunted something, but otherwise did not answer. Darwin meanwhile tried to make out something of the sounds that poured so volubly from Old Man's chest. Charles, who could speak no foreign language well, opined: "Their language does not deserve to be called articulate. Capt. Cook says it is like a man clearing his throat; to which may be added another very hoarse man trying to shout & a third encouraging a horse with that peculiar noise which is made on one side of the mouth."

But whatever Old Man said was articulate enough to York Minster. He burst out laughing at something the Fuegian had said to him. Although all the men of the *Beagle* had heavy beards and York Minster, as befitted a pure Indian, but a round dozen of scraggly hairs on his chin, Old Man had told him he was dirty and that he should pull out the hair on his face.

So, in this dismal, gloomy, wind-swept, hail-pelted region, civilized and uncivilized man faced each other. They had no means of communication except mimicry, of which the Indians were past masters. If anyone coughed or yawned or made any odd motion, the Indians imitated it. Whereupon Rowlett of the *Beagle,* who frequented the Zoo at Regent's Park, squinted and screwed up his face like a monkey. Immediately one of the towering savages, all daubed with color, returned the compliment and formed his face into an exact image of an African ground ape. When Charles exposed his white arm, Old Man seized it, smelled it, and looked his astonishment at its whiteness. Darwin, his arm held in a vise, could not help likening this display to the manners and motions of orangutans at the Zoological Gardens. And what now to amuse these giants? A song! The sailors formed a circle and burst into a rollicking sea-song. The Indians almost fell over in their astonishment. Then the sailors began to dance, and at once Old Man rushed up, grabbed an officer in tight embrace, and began to waltz over the frozen tundra.

The Land of Fire

Darwin showed himself an excellent observer. For the first time since their discovery in 1519 by Magellan, the natives of Tierra del Fuego were given an accurate ethno-history. Four tribal nations dominated these lands. The Tehuelches, called Patagones, were the mainland tribe and held sway over most of the southern portions of Patagonia. When horses were introduced, they changed from a sedentary hunting-fishing culture to one of more migratory character. The Ona, Huash, and Yahgan peoples, all linguistically related to one another, were scattered on the islets, coves, and sounds of Tierra del Fuego south of the Strait of Magellan. Their organization was typical of American Indians everywhere — strong filial ties, loose tribal organization. They had wigwams built of skins, or crude houses made of branches; clothing of seal, otter, or guanaco skins; ornamentation of feathers, leg-bones of gulls, and the time-honored face- and body-painting. Like the Eskimos, they made dance masks with pleasing schemes of decoration, as well as fish-spears, snaring nets, bow and arrows, pouches, bags, and baskets.

Living in a milder climate than the Eskimo, the Fuegians had developed no clothing beyond the skins they tossed about their large bodies. They had no bed, no blankets. They could sleep on the cold frozen tundra without covering, and trek all day in the endless rain and sleet picking up gulls' eggs or spearing fish. They ate with equal zest the putrefying carcass of a dead whale or bright yellow honeycombed fungus the size of a cabbage head. This they collected in large quantities and ate uncooked. Darwin — who in the not too distant future would declare that man and apes had a common origin — looked at the Fuegians and wrote: "Viewing such men, one can hardly man oneself to believe that they are fellow-creatures and inhabitants of the same world."

On the second day, in the Bay of Good Success, Darwin tried to penetrate the interior. A level piece of ground could be found nowhere. The land was all up and down. Heavy forests rose from the sea to a line 1,500 feet up the mountainside. They were succeeded by peat bogs on which grew minute alpine plants and here and there ferns and gray-colored lichens, which ended only at the line of perpetual snow. Darwin crawled over fallen trees, rugged hills, the whole in its tangled mess reminding him of the jungles of Brazil because of the mass of vegetation. There was violence everywhere — in the depth of the ravines, the contour of the mountains, the whirl of the winds, the beat of the rain, the very people of the land. "Death, instead of Life, seemed here the predominate spirit."

The day that the *Beagle* lifted anchor to round the Horn was clear, the sun warm, the air gentle. But as they moved southward and the last rock of the continent hove into sight, they ran into Cape Horn weather. A furious wind hit them, piling up heavy combers and tossing the ship about as if it were a match-box. Darwin was about to join that august company of Horn-rounders which had known the same winds, the same iciness as was now making him spew out his last night's dinner.

The cape had not been discovered until 1615, a century after Magellan had found the passage to the South Seas. The Magellanic Clouds, the southern star-clusters and nebulæ that this intrepid voyager was the first to see, still hung in the same skies. The natives that peopled the land were too primitive even to invent a means of remaking fire. So they kept the desolate hills raging in flames, and for that reason Magellan called it "Tierra del Fuego" — the Land of Fire. One day a strange figure, wrapped in guanaco skins, appeared over the hills. He was so tall that the discoverer himself reached only to his belt. Like Gargantua he wolfed a hamper of sea biscuits in one mouthful, he swallowed a bucket of water at one gulp. He was by turns amiable and violent, as giants are supposed to be. Magellan called him Patagão in Portuguese (Patagonia in Spanish) because of his gigantic feet (*Patas*). Thus the entire region became known as Patagonia. At the south of it Magellan found the strait. Now came others to capitalize on his discovery. Francis Drake sailed through in 1578 with his five ships, manned by the 164 gentlemen and sailors with whom he raised havoc among Spain's Pacific possessions. Seeing the breach in South America's walls being used by enemies, Philip II sent Pedro Sarmiento y Gomboa with a fleet of twenty-three ships and 3,500 men to stop that leak. He was to fortify the strait and colonize its bleak austerities. In 1582 Don Pedro, a resolute man, founded the city of Ciudad de Rey Felipe, wonderfully and strategically placed to command the entrance to the strait (for the Horn had yet to be discovered). But the Fuegian hosts swept down upon the city and decimated the settlers, and the "great plan" was wrecked.

When intelligence swept across the Spanish Main that the "great plan" had miscarried, more freebooters came down to use the strait. Cavendish, with many of Drake's old fighters, swept through its ice-bound waters in 1587; then followed John Davis, who discovered the Falkland Islands, two hundred miles east of the strait; then the doughty Hollanders, Joris Spilbergen, Isaac le Maire, and finally Captain Schouten, to whom we owe the discovery and the name of Cape Horn.

In 1615, after six months of unprofitable wandering in the raging environs of the straits, Captain Schouten put his ships into

Port Desire for beaching and careening. One vessel, the *Hoorn,* was most festooned with weeds and barnacles. He decided to "bream" her — that is, burn off the bulk of the befoulment. But the timbers, dried by the Patagonian air, suddenly caught fire and were completely enveloped. So perished the good ship *Hoorn —* only to find immortality when Schouten took his other ship, *Unity,* through the Strait of Lê Maire (between Tierra del Fuego and Staaten Island) into Drake's sea and finally round the last bit of rock on the American continent. To that promontory he gave the lost ship's name.

After that came the pirates, on their way to the hunting-grounds of the Pacific. There were Sir John Narborough, Dampier, Cowley, and Davis on the *Batchelor's Delight.* Woodes Rogers and Clipperton followed in the next century. The ships of Admiral Anson, too, came round the Horn to attack in the Pacific; and one of them, H.M.S. *Wager,* was lost on the inhospitable shores of the Land of Fire.

By the middle of the eighteenth century great changes had come over the sailing world since man navigated with only his astrolabe and cross-staff. Seamen now had Hadley's reflecting quadrant and Harrison's clock for determining longitude. And with these came the epoch of the scientific cruise. *La Boudeuse,* commanded by Louis Antoine de Bougainville, made its way through the strait in 1767. The machine had not yet been invented that would cut through rock and earth to make a canal at Panama. The Northwest Passage was proving to be a chimera. Only the Strait of Magellan was a real passage; it and it alone provided the "entrance into the South Seas."

Captain James Cook in 1769 followed in the wake of *La Boudeuse.* On board his ship were two "scientific gentlemen": Mr. Joseph Banks, wealthy and curious and English, who was to become for forty years the President of the Royal Society; and "an ingenious and learned Swede," Dr. Solander, a disciple of Linnæus. They landed at Fuego and gathered rock fragments and shells — the first orderly collecting ever done on those desolate shores. Banks killed an albatross, and the curse later fell upon Captain Cook. On another voyage he was killed — as was Magellan — in the far Pacific. Next in sequence came the voyages of H.M.S. *Beagle* and *Adventure.* These were to provide the world's maps with accurate soundings and lessen the hazards of the passage.

Charles Darwin was sensible to his part in all this history, for now the *Beagle* was rounding the Horn and, like the Ancient Mariner, it beheld:

[203]

. . . both mist and snow,
And it grew wondrous cold:
And ice, mast-high, came floating by,
As green as emerald.

The *Beagle* worked into St. Martin's Cove on Hermite Island (the nearest anchorage to Cape Horn), where they "kept Christmas merrily." Then the day following New Year 1833, "carrying a heavy press of sail," they went on to the region of the Woolya Indians at Navarin Island, between the Beagle Channel and Tierra del Fuego.

By the middle of January 1833 the vessel was making her way down the Beagle Channel, an alternative to rounding the Horn. Darwin compared it to Loch Ness with its chain of lakes and firths, its length one hundred and twenty miles and its average width two miles. It cut through the land in an almost straight line, bounded on each side by snow-covered mountains rolling on in indistinct undulations. To the south was Navarin Island. "His own land," Jemmy Button called it; and there FitzRoy decided to land him. They anchored the *Beagle,* put out three whaleboats and a yawl, and pulled over to sea-lion-infested Button Island. The natives had seen them already. Fires were lighted all along the beaches. As soon as they were ashore, the crew was instantly surrounded by fur-covered natives, demanding, begging, wheedling. They pointed to everything the ships possessed — biscuits, tarpaulins, muskets — and repeated ceaselessly the word *"Yammerschooner"* (badly spelled in Darwin's orthography), which meant: "Give it to me."

To Darwin's buttons, his pipe, his collecting kit — *"Yammerschooner."* Even to the whaleboat — *"Yammerschooner."* FitzRoy, remembering his lost whaleboat, threw around these a guard with muskets loaded and orders to fire at the first one who even came near.

All through the first week following their arrival the news spread. Members of the Tekenika (Jemmy Button's tribe) were told that the same boat that had taken Button had now returned. Several of them, entirely naked, came running so fast that when they arrived their noses were bleeding and their mouths frothing. Jemmy, at a great distance, saw his mother and his brothers. When they met, Darwin saw a curious display: "Why, their meeting was less interesting than that between a horse turned out into a field when he joins an old companion. There was no demonstration of affection, they simply stared for a short time at each other . . . the mother went to look after her canoe. . . ."

Jemmy, with his slick oiled hair, starched collar, kid gloves, and

shined shoes, dismissed them with a deprecatory air and apologized for their savageness. But this could not hide the real reason
for his shyness: in three years he had forgotten his own tongue.
It was at once laughable and pitiable to hear him speak to his
"wild brother" in English, and then add the Spanish *No sabe?* at
the end of every sentence.

Now the plans for the Fuegians went forward. Having been educated in the "reasonable air of England" for three years, and having seen all the advantages of civilization, it was believed that they
would return to their own land and teach their families the "things
of civilization." To assist in this, FitzRoy had brought along a Mr.
Matthews of the Missionary Society.

"Through all the meeting with the Fuegians he behaved," Darwin confided in his diary, "with his usual quiet resolution; he is
of eccentric character and does not appear to possess much energy
and I think it very doubtful how far he is qualified for so arduous
an undertaking." Matthews was to live alone with the members
of Jemmy's tribe, and bring the Indians' souls to God. The sailors
found a suitable place for a garden; they erected a shelter for
Matthews and began to cache the tools and the foodstuffs they
had brought along from England. "The choice of articles," Darwin said, "showed culpable folly and negligence. Wine glasses,
butterbolts, tea trays, soup tureens, mahogany dressing-case, fine
white linen, beaver hats, and an endless variety of similar things,
shows how little was thought about the country where they were
going to." The sight of so much stuff brought out the most indifferent Fuegians. They pressed forward with endless talk-talk and
jabber-jabber and much shouting of *"Yammerschooner."* Finally
FitzRoy drew a line over which, like the Rubicon, none could
pass. Then, the novelty somewhat wearing off, the Fuegians melted
away. So Matthews settled down to organize his "parish," and the
Beagle weighed anchor for a brief spell of chart-making.

Two weeks later they fell in with some natives in full regalia,
faces bedaubed with paint, the women festooned with pieces of
ribbon and bedecked with cloth in such extravagant folds that
they knew something was afoot. They got back to Matthews's
parish and arrived in a savage bedlam. The cove was filled with
Fuegians wrapped in pieces of tartan cloth and red linen; others
had cloth dangling from their mid-section, affecting for the first
time in their adult life a breech-clout. As soon as the sailors landed
(fully armed, of course), the Indians swarmed down on them yelling: *"Yammerschooner."* After a brief tussle they found Matthews
with a Fuegian sitting on his chest pulling out his whiskers. The
garden was trampled, much of the goods gone. There was Jemmy

Button, his clothes torn and ragged, repeating: "My people very bad, great fool know nothing at all."

Matthews, whose enthusiasm for God's work was at its lowest ebb since he had received the call, was hustled aboard the whaleboat.

In February 1834, on the return voyage (after Darwin had made his memorable trek across the pampas to Buenos Aires), the *Beagle* was back again in Tierra del Fuego, this time en route to Chile and the Pacific. FitzRoy had wanted to return not only to finish his charts, but also, although he never confessed it, to take a last look at his Fuegians whom he had left "with rather sanguine hopes of their affecting among their countrymen some change for the better."

Darwin had already developed a hatred, as he more than once said, for the "very sound of their voices." Their first and last word was *"Yammerschooner."* No bay or cove, however quiet and secluded it looked, was free of them. They always popped up to pester the arriving sailors, and were always underfoot until the last whaleboat had pulled away. "On leaving some place," Darwin wrote, "we have said to each other, 'Thank heaven we have at last fairly left these wretches,' when one more faint halloo from an all-powerful voice heard a prodigious distance would reach our ears . . . and clearly we could distinguish 'Yammerschooner.' "

But when the *Beagle* made the landfall at Woolya, all was disquieting silence. They began to feel that something had happened. Soon a canoe put off from shore, in it a solitary figure. Between paddle-strokes he could be seen trying to wash the paint from his face. When he came alongside, they saw that it was Jemmy Button.

"Poor Jemmy . . . now a thin haggard savage with long disordered hair . . . naked except for a bit of blanket about his waist . . . we had left him plump, fat, clean, and well dressed. I never saw," Darwin wrote, "so complete and grievous a change." Jemmy Button was a bit shamefaced, but he said he had "married" and did not wish to return to England. But — sad news for FitzRoy — York Minster and little Fuegia Basket had built a canoe and in an "act of consummate villainy" had stripped Jemmy Button of all his possessions. Once more FitzRoy loaded Jemmy with supplies, all shook hands with him, and he was set ashore. The *Beagle* weighed anchor. Darwin observed: "I do not now doubt that he will be as happy as, perhaps happier than, if he had never left his own country. Everyone must sincerely hope that Captain FitzRoy's noble hope may be fulfilled . . . by some shipwrecked sailor being protected by the descendants of Jemmy Button's tribe. . . ."

Ah, noble experiment! . . . In 1859 a group of missionaries was massacred by the Yahgans, led by Jemmy Button's son. Fuegia Basket, now a grown woman, often slept with the sailors who came into the land of Woolya. Jemmy's son a murderer; little Fuegia, who had been chucked under the chin by the King and decked with a blue bonnet by the Queen, a whore! Darwin had his last say: "Nature by making habit omnipotent and its effect hereditary has fitted the Fuegian to the climate and the productions of his miserable country. . . ."

As the *Beagle* stood out to sea, a shaft of white smoke curled up to the frosty sky. Jemmy Button was saying good-by.

The Jemmy Button incident must, in the nature of the broad canvas of South America's opening, seem more space-filling than its importance justifies. Yet it provided many additional incentives to exploration. It drew many readers to the various volumes * on the voyages of the *Beagle* and the *Adventure;* and these make the whole southern end of South America known in more detail than any other part of the entire continent. *L'affaire Jemmy* can take its place beside the haunting tragedy of Mme Godin, the War of Jenkins's Ear, and the captivity of Aimé Bonpland in Paraguay as the stories that brought attention to the continent.

Darwin, much as the affairs of the Fuegians absorbed him, felt that he was being cheated of important time, for the Land of Fire was most scanty in scientific material. "The zoology of Tierra del Fuego, as might have been expected from the nature of its climate and vegetation is very poor." † Among land forms, he found only a bat, "a kind of mouse — (Reithrodon) — two mice, two species of foxes, a few birds, sea-otters, guanaco, and deer." There were a scarlet-crested woodpecker, a few hawks and owls, but no reptiles, and only a few rare species of frogs. But poor as the land was in animals and insects, the sea was well stocked. It was filled with fish, and there were seals too. Whales fought, fed, and sported, and even mated in front of Darwin's inquisitive eyes. One marine form that aroused him to speculation was the sea kelp named *Macrocystis pyrifera*. He could not discover a single rock near the surface which was not shaggy with its floating masses. This slender sea-

---

* *Narrative of the Surveying Voyages of Her Majesty's Ships* Adventure and Beagle *between the years 1826–1836,* 2 vols. *Journal of Researches into the Natural History,* etc., by Charles Darwin, Vol. III. Also *Zoology of the Beagle* (1841) and *Geological Observations of South America* (1876).

† *Journal,* p. 225.

weed, not more than an inch in diameter, slimy, smooth, and green, grows to a depth of sixty fathoms. It is like the jungle liana. When Charles tried to count the different creatures that live on it, or within it, he grew bewildered at the number. Among them he found exquisitely delicate hydra-like polypi, the compound *Ascidiæ,* bivalves and other mollusks, small fish, and cuttlefish. "A great volume might be written," he said, "describing the inhabitants of one of these beds of sea weed."

He found, unfortunately, few fossils in the Fire-land. Yet geology had now begun to fascinate him with increasing intensity. He had received on the *Beagle's* visit to the Falkland Islands a packet of mail in which he found the final volume of Lyell's *Principles of Geology.* Whenever he could, he dipped into Lyell and was transported instantly to the most remote geological ages. His mind was stupefied "in thinking over the long absolutely necessary lapse of years." To merely think of the Andean system, and the infinities of geological time needed to create it, gave him a wonderful feeling. Why, millions of ages were but the infinitesimal part of eternity. If this was true about rocks and animals, what about man? Time only could have explained the presence of the Fuegians. He sat bolt upright in the worn hammock. Time! "What a scale of improvement is comprehended between the mind of one of these Fuegians and, say, an Isaac Newton." Whence had these people come? Had they remained in the same state since the creation of the world? What could have tempted a tribe of men leaving the regions of the north to travel down the cordilleras, to invent and build canoes, and then to enter one of the most inhospitable countries in the world? Time! Evolution! Migration! The Darwin brain was working.

In May 1834 the *Beagle* entered the Strait of Magellan for the second and last time. The skies were dark, glaciers hung poised on the side of the rock-bound mountains, ready to tumble into the sea. Icebergs of beryl-like blue floated by in huge masses; the albatross kept up a ghostly watch overhead. Amid squalls and gales they fought through the tangled confusion of bays and inlets and entered the Pacific. A few weeks later Darwin could happily write in his diary: *"July 23rd, 1834:* The *Beagle* anchored in the Bay of Valparaiso, the chief seaport of Chile."

CHAPTER XXI
Chile of the Crazy Geography

Everything in Chile appeared delightful, especially after the gloom and cold of Tierra del Fuego. The crisp atmosphere of Valparaiso, so dry, so clear, and the brightly shining sun made Darwin feel as if, like a butterfly, he had emerged into life from a cold pupa. The vista of the white houses with red roofs, the green trees, the blood-red earth, the rocky spurs of the Andes rising high, forbidding, and snow-topped, the clean harbor — it almost repaid one for the trouble of living. What a pity, Charles thought, that Rowlett could not have lived to see it. He had been stricken ill in Tierra del Fuego; the illness had gained despite the administrations of the *Beagle's* sawbones; on the 28th of June he died. There was an impressive ceremony on deck, made doubly so as Rowlett had been well liked. When his body was consigned to the embrace of the sea, Darwin remembered: "An aweful and solemn sound, that splash of the waters over the body of an old shipmate."

Yet Charles landed gaily at Valparaiso, astonished and pleased to find so many Britishers living there, and happier than words could tell to find an old schoolmate, Richard Corfield of Shrewsbury, who was a resident of Chile and a respected merchant. With educated society about him, bundles from home, letters from Henslow saying his collections from Montevideo had arrived and that they were excellent, Charles was in the happiest state since he had left England.

But something was wrong aboard the *Beagle* and it did not take the scuttle-butt of the ship long to pass the word that "FitzRoy is on his ear again."

Indeed, the strain of the survey of Tierra del Fuego had affected FitzRoy deeply. His plans grew grandiose. He thought to return to Tierra del Fuego and make still more charts of Patagonia; after that he would cruise along the coast of Chile and even cross into the South Pacific; perhaps he would circumnavigate the world! The mere thought of having to return to the "Tierra" and hear the pop-gutted, copper-skinned natives yelling *"Yammerschooner"* at him was enough to make Darwin plan to close his sea-chest and desert the *Beagle*. But there was no need of this, for many of the seamen who had survived the rigors of the subarctic sea fell ill. So did Darwin. For weeks he was partially immobilized in a hammock at Corfield's house — "a grievous loss of time as I had hoped to have collected many animals."

Yet FitzRoy persisted in his new plans — a year's survey of the coastline of Chile and Peru; then a sweep across the Pacific, a circumnavigation of the globe.

"Good God," Darwin wrote home, "who knows when the trip will end?" Two years had become three, and the prospect was that they would spend another two years on their surveying voyage. The "most comfortable reflection" that Charles could find was that "a ship being made of wood and iron cannot last forever and therefore this voyage must someday have an end."

While the *Beagle* was revictualing to go southward for a survey of the Chiloé Islands, which lie off the coast of southern Chile, Charles prepared to assault the Andes. He saw the cordilleras rising range upon range, towering majestically heavenward, topped with snow. This was enough to give him renewed strength for the geology that had usurped, for the moment, the place of animals in his interests. As soon as he could, he got his gear and his guides together and began the trek into the mountainous hinterland.

The lovely sweep of the valleys, the gemlike flowers, the browsing cattle, the curious, gentle inhabitants, all had the air of Switzerland. The clear turquoise sky, after the gloomy, perpetually storm-cast Tierra del Fuego, poured new life into Charles. "I did not cease from wondering at finding each succeeding day as fine as the foregoing. What a difference does climate make in the enjoyment of life! . . . How opposite are the sensations when viewing black mountains, half enveloped in clouds, and seeing another range through light blue haze of a fine day. . . . August 14th . . . and . . . I set out on a riding excursion for the purpose of geologizing the basal parts of the Andes. . . ."

As he mounted the flanks of the Andes, the land of Chile, like an immense relief map, was spread before his astonished eyes. "Chili," he observed, "as may be seen in the maps, is a narrow strip of land between the Cordillera and the Pacific. . . ."

Indeed a narrow land-strip, 2,600 miles in length, composed of parallel mountain ranges, level basins, deserts, and narrow, fertile valleys. In the north, the Atacama Desert and the nitrate fields; in the central part the fertile valleys, the sites of the growing cities, Santiago, Concepción, Antofagasta; in the south, a region of tarns and lakes, thickly treed and still held by the fierce Araucanian Indians. With the volcano-studded Andes as its backbone, the edges of Chile's territory were scalloped — one by three hundred mountain peaks, including the great snow-topped, smoke-ringed Mount

Aconcagua, the tallest in South America, and the other by the saw-toothed shoreline of the Pacific.

In climate Chile was not one, but three: northern Chile, where it never rained; central Chile, where it rained in winter; southern Chile, where it rained all the year round. This was the land of the crazy geography, which fell in conquest to Diego de Almagro in 1536 and was settled by Pedro de Valdivia some years later. When Pizarro had completed the conquest of the Incas, Almagro made a long, torturous trek into the Atacama Desert. He returned with reports of gold. Pedro de Valdivia followed with a well-organized expedition of 150 Spaniards and one German, a Herr Blumen. They cut through the desert, crossed a sharp range of mountains, and plunged into a rich valley with wide and generous earth. Valdivia began to colonize. Opposition mushroomed in the vigorous persons of the Araucanians, who, since the earliest days, had held the land. A century earlier the Inca Tupac Yupanqui, with 20,000 stout bowmen and rock-tossers, had attempted to subjugate them and had failed. Valdivia had even worse going. In 1551, while leading his men against them, he himself was killed. Yet nothing could halt the tide of conquest. Spaniards of the more sturdy type poured into Chile — those who would take from the land its real riches, fruits of the soil. Since the climate and the land most approximated those of Europe, and since there were no slaves or Indians to work the lands, the Spaniard used his own hands. This helped form the character of the Chileño. By 1770 there were 80,000 people in Chile. At the close of the colonial epoch there were not more than a half a million.

Throughout the *tiempo colonial* the government of Chile, as elsewhere, continued in the spirit of Spanish absolutism. "Monarchs are the sacred viceregents of God himself for the temporal government of his people," said the Viceroy of Peru in 1796 when he made Chile a Capitanía General. Chile continued to attract vigorous types, notably Basques, "the toughest and most diligent of all Iberians." Even Irishmen arrived; one Ambrosio O'Higgins, to name the first and greatest, rose from storekeeper to be Capitán General of Chile.

Not long after Charles Darwin was born, there were rendings in the social fabric; revolution broke out in South America. Chile threw herself into the struggle against Spain. In 1814 the loyal Spanish forces captured Santiago; in 1817 the ragged Chileños crossed the Andes with José de San Martín and in a series of battles extending over a period of five years decisively defeated the Spanish armies. Chile was now quit of Spain. Then came the reaction. It was the same here as in Argentina. Darwin, who had seen the forces of reaction, the path of dictators, the rise of ruthless men in Uruguay and Argentina, saw in Chile as elsewhere that the people's war did not bring a people's victory. Once more, as in the past, there was the dichotomy between the landed gentry and the peons. In Chile the landed ones, the *pelucones,* had talked and waged the people's war as long as it took to oust Spain. This done, they promptly put the *pipiolos,* the common folk, back in their place and so into peonage. The great estates became greater, the privileges of the landed ones extended. Bernardo O'Higgins, the revolutionary son of the Irish peddler, who had become Capitán General, was exiled to his death in Peru. *La Fonda aristocrática* had triumphed, and with it Señor Diego Portales, who was at once President in perpetuity, dictator, leader of the conservative party, and author of the 1833 Constitution. Darwin had been received by Portales and carried a passport signed by him.

So Darwin mounted the Andes to tap the ancient rock with his geological hammer, to collect plants, to shoot a condor, "thoroughly enjoying scrambling about these huge mountains." He made no provisions for food or shelter, for he needed none. Along the way through the pleasant valleys he could always find haciendas where the stranger was most hospitably given *posada.* Darwin never tried to curb his curiosity; whether it was fossil, llama, puma, or woman, his creative curiosity followed him everywhere. So we have in his journal an account of a stay at a hacienda "where there were several pretty señoritas."

By March 7, 1835 he was well on his way to Portillo, the 10,000-foot-high pass between Chile and Argentina. He was completely absorbed in the vivid stratification of the wall-steep cordilleras. Everywhere he dismounted, collected geological specimens, and pondered all that came before him. Once again the vastness of geological time came home to him as he listened to the mountain torrents carrying down their countless pebbles. "The whole race of animals have passed away from the surface of the globe during the period throughout which, night and day, these stones have gone rattling downwards in their course."

At the Chile-Argentine border-line, the custom-house officers were "very civil," thanks to the letters he carried from Señor Diego Portales. The people were most hospitable, and small acts of gallantry brought acknowledgment in his diary: "I must wonder at the natural politeness of almost every Chileño . . . for instance, we met a little old Negress riding astride on a mule. She had a goitre so enormous that it was scarcely possible to avoid gazing at her for a moment. But my two companions almost instantly by way of apology, made the common salute of the country by taking off their hats. Where would one of the lower classes in Europe have shown such feeling of politeness to a poor and miserable object of a degraded race?"

Charles was mounted on a mule, the largest his companion could find. But this stoop-shouldered six-foot-two Englishman was an immense cargo. Aware of this, Charles began his panegyric of the mule, a common eulogy from those who use it in the Andes: "With what delicate slim limbs, without any proportion of muscle these animals support so great a burden! That a hybrid should possess more reason, memory, obstinacy, social affection, powers of muscular endurance and length of life than either of its parents seems to indicate that art has here outdone nature."

He was now entering a vertical, rock-hard world where raging streams poured down beside the narrow mountain path with the roar of the sea. The lofty mountains, the pretty alpine flowers, the valleys filled with stratified alluvium, the utterly bare hills of precipitous porphyry, the picturesque central pinnacles of the snow-topped Andes, were paying handsome dividends, for Darwin was laying down with his acute powers of observation and his small geological hammer the first complete picture of the geology of this unknown continent. Humboldt had begun its survey, but he was limited in his interpretation by the geological concepts of Herr Werner of Freiburg. It was Darwin who gave South America its first full geological survey in modern science.

Pumas crossed his trail. Condors wheeled in the sky. Hummingbirds dipped down to thrust their feathered tongues into the dainty, fragrant alpine flowers; and in the valleys and on the peaks he saw guanacos and vicuñas, ruminating cousins of the llama. No works of man had as yet come into these mountain fastnesses. The Chilean Andes were still inviolate. Darwin stood there alone and in ecstasy. The view of the shining, snow-capped peaks, under the intensely turquoise sky, was utterly superb. "I felt glad I was alone," he recalled. "It was like watching a thunderstorm or hearing in full orchestra a chorus of the Messiah."

Darwin kept climbing and chipping, collecting and observing, until *soroche,* mountain sickness, came over him. His breathing became labored, his heart beat like a trip-hammer, he was in the bleak region that the Chileños called the *puna.* His guides told him that "all the waters here have *puna* — where there is snow, there is *puna,* as if *puna* was not the result of altitude, but was some subtle malignant quality of the Andean atmosphere." But now he found fossils, thousands of small exposed fossils, and in his excitement he was no longer aware of the altitude. As he lay panting on the side of the bare Andes, chipping away at the fossils, he felt that feeling of exhilaration which comes in rarefied atmosphere. His guides told him that it takes foreigners a whole year to accustom themselves to the heights. The natives recommended onions for his attack of *soroche*. "I know," Darwin said, "that the onions have sometimes been given in Europe for pectoral complaints; it may possibly be of real service: for my part I found nothing so good as the fossil shells. . . ."

On April 9, 1835 he entered in his diary: "We were now on the high road to St Jago [Santiago] & crossing the Cuesto of Chacabuco, reached at night the village of Colina. From this day till I reached Valparaiso I was not very well & saw nothing & admired nothing. (10*th*). We reached St Jago by the middle of the day, having been absent 24 days, & being well repaid for my trouble."

And at Valparaiso there was good news, or what Darwin thought should have been good news. Captain Robert FitzRoy had been promoted in recognition of his splendid work in surveying South America's coasts. The Captain was not too elated over this because the Admiralty had failed to make some gesture toward his two executive officers, Mr. Stokes, mate and surveyor (and one day Admiral of the Fleet), and John Wickham, Lieutenant (who was to become a captain in the Queen's Navy and Governor of Queensland). Now FitzRoy decided to cruise the Humboldt Current northward along the desert areas of Chile. And once more Charles, thinking of the dreary weight-dipping, the depth-taking, the dull skies, the streaming line of terns, gulls, cormorants that followed the current, decided to turn back to the land. He bought four horses and two mules for twenty-five pounds sterling and set off along the rainless littoral of Chile.

The trek along the coast was as dull as the barren, sterile countryside. It was literally indescribable because there was nothing to describe — nothing that held the eye or exalted the spirit. Somber, dry, colorless, and flat, the Atacama Desert induced in Charles a strange depression or lassitude. At Coquimbo he found the first town, a copper-mining village. The miners still used the primitive methods of Agricola. They dressed as if performing in an extravaganza — scarlet skull-caps, long purple shirts, leather aprons, all dominated by a broad, bright-colored sash. The food was bad; there was scarcely a flealess night. The more northerly the course, the drier the land. It was not a land for a naturalist. Darwin even grew tired of entering "barren and sterile" in his diary. Sometimes, here and there, he would find by diligent search some little bush, cactus, or lichen, scarcely enough to inspire him to dismount and take out his botanical press. "It was almost a pity," he wrote, "to see the sun shining so constantly over so useless a country; such splendid weather ought to have brightened fields and pretty gardens."

By June 10 Darwin had stumbled into the seaport of Copiapó; from the top of the treeless hills he could see the *Beagle* riding at anchor in the indentation of the coastline, which was the "harbor." On the 16th of July they weighed anchor for Lima. Darwin did not leave Chile with regret, yet his *Journal* contained more than a hundred pages devoted to this then little-known land, one hundred pages of clear, sharp description. This for the year 1835 was encyclopedic. For the first time a general reader could feel this land, hear of its foibles, grasp its geological foundation, sink into its ancient history. Darwin had drawn the first scientific portrait of Chile; now he was on his way to Peru.

As the *Beagle* bounced along on the Humboldt Current, Darwin suddenly realized that he was coming onto sacred scientific ground — "land Humboldt had traversed." Alexander von Humboldt, beginning at Venezuela, had gone to Cartagena, then down the Andes to Lima. Darwin began his explorations in Brazil, swung about that great country, swept down past Patagonia and round the Horn, then came up through the Chile of three climates to Peru. Between them they had circumnavigated the whole of South America.

"I cannot say I liked the very little I saw of Peru," Darwin wrote of his six weeks in the ancient land of the Incas. Callao, the port of Lima, he found filthy and ill-built. The atmosphere was heavy with foul smells, the people depraved and drunk and of "every imaginable shade of mixture" — Indian, Negro, and European. The sky was overcast, making the dilapidated tile-roofed buildings the more gloomy. A thick *garua* drizzle, "Peruvian dew" he called it, fell without cease, muddying the streets and dampening his clothes. In addition, Peru was in its annual state of political fomentation. There were four *caudillos* contending for supremacy, and the uncertain political conditions kept Darwin from going far into the interior. But he took the coach that ran twice daily from Callao to Lima and spent five pleasant days in that city. There was some consternation on the short ride when banditti appeared on the hill. Darwin was told that not many months before, "Mr. Wilson, the Consul General, Lord Clinton, and a Frenchman were riding and were attacked by a party of soldiers — robbers who plundered them so completely that they returned naked, excepting for their drawers." The robbers were actuated by warm patriotism; they waved the Peruvian banner and alternately cried: *"Viva la Patria!";* "Give me your jacket"; *"Libertad, Libertad!"* "Off with your trousers!" But nothing happened, and Charles arrived in Lima with his pants, his money, and his curiosity.

Darwin liked the city. He confessed that he enjoyed the hospitality, the lively conversation, the contacts with so many famed people through the British Consul, Wilson, who acted as his cicerone and who had been an aide-de-camp to Simón Bolívar and knew most of the important people. Englishmen he found by droves in roles of merchants and exporters. They seemed to have become more benign under Peru's influence. There is no doubt, as Darwin noticed, that a "residence of some years in contact with the polite and formal Spaniards certainly improves the manners of the English merchants."

The women of Lima were improving the Darwinian æsthetics. He confided to his diary: "Their close elastic gowns fit the figure closely and oblige the ladies to walk with small steps which they do very elegantly and display very white silk stockings and very pretty feet. They wear a black silk veil, which is fixed around the waist behind, and is brought over the head and held by the hands before the face, allowing only one eye to remain uncovered. Then that one eye is so black and so brilliant and has such powers of motion and expression that its effect is very powerful. Altogether the ladies are so metamorphosed that I, at first, felt as much surprised as if I had been introduced amongst a number of nice round mermaids. . . ." Fine words, coming from the incipient author of *The Origin of Species!*

Darwin did some bird-collecting outside of the city, and came across *huacas,* ancient mounds of the Incas; but with these he was not too impressed. His collecting was desultory and unprofitable. The last months had been dull and he yearned for home. England was often in his mind; Shrewsbury, his family, his well-loved sisters and his friends. Deep in melancholia, he wrote: "This voyage is terribly long. I do so earnestly desire to return, yet I dare hardly look forward to the future, for I do not know what will become of me."

What would become of him? Darwin asked that, and the answer was not far off. A pendant of South America, the Galápagos archipelago, was about to cast his destiny. But he was oblivious of all save his geological notes on South America as H.M.S. *Beagle* began its 1,200-mile trip to the Galápagos.

Four views of the Galápagos, made during Darwin's memorable visit to this volcanic archipelago in 1835. On these cinder-heaps Darwin was first stimulated to think about the processes of evolution. (1) Charles Island. (2) Chatham Island. (3) Albemarle Island. (4) Watering-place on Chatham.

The reptiles of the Galápagos provided Charles Darwin with the stimulus to ravel out the processes of evolution. Above, the giant tortoise, reaching as much as five hundred pounds in weight; below, the head of the land iguana, denizen of the cactus-studded Galápagos.

CHAPTER XXII
The Galápagos Begets Evolution

THE GALÁPAGOS ISLANDS were the most desolate regions that the *Beagle* had visited in its twenty-thousand league voyage. Black metallic cinder-heaps, they rose out of the clear, pellucid Pacific to towering heights, as barren as the cinder-heaps that surrounded the iron furnaces near Wolverhampton.

What had Darwin expected? At least to see palm trees, gaudy-colored birds, jungles; and to hear the raucous screech of parrots or the shrieks of howling monkeys. Instead he found volcanic deserts. There was a reason for this. The Galápagos (or Enchanted Islands), while only 600 miles from the mainland of South America and split by the equator, were bathed by the cold Humboldt Current.

H.M.S. *Beagle* had followed this current on an uneventful voyage from Lima. It reached the Galápagos archipelago on September 15, 1835, and on the 17th put into the harbor on the lee side of Chatham Island, the westernmost of the group. Darwin had hoped for some relief from the broken terrain, the parched deserts of Chile and Peru. Now, when he landed on Chatham, he saw his hopes dashed; nothing could have been less inviting. Broken fields of black basaltic lava thrown into rugged waves rolled up to a height of some 3,000 feet. The tumbled masses of blackish, greenish stuff seemed like the dross of an iron furnace. Its inlets were sparsely fringed by mangrove thickets, its sand-strips by shortlived succulents, and its clinker-bound interior by wretched little weeds, "which would have better become an arctic than an equatorial Flora."

FitzRoy was right in thinking the islands "fit for Pandemonium." The heat, the stillness, the bleak skies, the lava-bound littoral, were like some cultivated part of hell. No one would have guessed, least of all young Charles Darwin, that here on this blighted moonscape would be born the theory of evolution. Three centuries of scientific exploration in South America were to receive their culmination on these islands.

While the *Beagle* carried on its survey, the first and perhaps to this day the most thorough to be made, Charles went ashore. There, surrounded by the leafless trees, the meager, ill-smelling *muyuyu* bushes, and the giant cacti, he investigated the geology of the Enchanted Islands. On every hand there were gaping craters, fumeroles, "cones, vents, truncated cones . . . extraordinarily numerous." Chatham, he perceived, had been permeated like a sieve by subterranean vapors. Here and there the soft lava had been blown into great bubbles which, when hardened and brittle, had collapsed and fallen in, leaving circular pits with deep sides. Chatham was typical of all the islands, of which there were ten large ones and a score smaller. The whole archipelago, scattered over a water area of 23,000 square miles, had a total land surface of not over 2,800 square miles. More than half of this was comprised in Albemarle Island, the largest of the archipelago.

Here Charles seemed to have been brought face to face with creation. The islands were geologically recent. Smoke still poured from the serrated mouths of active volcanoes, lava still belched out of the broken dark caverns. Darwin now, in the moon-shadows of this strange, haunting, gloomy scene, felt himself face to face with the innermost mysteries, the origin of things. He grasped, almost instantly, that the islands had been created by epochal eruptions beginning on the ocean floor. For countless æons the lava shot out and built up layer upon layer, until its shaggy, smoking basalt head burst above the boiling waters of the Pacific. Then for centuries more the lava cooled and solidified, forming islands bleak, hard, twisted — and without life. But mangrove roots, breaking off in the ebb-tides of the continent, floated out on the swift-moving Humboldt Current and took refuge on the harsh, cruel littoral. Sea kelp and other leathery algæ found a respite from their eternal floating and draped themselves about the rocks. Rain and sun, sun and rain, reacted on the hard lava, and parts of it began to erode into thick, pasty black earth. Here primitive plants, carried on the tropic currents of air, found refuge and thrust up stems. The islands began to assume earth's green mantle.

Then came the avifauna in casual accidental migrations: boobies, albatross, penguins, frigate birds, cormorants, following the currents that were rich with sea-life. Finding the Galápagos free from enemies, they remained.

Charles could now see it plainly, with a strange feeling of exaltation. Gradually the puzzle of life began to fall into place.

The second day was glowing hot as the sun broke through the mists and reflected on the clinker-bound terrain. Darwin set off through the prickly bush in search of plants. Suddenly he was brought up short by the sight of two immense forms moving toward him — two gigantic tortoises (*galápagos* in the Spanish idiom) of more than two hundred pounds each. One stopped to eat some prickly pads of cactus, its long reptilian neck and staring blank eyes as primordial as the raw earth itself. Darwin moved, the giant tortoise sensed him — and dropped with a hiss to take refuge within its shell. Surrounded by the cacti, the green lichen-covered lava, the smoking craters, and the great reptiles, Charles seemed to be dragged back to antediluvian times.

Once these giant tortoises had lived in teeming millions all over the world, when the orb was young, verdantly luscious, and rep-tilian. But time had overwhelmed these relatively defenseless shell-bearing reptiles, and now their last places of refuge were Pacific Islands — the Galápagos, off South America — and the Sey-chelles, Réunion, and Mauritius in the Indian Ocean.

Life began for them, Darwin discovered, in an egg, a round bil-liard-ball-sized egg, placed in a hollow that the mother tortoise scraped in the coarse soil. Breaking out of its shell after five weeks of incubation, the little tortoise — weighing about two ounces — scrambled past those eggs still unhatched and burrowed through the soil to the surface. Once clear of this hypogeum, the tortoise took off to the cool higher interior, feeding on tender young grass, bits of cacti, and, as it became cyclopean, on the giant spine-infested pads of the opuntia. Of all the wonders that Darwin had seen in his four years in South America, these great tortoises were the most bizarre, the most enigmatical. It was said that they could not swim. Then how did they get on most of the other islands, how did they reach the Galápagos in the first place?

With these questions still burrowing into his mind, Darwin got back on the *Beagle* in time to be transported to Charles Island, a hundred miles southwest of Chatham. Here they found people, 300 in number. An Englishman, Mr. Lawson, was the Vice-Governor; he was overjoyed at seeing a ship of the King's Navy in these en-chanted waters.

Charles Island, the most fertile of the archipelago, had a dif-ferent aspect from Chatham. With Lawson as their cicerone, they passed through coarse-leafed, spined thickets like those on Chat-ham, and followed the rise in the island. The atmosphere began to change. Four and a half miles from the harbor, 1,000 feet in altitude, they came upon the colony, set among trees, real trees, leaves and all. They were fanned by fine southern breezes, their sight was refreshed by green vegetation, they saw large coarse ferns and grasses and thick-trunked, albeit stunted, trees. There were also cultivated crops: sweet potatoes, bananas, and coffee. And what was more exciting, mud, black mud, rich black earth. "Since leaving Brazil, we have not seen so Tropical a Landscape. . . . It will not easily be imagined how pleasant the change was from Peru & Northern Chili, in walking in the pathways to find *black mud* and on the trees to see mosses, ferns & Lichens & Parasitical plants adhæring. . . . The inhabitants are in number 200–300: nearly all are people of color & banished for Political crimes from the State of Equator (Quito & Cuayaquil &c.) to which this Archipelago belongs. It appears that the people are far from contented. . . ." Indeed, they hardly could be, living in caves like troglodytes and eking out an existence, Robinson Crusoe fashion, as their share in the "people's victory" of the late revolutions and counter-revolutions that shook South America and demolished the Gran Colombia of Simón Bolívar.

It was in 1831 that President Vicente Roca Fuerte had looked upon the Islas Galápagos, the way-station of whaling ships, though unclaimed by any nation. He had formed an agricultural colony to settle them; the schooner *Mercedes* was victualed for the 600-mile voyage and put under the command of Colonel Ignacio Hernandez. In 1831 the islands of pirates and giant tortoises were officially annexed by Ecuador and renamed Archipelago de Colón, a name which no one, not even the Ecuadorians, used. But soon, instead of being an agricultural colony, the group became a political Devil's Island of the Republic of Ecuador.

H.M.S. *Beagle* remained six days at Charles Island, where Darwin collected avidly. Already there was creeping into his diary the significant and stimulating question: "September 26th & 27th. I industriously collected all the animals, plants, insects & reptiles from this island. It will be very interesting to find from future comparison to what district or 'centre of creation' the organized beings of this archipelago must be attached."

Lawson, the English resident, observing Darwin's immense interest in all the island's phenomena, especially the giant tortoises, told him that these differed from island to island; further, that he could tell by a glance at a tortoise's shell from which island it came. Charles admitted that "he did not for some time pay sufficient attention to his statement," for he collected blindly, mixing the specimens of all the islands. This shows how dormant Charles's speculative sense had become since he dug out the fossils in Patagonia, which bore such remarkable likeness to living South American animals.

When the *Beagle* moved on to Albemarle, he once more came upon giant tortoises and noted the difference in their shells — and Lawson's remarks struck home. Here was a constellation of islands "formed of precisely the same rocks," quite similar in climate, rising to nearly equal heights, "and yet so differently tenanted." The Galápagos were a little world in themselves.

The *Beagle* took the time-honored voyage through the strait that lay on the lee side of that great clinker, Albemarle. To the south of it was Narborough with its spouting volcano, which lay, as Melville had it, "in the black jaws of Albemarle like a wolf's red tongue in his open mouth." And, as had most ships before it, the *Beagle* anchored in Tagus Cove. On its volcanic black walls, worn smooth by the endless friction of water and air, were painted the names of ships that had used the cove. There, faintly legible in red, the color of terror, was the name of the pirate ship *Batchelor's Delight,* which had frequented the islands in 1640. Darwin recalled that it was that bloody crew — William Dampier, Ambrose Cowley, John Cook, and the most famed Lionel Wafer, the "barber-chirurgeon" — who had made the first chart of these waters and had given the individual islands their English names.

The Galápagos had been discovered by the Spaniards by accident. In 1535 the good Bishop of Panama, Tomás de Berlanga, was caught in the outward sweep of the Humboldt Current and brought to the water-parched Galápagos. But the Spaniards never returned. Later the pirates used the islands, named them, and began their literary history. And it was the English who mapped them in anticipation of the whaling traffic soon to arise in the Pacific. In 1794 Captain James Colnett came round the Horn into the Pacific, made the landfall at the Galápagos, left the name of the sloop *Rattler* painted on the rocks of Tagus Cove, and surveyed more of the islands. He christened those left unnamed by Ambrose Cowley — Hood, Gardiner, Chatham, Duncan, Barrington — all admirals of the Blue. And in the bay at Charles Island Colnett set up a large barrel which became known as Hathaway's Post Office. Here whalers left their letters — items of home interest, the number of whales they had caught — which they expected to be picked up by other whalers; and this proved their undoing. For when war was declared between Great Britain and the United States, Captain David Porter in the U.S. frigate *Essex* came to the Pacific, made for the post office, and ransacked the letters. Thus he learned the type, tonnage, and number of British whalers that moved in the Galápagos cluster, and set out to seize them as prizes.

Since that time the Galápagos had become a whaling station. But the enchantment of the isles was at work. Men were lost in the tantalizing sameness of the landscape; thirst-crazed sailors and scurvy-ridden men were brought to madness. The marlinspike was used in many a lurid struggle on the enchanted, lava-bound shores, and many a man was left to be "tucked in with the clinkers."

Charles saw evidence of this at James Island, where the *Beagle* next moved. "A few years since the sailors belonging to a sealing vessel murdered their captain in this quaint spot: and we saw his skull lying among the bushes. . . ."

Here Darwin went ashore with Benjamin Bynoe, acting surgeon of the *Beagle*. His knowledge of anatomy and the restless insistence of Darwin caused him to quit ship and take to the lava-strewn hills, to collect and skin some of the giant land lizards that colonized the eroded parts of the island. They lived ashore for a week.

"In the low dry region," Darwin recorded, "there are but few Tortoises: they are replaced by infinite numbers of the large yellow herbivorous Lizard. . . . The burrows of this animal are so very numerous that we had difficulty in finding a spot to pitch the tents. These lizards live entirely on vegetable productions; berries, leaves, for which they frequently crawl up the trees. . . . I suspect such habits are nearly unique in the Saurian race." Such were Darwin's first comments on the land iguanas of the Galápagos.

Like the tortoise, with which it shared the island, this iguana ate cacti; like the tortoise it laid its oval eggs in the sand to hatch. Heavy and squat, a little less than a yard in length, the land iguana was a fitting complement to the sea iguana. While the land iguana was tied to the land by its inability to swim, the Amblyrhyncus sea iguana was endowed with webbed feet (which, curiously, it never used for swimming) and a long-spined, spiked tail, which it used as a paddle to push itself above and below the surface of the water.

Here was a world purely reptilian in character; there were no mammals. All the animals were, in a sense, unique; still, they were definitely American types. Why? Charles pondered this often in those last days on James Island. There, among the remains of tortoise shells, the meat of which they had eaten *con cuero,* there in front of the coarse red soil which an iguana was excavating for a nest, Charles allowed his speculation to run riot. Here where "most of the organic productions were aboriginal creations . . . found nowhere else in the world . . . there remained even a difference between the inhabitants of the different islands . . . yet all showed a marked relationship with those of America, although separated from that continent by 500–600 miles of water." Here, "seeing every height crowned with its crater and the boundaries of most of the lava-streams still distinct, we are led to believe that within a period geologically recent the unbroken ocean was here spread out. . . . Hence both in time and space we seem to be brought somewhat near to that great fact — that mystery of mysteries — the first appearance of new beings on the earth. . . ."

How account for the fact that there were mutations, differences, even within the islands themselves? There were only two ways: either the tortoises, iguanas, and birds were created independently,

simultaneously, or successively for these islands; or they were derived from a common ancestry. If they were part of a "common
ancestry," and derived from their South American prototypes, one
could explain their presence on the Galápagos by some as yet unknown migration. Yet if species were not mutable, not subject to
modification due to environmental factors, then why did the
species on the Galápagos differ from island to island? But if species do change, do modify, are subject to mutations, then the puzzle is unraveled. Now, the species of the Galápagos are peculiar to
those islands, although they show distinct relationship with the
species of the South American mainland. If there were mutations
in the Galápagos among the species, there were mutations elsewhere. How blind he had been! This was what the fossils that he
had unearthed at Bahía Blanca had said to him: "We are of the
past, but we are also of the present. Do you not see how similar
we are to those living today? We are the overt testimony of the
unrolling, the evolution. . . ." So that was it. Geology spoke of it,
paleontology affirmed it, and before his eyes in the Galápagos the
very tortoises carried the solution on their backs, and the brown
dusky finches in the shape of their beaks.

For years the Galápagos would haunt Charles Darwin. . . .

In 1837, after his return to England, he confided in his note-
book: "In July opened first note-Book on 'Transmutation of the
Species.' . . . Had been greatly struck from about month of previous March (1836) on character of S. American fossils — & species
on Galápagos Archipelago. — These facts origin (especially latter) [i.e., the Galápagos] of all my views." From barren volcanic
islands tenanted only by lost-world reptiles, islands disdained by
the Spanish for centuries, came the work which was to give science
the greatest stimulus it had had in two thousand years.

In such fashion, and by such slight unforeseen incidents, was
South America opened — not by the musket or the cutlass, or the
ravages of conquest or revolution, but by the slow ponderings and
gropings of explorer-scientists. Years later the Galápagos puzzle
would find complete exposition in *The Origin of Species:* *

"The most striking and important fact for us is the affinity of the species
which inhabit islands to those of the nearest mainland without being
actually the same. The Galápagos Archipelago, situated under the equator . . . here almost every product of the land and of the water bears
the unmistakable stamp of the American Continent . . . the close affinity of most of the birds to American species . . . is manifest in every
character, in their habits, gestures, and tones of voice. So it is with the
other animals and with a large proportion of the plants. . . . The natu-

* Modern Library edition, pp. 310 ff.

ralist looking at the inhabitants of these volcanic islands in the Pacific, distant several hundred miles from the continent, feels that he is standing on American land. Why should this be so? Why should the species which are supposed to have been created in the Galápagos Archipelago and nowhere else bear too plainly the stamp of affinity to those created in America? There is a considerable degree of resemblance in the volcanic nature of the soil, in the climate, height and size of the islands, between the Galápagos and Cape Verde Archipelagos: but what an entire and absolute difference in their inhabitants! The inhabitants of the Cape Verde Islands are related to those of Africa, like those of the Galápagos to America. Facts such as these admit of no sort of explanation on the ordinary view of independent creation: whereas . . . it is obvious that the Galápagos Islands would be likely to receive colonists from America, whether by occasional means of transport or (though I do not believe this doctrine) by formerly continuous land . . . such colonists would be liable to modifications — the principle inheritance still betraying their orginal birthplace."

At last the *Beagle* came home — home to England, after taking its long course across the South Pacific, touching at the Society Islands, New Zealand, Australia (where they dumped off Mr. Matthews, one-time missionary to the Fuegians) , then into the Indian Ocean, round the Cape of Good Hope, then once more into the South Atlantic to the coast of Brazil. Now the homebound pennants were put up and H.M.S. *Beagle,* flying before the wind, came back to England after a historic voyage of five years and one hundred and sixty days.

The evolution of Charles Darwin from clergyman to naturalist was complete.

CHAPTER XXIII
"I Am an Author"

I AM AN AUTHOR."
To his utter surprise Charles Darwin woke one morning and found himself the celebrated author of the third volume, *Journal & Remarks,* of the official publication of the voyages of the *Beagle.** The Victorian modesty of young Darwin is most refreshing, for despite the scarcity of books on South America he really believed that his five years of intensive research on the mainland of that continent and its islands was not important. He thought much of his *Journal* was "childish" and "ridiculous" and hardly worth the publishing. He had even expressed his willingness, at Fitz-Roy's suggestion, to have the *Journal* absorbed in the official account: "FitzRoy . . . proposed me to join him in publishing the account; that is for him to have the disposal of & arranging of my Journal, & to mingle it with his own. Of course I have said I am perfectly willing, if he wants materials or thinks the chit-chat details of my Journal are any ways worth publishing." Had this proposal (happily not carried out) come to pass, the work of Charles Darwin, the opening of South America, perhaps even the theory of evolution would have been seriously delayed.

The *Journal* was published in 1839. It caught on at once; much to Captain FitzRoy's consternation, the demand for the third volume so outstripped that of the other two volumes that Darwin received an offer next year from Colburn, a London publisher, for a reissue of the *Journal* alone. The volume was given a title that its importance justified: *Journal of Researches into the Natural History and Geology of the countries visited during the Voyage of H.M.S. 'Beagle,' round the world under the command of Captain FitzRoy, R.N.* But the *Journal* had greatly changed from the diary that Darwin had sent home in batches to "amuse the family."

When Darwin returned, he (like Humboldt) distributed his collections to specialists, and the *Journal* began to take on all the aspects of an important major contribution. To Professor Owen went the fossils, to Waterhouse the skins and skeletons of the recent mammalia, to Gould the birds; Thomas Bell received the rep-

---

* *Narrative of the Surveying Voyages of Her Majesty's Ships* Adventure and Beagle *between the years 1826–1836, describing their examination of the Southern Shores of South America,* etc., etc. 1839. Vol. III, *Journal & Remarks, by Charles R. Darwin 1832–36.* 1839.

tiles, and Hooker the plants. On these they reported, and these reports Darwin gathered up and incorporated into the book. Of the original diary he tossed out more than half, and set himself to copying, recasting, and expanding the original entries in line with his further researches. As soon as he had the reports from the specialists, he added over 100,000 words which explained and elucidated the material that he had gathered. In the matter of style, he kept the *Personal Narrative* of Alexander von Humboldt ever before him as a model, and made the work almost entirely a "popular scientific treatment." And what a concourse of phenomena — Brazil, flatworms, sea discoloration, jungles of Bahia, insects, butterflies, lush-eyed señoritas, dictators, fossils, bolas, ostriches, climate, zoology. All this was completed in a year's solid work, so that by July 1837 the complete *Journal* of 240,000 words was out of his hands and in the printer's. When the printer's proofs came to him, Darwin could hardly believe in his transformation into an author. "If I live till I am 80 years old," he wrote to Professor Henslow, "I shall not cease to marvel at finding myself an author; in the summer before I started if any one had told me that I should have been an angel by this time, I should have thought it an equal impossibility."

Hardly had the ink dried on the unbound copies of the *Journal* when the book was passing from hand to hand. There was hardly a scientist in England who did not read it within a month after its publication. Professor Lyell, to whom it was dedicated, was deeply moved by the book; Horner praised the clarity of its style; young Joseph Hooker, the botanist, slept with it under his pillow so that he could take it up the moment he awakened. In far-off Yorkshire a tinsmith-botanist was reading it to another botanist, Richard Spruce, on whom the book would have an important effect. Reviewers spoke of the charm of the narrative, "a charm that could only come from the freshness of the heart of a strong intellectual man and an acute observer." When others compared it with Humboldt's *Narrative*, Darwin overflowed with happiness. In a few weeks Volume III was out of print; Colburn, the publisher, approached Darwin and in his "astonishment over being an author" he signed away his rights. To his sister Susan he wrote: "Talking of money, I reaped the other day all the profit I shall ever get from my Journal, which consists in *paying* Mr. Colburn £21 10s for the copies which I presented to different people: 1337 copies have been sold. This is a comfortable arrangement is it not. . . ." That, financially, is all that Darwin ever reaped out of his scientific conquest of South America. But the work was paying handsome dividends not only to the publisher, but to the whole scientific world. A copy sent to Humboldt was translated into German. Humboldt was so delighted with it that he sent a copy to France, where it was quickly translated. Even in Spain an edition was brought out. In the space of a decade the *Journal* became a classic. Already a century old, it is still being reprinted.

An amazing impulse was created by the publication of the *Journal*. For the first time South America was shown in a charmingly written, authentically narrated book — a whole view of South America. New expeditions, stimulated directly by Humboldt and his *Personal Narrative* and by Darwin and his work, descended upon the continent. To Peru between the years 1834 and 1837 went Count François de Castelnau; Robert Schomburgk went to British Guiana to link that unknown part with "Terra Humboldtiana." The Italian Codazzi went to Colombia; Pissis and later R. A. Philippi explored Chile; Burmeister went to Brazil, Raimondi to Peru, where Ave-Lallement and von Tschudi followed him. Professor Karsten went to Venezuela. The geologist Wagner sailed to Ecuador. There was one great area still to explore in detail — the Amazon — and this remained the special province of Britishers. Alfred Wallace was on his way there with Henry Bates, the entomologist; and one other, Richard Spruce, who would make the whole of the great Amazon Valley his laboratory, was getting ready for his part in opening South America.

If Charles Darwin was astonished in 1839 to find himself an author, he was more astonished to find himself married in the same year to his cousin, Emma Wedgwood. They took up residence at No. 12 Upper Gower Street, London. There Darwin settled down to work on his collections and to rear a family.*

With the publication of the *Journal* and Darwin's election as a Fellow of the Royal Society, the Linnean Society, and the Zoological Society, no one in his family or out of it ever again mentioned anything about the "very quiet parsonage" which he had envisioned as his future home on his return from South America. He was now the complete scientist.

Darwin turned to the task of harvesting the mountain of specimens and the notes he had made in South America. This led first to the *Journal* (1839), then the *Zoology of the Beagle* and *The Structure and Distribution of Coral Reefs* (1842), the *Geological*

---

* In all, Darwin fathered ten children. The six sons were William Erasmus, Charles Waring, George Howard, Francis (destined to be elevated to knighthood), Horace (also to be knighted), and Leonard, who entered the Royal Engineers and retired a Major. This gentleman, with whom I was in touch for the period of the Darwin Galápagos centennial, died in March 1943 at the age of ninety-three. There were also four daughters.

Observations on the Volcanic Islands, then back to South America again with the publication of *Geological Observations on South America* (1846) . By this time he was well on his way. Yet always in the back of his mind was that tantalizing question of the origin of life. Every time he went over his Galápagos collections, the same vague doubts of the stability of the species flitted across his mind. Evolution was in the air. He had more and more returned to the problem of the origin of the species, and his scientific friends were after him to publish. His priority must be established. But Darwin was both a careful man, and a modest one. He must have more facts, more proofs.

Then in that horrible winter of 1854, when the Crimean War was raging, and the charge of the Light Brigade took its pitifully heroic place in military history, Darwin worked on the outline that would one day become *The Origin of Species.* And another was working, too. Alfred Russel Wallace, then living in the Malay Archipelago, had been led to consider independently the origin of species and had drafted an essay *On the Tendency of Varieties to Depart Indefinitely from the Original Type.* He sent it to Darwin, who received it in the morning's mail, "containing no more than a few thin sheets of paper closely penned." Would Mr. Darwin, wrote Wallace, if he considered the paper important and believed that it would supply the missing factor to explain the origin of species, send it to Professor Lyell. Darwin had been forestalled! "I never," he wrote when sending the paper to Lyell, "saw a more striking coincidence; if Wallace had my own sketch written out in 1842, he could not have made a better short abstract: Even his terms now stand as heads of my chapters."

"Men do inevitably desire priority," writes the excellent biographer of Darwin.* "It is a fundamental human instinct. Life may be largely a matter of repetition, but it reaches out continually to newness; it exists for the sake of newness, to do the new things, or, more deeply still, to *be* the new thing. Who has never created something unique, his alone, has never lived. . . ." And how did Darwin handle this matter of priority? "I would rather burn my whole book," he wrote, "that Wallace or any other man should think that I behaved in a paltry spirit." What followed are the most honorable pages in the history of science: both papers were read at the Linnean Society on the same evening, and published at the same time.

Darwin then went to work, and by 1859 the public was offered the long-awaited work *On the Origin of Species by means of Natural Selection, or the Preservation of Favoured Races in the Strug-*

* *Charles Darwin,* by Geoffrey West, p. 233.

[228]

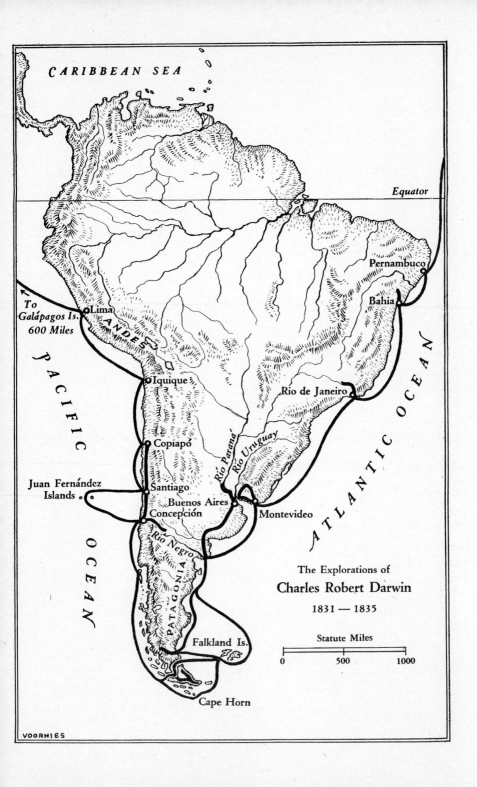

CARIBBEAN SEA

Equator

Pernambuco

Bahia

To
Galápagos Is.
600 Miles

Lima

ANDES

PACIFIC

Iquique

Rio de Janeiro

Copiapó

Río Paraná

Río Uruguay

Juan Fernández
Islands

Santiago

Buenos Aires
Concepción

Montevideo

OCEAN

Río Negro

PATAGONIA

ATLANTIC OCEAN

The Explorations of
Charles Robert Darwin
1831 — 1835

Statute Miles

Falkland Is.

0   500   1000

Cape Horn

VOORHIES

gle for Life. A memorable year, 1859: Alexander von Humboldt was on his death-bed; Karl Marx, banished from Paris, was publishing his *Introduction to the Critique of Political Economy;* and the pages of *The Origin of Species* were agitating society everywhere. The rest of the history is well known. The men who rose to champion Darwin and his work, the long list of those who denounced him, the vilification and billingsgate heaped upon one of the most gentle men who ever lived — all this belongs to history. That single book provided the main stimulus for biological research for half a century.

The man Darwin took all the controversy in the way he had taken most of the events of his life, without apparent agitation, and went back to the study of his barnacles and the writing of *The Descent of Man.* In all, between spasms of pain (an inheritance from the *Beagle* voyage), Darwin composed some twenty books, all stemming from his original source of inspiration, the voyage of the *Beagle* and his expedition of five years about the coasts of South America.

By April, 1882 his spasm-racked body had brought Darwin to the end of the journey. In his last seizures of pain, nausea, and vomiting, he grasped the hand of Emma Darwin and managed to mutter:

"I'm not the least afraid of death."

The body of Charles Robert Darwin was laid to rest in Westminster Abbey beside Sir Isaac Newton. Even in death they had come together. It was Newton's speculation on the shape of the earth that had sent La Condamine scurrying to the new continent; then came Humboldt, whose writings about South America inspired Darwin to take the voyage that not only helped to open South America, but sent other knowledge-thirsty men to the same continent. Already explorer-naturalists were in the Andes, coursing the pampas, trekking the llanos. Only one vast area waited to yield its secrets to the world — the Amazon.

And to the Land of the Amazons in 1849 went Richard Spruce, inspired by Charles Darwin.

PART IV

❀◈❀◈❀◈❀◈❀◈❀◈❀◈❀◈❀◈❀◈❀◈❀◈❀◈❀

CHAPTER XXIV
Richard Spruce, Yorkshireman

A PERFECT GALE was blowing, but fortunately in the right direction. It caught up the lateen sails of the *Tres de Junho*, pushing its 80 tons burden up the main stream of the River Amazon. The air was vibrant, the sun hot, the sky blue with the texture of porcelain. Suddenly this Amazonian afternoon was split with a throbbing, wheezing sound that began like the death spasms of a sacrificial pig; then the throbbings changed into musical notes — and over the swift-flowing yellow waters floated the spirited air of a Yorkshire jig. The brown eyes of the Indian deck hands all turned to the hammock on the poop, drawn to it by this strange music. A large blue and green parrot stopped plucking its feathers and cocked its head. Tinga, the woolly monkey, pulled itself to the ends of its chain and looked toward the sound. The natives, earth-brown, with only a sad pair of pants to hide their nakedness, closed in on the hammock and stared down on the ruddy complexion of Richard Spruce, Yorkshireman, botanist, and bagpipe-player.

Oblivious of the straining eyes and gaping mouths, Spruce curled his long legs in the hammock and played the sprightly tunes of his native moorlands of Gansthorpe. As he puffed away, his blue eyes took in the infinitely long façade of trees, trees, trees, trees. What a place for a botanist! How might he convey, to one who had not seen it, the immensity of the Amazon? The ocher-colored river, which drained half the South American continent, flowed by him at the rate of 500,000 cubic feet a second. It was not like a river, it was like the stark desolation of the sea. No wonder the natives called it *Parana-tinga* — the Ocean-river.

The water was rising. Great floating islands — *Ihlas de caapim* — swept by. Grass islands moving on the Amazon's relentless turgid flow to the sea, they were filled with water-hyacinths, brittle grass, and bastard cane. If a vessel was unfortunate enough to become entangled in one of these, it would become engulfed; and there were many other things to engulf one in the Amazon. Large trees shot by, trees that dwarfed anything that Richard Spruce had ever seen. A branch of a jungle giant bumped into his sloop, and for a moment floating tree and sailing craft were locked in mortal embrace. The Indians rushed forward to disentangle the flotsam, but they were not there before Richard Spruce. He dropped his bagpipe, leaving the air to rush out in a painful squeak, picked up his lichenologist's hammer, and quickly, carefully, ripped from the shattered tree a lichen, pancake-size, that encrusted the trunk in vivid yellow and red. He went back to his hammock, took out his botanical press, and put the lichen between two pieces of pressing paper. He then leaned back to make his notes. "Family: Graphideæ. Date: October 10, 1849. Locality: In the middle of the Amazon, halfway between Santa Maria de Belém de Grão Pará and Santarem, 200 miles up the Amazon. . . ."

"Two hundred miles up the Amazon." Richard Spruce rubbed his lean young face thoughtfully, and his blue eyes lighted up as they had always done when he thought of the wealth of plants that this wild unknown region would yield. He had read, in fact he still carried with him, a dog-eared copy of Charles Darwin's *Voyage of the Beagle*. He had wanted ever since he had first read that book to do for the botany of South America what Darwin had done for zoology. Now, in 1849, when the world hovered on the brink of revolution, Spruce's desire had come true.

Spruce marked a new turn in South American exploration; for the first time the professional naturalist appeared. La Condamine had wealth; Humboldt spent most of his personal fortune in exploring South America; Charles Darwin came from parents who, while not wealthy like Humboldt and La Condamine, were so well established financially that he did not have a single financial worry the whole of this life. But Spruce was poor. Like Wallace and Bates, who were on the Amazon at the same time, he reflected the change that had come over the world since the fall of Napoleon and the coming of the industrial revolution. These naturalist-explorers were men of substantial British families. Their interests and enthusiasms were as great as those of their predecessors, but they did not have means at their disposal.

Ever since Linnæus had inspired men to open the green world, collectors had taken to ships, to the jungle, to the heights, to gather and codify the plants of the earth. South America, for obvious reasons, had remained largely untouched. The plants that had been collected by the Spaniards had been either destroyed, as were those of Mutis in the revolution in Colombia, or left to molder in the archives of Spain. South America, where distances are great, where facilities are limited, where rainfall and insects ceaselessly conspire against the collector, had always defied the botanist.

Spruce was not trained for his task as tropical botanist. He was self-taught, as Darwin, Wallace, and Bates had been self-taught. His love of plants came to him early on the Yorkshire heaths, grew through the years, and in the end created the botanist who opened the green world of the Amazon. He possessed in a marked degree the faculty of order shown in his unvarying neatness of dress, his carefully formed handwriting, and the orderly arrangement of all his surroundings. Whether in his little grass-thatched cottage in Yorkshire or in a wattle-and-daub hovel on the Amazon, his writing materials, his books, his microscopes were always well arranged. Neat in thought, neat in his externals, neat in his collecting, such was the person of Richard Spruce. These qualities came from his inheritance, for Dick Spruce was one of a long line of vigorous Yorkshiremen, solid, inquisitive, exacting and stern taskmasters to themselves and others. As for his development, Dick was educated by his father, Richard Spruce, Sr., the highly respected schoolmaster at Gansthorpe. So far as the records show he had no formal schooling, no systematized learning. While he was very young, his mother (who was an Etty and a relative of the Yorkshire painter William Etty) died. When Dick was fourteen, his father remarried; he had eight daughters by his second wife. Under these circumstances, Dick Spruce had more or less to fend for himself. He learned Latin and Greek from old Dr. Langdale, who had been educated for the priesthood and whose scholarship was of high order. And in attending these classic lessons he had to cross the mist-ridden moors. There he acquired a love for plants and flowers. At sixteen, wholly without prompting from outside, he began to set down a list of the plants he found on the moors. At this time his stepsisters were being born, it seemed, as fast as gestation would permit, but his father found time to get him books on botany and to take a few botanical excursions with him. It was evident that young Dick had the true spark. The list of plants that he was able to name, to identify, contained 403 species. Later he drew up another list of 485 flowering plants, many of which were of sufficient rarity to be included later in Baines's *Flora of Yorkshire.*

At the age of twenty-two Spruce became a tutor in a school at Haxby, four miles from York, and a year later took the post of mathematical master at the Collegiate School at York. He was then very undecided about his future. His duties as schoolmaster gave him little time for botany. His only relaxations from teaching were visits to Sam Gibson, the tinsmith, near Halifax. Gibson was one of a considerable number of north-country men of the early nineteenth century who became interested in the green world about them. Spruce, the schoolmaster, would sit by the forge of Gibson, the tinsmith, and talk of flowers and plants, while the fire crackled and the bellows puffed.

Sam Gibson had a copy of Hooker's *British Flora,* so begrimed and blackened that Spruce was scarcely able to read it. A real friendship grew up between these two, and Spruce confided his innermost thoughts to the tinsmith. He hated teaching. He loved botany. Yet what could he do? He had not the formal background to secure a post in a museum; he had all but exhausted the moors of Yorkshire botanically; he had not the funds to travel. Gibson was for his giving up the teaching. He encouraged Spruce's botanical excursions; he introduced him to other botanists. Thus he kept alive an enthusiasm which might have died from inertia.

Then, in 1839, came the awakening. The press announced that there had just been published a *Narrative of the Surveying Voyage of Her Majesty's Ships Adventure and Beagle.* The third volume was Charles Darwin's *Journal.* Gibson borrowed a copy, put it into the hands of Dick Spruce. The next day the classes at the Collegiate School suffered. The teacher used every available moment in devouring this unknown young naturalist's writing about South America. The sections about botany drove Spruce to utter distraction. Wouldn't it be wonderful to do for botany in South America what this Charles Darwin had done for zoology and geology? South America was calling. La Condamine, who opened South America, had inspired Humboldt; Humboldt had inspired Darwin; and now Darwin was inspiring Spruce.

But all things conspired against a journey to the Amazon. The dog-eared copy of Darwin's *Journal* had to be put away. One had to live. Spruce found schoolteaching distasteful, but it was his one livelihood.

By the age of twenty-two he had reached the limit of his growth — six feet two, thin for his height, dark, with fine features of a southern type. He was extremely courteous and very dignified in manner, with a fund of quiet humor and a great love for anecdote. Frustration doubtless helped to bring on the symptoms of lung trouble, as did confinement in the classroom and mental worries, not to mention the inclement weather of the Yorkshire moors, and the miserable stipend he received as teacher at the Collegiate School. He had a lung attack that was almost fatal; he had an attack of gall-stones that caused the "most excruciating pain it is possible to conceive."

Then fate came to his aid. The school broke up. It was the turning-point of his life. He was forced out of teaching. He had begun to acquire among botanists an excellent reputation for careful collecting. His articles in the *Phytologist,* which had begun publication in 1841, brought him to the attention of the curators of Kew Gardens. So when he went to London in 1844, he was not entirely unknown. He still wanted to go to South America, but there seemed no way to acquire the necessary funds. Sir William Hooker, at Kew Gardens, sought for him the curatorship of some colonial botanical garden, but this plan was dropped as "uncertain of attainment." Hooker suggested Spain, botanically the least known of European countries. At the moment the government of Isabella II was so torn with revolution that it would not be safe to travel there, but as soon as matters quieted down — well, he would try to arrange things. And what about funds? Spruce was mouse-poor. Hooker presented him to George Bentham, the botanical collector who had just come back from the Pyrenees. Bentham suggested that a really good collector like Spruce could easily pay his expenses by the sale of dried plants, well preserved and accurately named, to museums and herbariums.

Spain was not South America, yet at least it was a start. Humboldt, who had started in Spain, ended in America. Then, too, the cold, mist-swept Pyrenees would gratify Spruce's "irresistible inclination to study my beloved mosses." George Bentham became his botanical agent. He undertook to dispose of Spruce's collections as received, and meanwhile advanced him a sum on account. In April 1844, at the age of twenty-seven, Richard Spruce set out for Spain. It was only a roundabout route to South America.

Spain and the Pyrenees held him for two years; he learned to speak Spanish and French; his superb collections, the best-prepared in the history of botany, began to pour into the herbariums; and the illness, the lung, mind, and stomach troubles, disappeared completely. His return in April 1846 found him known and accepted among botanists. He published *Notes on the Botany of the Pyrenees,* and began the outline of an elaborate work, *The Musci and Hepaticæ of the Pyrenees.* Now that he had tasted an explorer-naturalist's life, he could no longer be satisfied with Yorkshire. "I yearn," he wrote to a friend, "to be independent, and I hope the next time I go out it will be to settle in some comfortable office; but I must be contented to wait until some opening occurs, and in the meantime, what my hand has found to do, I will do with all my heart, for my heart is in it. . . ."

His independence came quickly enough, but not precisely the "comfortable office" that he desired. South America was calling.

Spruce had gone to London in 1848 to attend the sale of one Dr. Taylor's books and herbarium (for in those times bird skins and pressed plants were auctioned off as books and furniture are auctioned today). There he met Hooker and Bentham. They spoke of his successful tour of the Pyrenees. "And now what about South America?" asked Bentham. Spruce was all interest. South America? Yes, he could do in the Amazon what he had done in Spain. Collect, and sell the plant sets. Spruce went to the British Museum and looked over the wealth of insects, animals, and birds' skins that Alfred Wallace and Henry Bates were sending back from the Amazon.

Spruce spent the winter of 1848 and the spring of 1849 at Kew Gardens, preparing himself for tropical collecting by studying what material was there. George Bentham agreed to advance the necessary funds and to receive his botanical collections, name the already described species, sort them into their several genera, and send them to the various subscribers in Great Britain.as well as in different parts of Europe. In return for these invaluable services he was to receive the first complete set of the collected plants. Spruce had eleven subscribers to begin with — which meant that he would have to collect eleven specimens of the same plant. But this did not deter him.

At thirty-two, the age at which La Condamine landed in America, and a century to the day after Jean Godin started down the Amazon to begin the woeful odyssey of his wife, Spruce left England. Of the beginning Spruce wrote simply:

"I embarked at Liverpool on the 7th of June, 1849, on board the brig, *Britannia,* Edmund Johnson, commander, with a crew of twelve men. My fellow passengers were Mr. Robert King, a young man who agreed to brave the wilds of the Amazon as my companion and assistant, and Mr. Herbert Wallace, who was going out to join his elder brother. . . ."

On July 12th the *Britannia* made the landfall of Pará. Spruce, as he lay in his hammock on the sailboat *Tres de Junho,* could still recall that day of days. At sunrise they saw low cliffs, like a dense residuum of night; then with the rising sun there appeared on the horizon a long band of glowing saffron; and as they neared the coast a parapet of black filigree, which Spruce's botanical eye knew to be the crowns and fronds of palms, showed itself in rigid silhouette. Then they had entered the mouth of the Amazon and had followed the yellow water for miles until they came to the edge of the forest on the banks of the mightiest river in the world. Spruce had almost swooned with delight at those massive jungles. These were not the forests of England, full-leafed, of dull mid-summer verdure. This was a solid phalanx of trees, uniform, shadowless, without break. The forest poured down to the river's edge; roots of the tall trees were awash in the yellow waters; clumps of palms threw their fronds above the jungle roof. Now the individual trees, featureless and formless from a distance, took on shape. There was a giant silk-cotton tree with roots like the buttresses of a Gothic cathedral; there was a tall Santa Maria with silver-glinted leaves like a mahogany; there were graceful palms everywhere. Vines looped across the warp of the trees, supplying the woof that knitted the whole jungle organism into one great pattern of green and brown. Then the mouth of the river became lost in channels, lagoons, tangling waterways. Canoes shot across the water, small craft with lateen sails passed under the bows of the steamer *Britannia*.

Santa Maria de Belém lay a few miles up the delta on the Pará River. Belém (not Pará, for Grão Pará was the name of the state, not a city) was of striking appearance from the distance. It was hemmed in by the jungle, a dramatic background to that flat congestion of white buildings with their red-tiled roofs. Spruce landed on the mole; "rather paltry," was his opinion of it. He walked along the esplanade shaded by mangoes and strangler-fig trees, past the two-storied buildings, past idle soldiers carelessly carrying their guns in their arms. Negresses lounged by in showy English prints, indolent in movement, but fashioned in tantalizing curves. It had an air, this Belém of Pará, not the staid quiet air of Gansthorpe, but a gaudy, tropical, indolent character — precisely what he had expected. An Indian dragged along a giant turtle by its flipper. A gorgeous red and green parrot screeched, raucous and squawking, at the setting sun. A monkey tried to drag away its heavy chain in front of the offices of the Messrs. Campbell, "colonists of long standing" and friends of naturalists. In went Spruce to present his letters of introduction. A few clerks, immaculate in white, bent over their books; Negroes with kinky hair, and brown-bodied Indians hauled freight in the shadows of the warehouse. Then James Campbell, the elder of the two brothers, burst out of his office, welcomed Spruce to Amazonia, and quickly installed him in his house.

In 1849 great hopes were entertained for Belém. It was the entrepôt of the Amazon, and by all odds should have become a vast emporium for all the wealth of the great river basin. Already, as

Richard Spruce (1817–93), one of the greatest botanical explorers in history. An inscription on this picture reads: "On my 47th birthday, Sept 10 1864."

The Brazilian forest. In a jungle such as this Richard Spruce looked upon the beginning of a jungle three million square miles in extent.

Spruce gathered the plants that festooned the city, there was much talk of what the steamboat would do for Brazil. There was talk of constructing a railway. Both the United States of America and Britain were pressing for the opening of the Amazon to world traffic. Lord Clarendon carried on a long diplomatic correspondence on the matter, but the North Americans, "more tenacious to their projects and less deferential to diplomatic precedent," went to work in a more decided manner. Lieutenants Herndon and Gibbon were deputized by Congress to survey the Amazon, which they did about the time that Spruce arrived in Belém. They followed the upper river in Peru and descended its full length to the sea. By 1851 they returned to Washington, and their two-volume work, *Exploration of the Valley of the Amazon,* was released. "I have no hesitation in saying," thus spoke the authors, "that within 50 years Rio de Janeiro will be a village compared to Pará. Santarem will be the Saint Louis of Brazil, and Manáos its Cincinnati. . . ." These explorers even quoted Byron's verses about the castled crag of Drachenfels, and compared the Amazon to the Rhine.

Richard Spruce heard all this talk, but it impressed him little. He had plants to collect, and all nature was open to him. He collected the gay flowers from the villas embowered with papayas, mangoes, palms, and mimosas. He filled his plant presses with all the botanical novelties that met his eye, and his stomach with the as yet strange and exotic stuff from Brazilian tables. He feasted on bananas, raw from the golden clusters in the market, fried in grease, mashed with sugar. Of this amazing proof of nature's fecundity, like his own countryman Tomlinson, he might have said: "If I could sing, I would sing the Banana. . . . The plantain jets upward with a copious stem, and the fountain returns in broad rippled pennants, falling outwardly, refined to points, when the impulse is lost. A world could not be old on which such a plant grows. It is sure evidence of earth's vitality. To look at it you would not think that growing is a long process, a matter of months and natural difficulties. The plantain is an instant joyous answer to the sun. The midribs of the leaves powerful but resilient, held aloft in generous arches, the broad planes of translucent green substance. . . . It is lush and solid, though its ascent is so aerial and its form is content to the eye. There is no green like that of its leaves except at sea. . . ."

Three months were spent in Pará. Although disclaiming any linguistic ability, Spruce had begun to speak Portuguese with a mastery many of the other English colonists of long residence failed to obtain. He readied himself for the trip up the Amazon. A brig of eighty tons, the *Tres de Junho,* had come down from Santarem with a cargo for the Campbell brothers. Bates and Wallace were stationed at that river city, 475 miles upstream. This seemed a likely place for Spruce's headquarters. He obtained passage, and a letter of credit from Campbell. He changed his five-pound notes into copper money of the country, and then he turned to provisions. Food was a necessary item. He obtained piles of the hard-toasted bread *farinha,* and vast stores of salted *pirarucú* * in large, strong-smelling slabs, which only necessity and much practice could bring one to relish. Eggs, coffee, and a sort of canteen called a *patuabalaio,* an indispensable article at that period for a traveler, completed the equipage. Spruce boarded the *Tres de Junho* on the 10th of October 1849.

As soon as they had passed the wide Bay of Marajo, the trades began to blow and the waves rolled almost as much as in the open sea. The *Tres de Junho* passed into an arm of the great stream, and Spruce found time to brace himself in his hammock and write a note to his friend Bentham:

"We are now at length fairly in the Amazon. Its muddy waters vary from a dull yellow color to that of weak chocolate . . . we must henceforth depend entirely on our sails. We were, however, in only one of the channels or *Paraná-mirís* of the King of Rivers, not exceeding two miles in breadth. . . . Throughout the dry season the easterly wind — a continuation of the trade-wind of the ocean — blows up the Amazon at least for several hours a day and sometimes day and night without remission."

The wind that was blowing Spruce up the Amazon was also blowing him into botanical immortality. He had few predecessors. La Condamine had gathered some plants on the first scientific journey down the Amazon a century before; Humboldt and Bonpland stopped short of the main river on the banks of the upper Río Negro; von Martius and von Spix, who floated to Brazil on the wings of Humboldt's enthusiasm, laid down the first basis of botany in the Amazon, where they remained and collected for three years; Eduard Pöppig, who had worked in Chile and Peru, came down the Amazon collecting here and there; Count François de Castelnau finished his expedition on the Amazon and added somewhat to the pile of known plants. And this was about all. The whole Amazon, botanically speaking, belonged to Richard Spruce.

* An important Amazonian food fish. Specimens have been reported as much as eight feet in length.

The higher he sailed, the more the Amazon became the *Parand-tinga*, the King of Waters. Nowhere in the whole world was there anything comparable to it. It was not a river, it was a congress of rivers that drained over two and a half million square miles of land. Compared with it, the rivers of Europe were gutter trickles. Commercially the Amazon was dead; culturally it was nothing. The Indians had moved inland, the *mamelucos* (half-castes) had taken up white man's ways, and the missionaries had lost their force. Once the whole Amazon had been controlled by the God-intoxicated padres; now it hung midway between exploitation and apathy. A new group of men were coming to take the padres' place — the naturalist-explorers.

They were precursors of big business.

CHAPTER XXV
The Great Mother Forest

To Richard Spruce the Amazon appeared as a monstrous tree. Its tributaries, its streams, its brooks were the boughs; its ascending and spreading ramifications were the twigs, the branches. His mind saw that dark region where the river-branches lost themselves as an impenetrable density of green. One enters these green mansions and vanishes; and vanish Spruce temporarily did, on the edge of a primeval forest just below Santarem.

"There were enormous trees," he wrote, "crowned with magnificent foliage, decked with fantastic parasites, hung over with lianas which varied in thickness from slender threads to huge, python-like masses, rounded, flattened, twisted with the regularity of a cable. . . . Fancy if you can," ran his letter home, "two million square miles of forest. . . . The largest river in the world flows through the largest forest. . . . Here our grasses are bamboos, sixty or more feet high. . . . Our milkworts are stout woody twiners, ascending to the highest top of trees. . . . Instead of your Periwinkles, we have here handsome trees exuding . . . a most deadly poison. Violets are the size of apple trees. . . . Daisies, born on trees like Alders."

Richard Spruce rubbed his hands over all this botanical loot. Yet how was he to obtain this treasure? To identify the plant he must have leaves, fruits, and blossoms. And these were, as far as he was concerned, heaven-high and out of reach.

"Both flowers and fruits were for a long time sour grapes to me. Like Humboldt, I was at first disappointed in not finding some agile and willing Indians to run like cats or monkeys up the tree for me. . . . At length the conviction was forced upon me that the best, and sometimes the only way to obtain the flowers and fruits was to cut down the tree: but it was long before I could overcome a feeling of compunction at having to destroy a magnificent tree, perhaps centuries old, merely for the sake of gathering flowers."

Spruce readily comprehended that the "natives themselves think no more of destroying the noblest trees, when they stand in their way, than we the vilest weeds . . . a single tree cut down is no more missed than when one pulls up a stalk of groundsel . . . in any English corn field." And the Indians were filled with astonishment when Spruce told them that in his country most of the forest had to be planted.

"Trees planted? Why, here," said they, "when one wants to plant a tree, one must first cut down a dozen to make room for it."

". . . Thus I reconciled myself to the commission of an act whose apparent vandalism was, or seemed to be, counterbalanced by its necessity and utility. In the same way I suppose a zoologist stifles his qualms of conscience at killing a noble bird or quadruped merely for the sake of its skin and bones. I do not know whether Alexanders and Napoleons made use of any such process of reasoning to justify to themselves the waste of human life entailed in their victories; but if the bodies of the slain at Arbela or Austerlitz could have been collected and preserved — stuffed and set up in attitudes of mortal agony — under cases in one vast museum, what instructive specimens they would have been of the fruits of war."

Hours might be spent in felling a single tree. The crashing giant then brought down others in the fall, along with a tousled head of epiphytes and parasites. Orchids were plentiful; so were the giant cyclanthuses with their enormously broad bifid and fan-shaped leaves. Lianas, which were strung from tree to tree (*sipos*, in the Tupi language), came down with the fallen masses, dragging the parasites down like bell-ropes. Spruce gathered the many species that festooned a single tree. There was the sarsaparilla, a liana important in the commerce of his time; there was the *yurupari-pina*, the devil's fish-hooks, with broad, sharp thorns that could wound a man severely. Brown, earth-colored termites' nests would tumble down with the trees. Ants rained on his head. The falling of a tree began a virtual pandemonium in the jungle. The monkeys would first scream and run, then return to scold. Green and red parrots screeched; toucans with gaudy-colored harlequin beaks would fly down to investigate all this disturbance.

The jungle was really never still. Cicadas hammered away until the jungle pulsed with sound. Frogs joined in with a rapidly beating "peng, peng, peng," sounding to Spruce as if he were in the midst of a boiler factory. The air seemed to tremble in the rhythmic clangor. Spruce hated to leave this magical forest, but the captain was impatient. He reluctantly climbed aboard. The *Tres de Junho* plowed on up the Amazon.

Parrots squawking in the quiet air announced the dawn. An alligator floated by, a flock of giant jabiru storks flew over low enough for an Indian on the *Tres de Junho* to level his bow at them. A strip of white beach came into view, then some sharp hills filigreed with palms, and then immediately below it a line of houses. This was Santarem. Here the Río Tapajoz, enormous and black, entered the Amazon from the south and its inky waters sharply contrasted with the yellowish main stream. Fully thirty miles wide at this spot, the Amazon was an immensity of water, a mobile plain of muddied silver. It looked every inch what the natives called it, the Ocean-river; and indeed it is generally supposed now that the Amazon, at a time too distant for computation, was in fact a shallow sea separating the Andes, the highlands of central Brazil, and the mountains of Guiana. The action of rain, the flowing rivers from these highlands, gradually filled up the shallow sea with silt, and this gave rise to the gigantic, low-lying jungle whose secrets Richard Spruce was to lay bare in his seventeen years' sojourn.

The *Tres de Junho* maneuvered to miss an acre-wide floating island, tacked, filled its sails with the heavy persistent breeze of the *vento geral*, and so, within seventeen days to the hour, brought Spruce to Santarem.

Captain Hislop waited for him under a statuesque silk-cotton tree on the bank. Hislop, ruddy and sturdy, monstrously tall alongside the Indians, shared the shade with a covey of storks, some cattle, and a row of chocolate-colored babies that rested astride the hips of their Indian mothers, naked save for a string of beads.

This man was the patriarch of Santarem. Despite the fact that he spoke Portuguese in a booming voice, with an accent too Scottish to be fully understood, he had built up an extensive trade in diamonds, gold-dust, rubber, and tonga beans that had reached up to Cuyaba, the capital of the mountainous province of the Matto Grosso. After forty-five years he had given up that vast trade, "having suffered serious losses," as he explained, "from the roguery of his agent and the failure of his creditors." Now he dealt only with Pará.

Hislop found Spruce a house — a wattle-and-daub affair, with palm-plaited roof, a single room, a floor of tile ("instead of mother earth, as in the houses of inferior class") and no single article of furniture. Hislop dug up a few chairs and sent over some planks, from which, with a pile of bricks, Spruce and his assistant, Robert King, extemporized a table on which to put their plants. Slaves were sent to do their cooking, and other English residents — Mr. Jeffries and Mr. Golding — lent further articles. Within a few hours Spruce was ready for his assault on the jungles of Santarem.

The night of their arrival Hislop had the whole English colony over for dinner. Alfred Wallace had returned from collecting, bringing his friend and co-explorer, the quiet, unobtrusive Henry Bates. Jeffries and Golding arrived. And Hislop opened the brandy bottles he kept for such occasions.

Captain Hislop was a true Chesterfieldian, who held that his dinner guests "should not fall below the number of the graces nor exceed that of the muses." From the opening of the first bottle, through the courses of farinha, fish, and roasted manatee flesh, he held the floor. He was an avid reader of newspapers, of which he kept great moldy files, swarming with spiders, wasps, and termites. He discoursed on the past with the same interest as the present, mixing the first Napoleon with Napoleon III, who had just seized France's government in a *coup d'état*. It made no difference, he said, how he read the papers, whether they were ten years old or only six months. Of books he had read but two, Volney's *Ruins of Empires* and the Bible, and by "combining their contents, he had framed for himself a creed of very motley complexion." If the port lasted long enough, he would eventually get to the subject of Moses. . . . Henry Bates, who had heard this before, busied himself in collecting the insects that poured in, attracted by the kerosene lamps. Winged ants, flying termites, night cicadas, mayflies, mosquitoes fell in myriads about the light, and all the taciturn bespectacled Bates had to do was to sweep them into his collection-box.

Bates was twenty-three years old when he came to the Amazon with Wallace. He had been there two years now and was destined to remain nine more. He had found the Amazon an Elysium for the entomologist. He collected 14,000 different species of insects, of which 8,000 were new to science. Like Wallace and Spruce, he was a superb self-taught naturalist. By patient collecting and observation, he became the discoverer of protective mimicry. And long before Darwin had published his *Origin of Species*, Bates had written: "Nature writes on a tablet the story of modification of the species."

Self-effacing, modest to a fault, Bates was primarily an entomologist. Still, his interests were broad enough to include birds, reptiles, marmosets, turtles. "His eyes," as Cutright puts it, "were clear, his brain was active and his pen was graphic," but he did not make extensive journeys, and he kept to certain defined areas. Urged on by Charles Darwin on his return to England, he wrote *The Naturalist on the River Amazon*, which described the region more fully, more accurately, more completely than any book before it. It became, for a while, the guide-book for those who would exploit the riches of the Amazon. But it was Alfred Wallace and Richard Spruce who found an immediate interest in each other. Their friendship was to last over half a century, and Wallace, in the ebb-tide of his life, was to take over the editorship of Spruce's journals.

Wallace was younger than Spruce by some seven years. He had been born at Usk, Monmouthshire, in 1823, and like his illustrious South American predecessor Humboldt he lived ninety years. His early life paralleled that of Richard Spruce. He was interested in botany, he was a self-taught naturalist, and he taught school. He had met Henry Bates, and their common interest, stimulated by reading Darwin and Humboldt, led to the formation of plans to visit South America. Wallace was twenty-five years old when he landed in Brazil. His love of the unknown, his insistence on covering a great deal of ground, brought him far up the Río Negro, where the privations of an explorer's existence brought about a general deterioration of his health. He remained only four years on the Amazon. Ill with malaria and intestinal difficulties, he took ship to England only to meet misfortune and tragedy. Seven hundred miles from Bermuda his ship took fire; he was saved only by mere chance; his entire collection, formed in those four years of tireless effort, perished in the flames that enveloped the steamer *Helen.*

In 1853 Wallace published *A Narrative of Travels on the Amazon and Río Negro,* the best book on the country before Bates published his own. Wallace's later career took him to Asia, and he belongs not to South America, but to Malaya, Celebes, and Timor.

Captain Hislop was still holding forth when the explorers, heady with port, stumbled home through the still Santarem night.

Spruce spent a whole year in the vicinity of Santarem. It was a good collecting station. As it was a center of river traffic (despite the fact that it was dismal and forsaken), Spruce could get paper which he needed for pressing his plants. Then, too, when he had got sufficient plants together, he could send them down to the Campbells in Pará, who acted as his shipping agents. The year in Santarem gave him the feel of the land. His Portuguese improved, he broadened his vocabulary of *Tupi-Guaraní,* an important Indian tongue on the whole Amazon. And he had an unusual opportunity to reap a cross-section of Amazonian plants. Instead of the jungle-clad plains and artificial pastures which were carved out of the jungle at Pará, Spruce found at Santarem natural undulating savannas, sloping gently upwards from the blue-black waters of the Río Tapajoz.

Every morning, after a cup of black coffee prepared by a Negro slave, he and young Robert King, with a native enticed from his hammock, loaded themselves down with plant presses and took to collecting. By following Igarapé d'Irurá, a brook of clear water which took its rise in the 600-foot-high hills back of the town, they reached their collecting-grounds. Almost all the plants were new to science, and those that were not had to be collected again so as to give a rounded picture of the vegetation of the Amazon. Spruce began by selecting what in his mind represented a typical ecological zone of the region. He collected all flowering or fruiting plants within that zone. Then, when this had been in a sense exhausted, he would select the important trees and plants from a wider range.

Cashew trees were exceedingly abundant. Their leaves were of a delicate red-brown, garnished with numerous pear-like yellow and red fruits, tipped with kidney-shaped nuts. There were palms of all descriptions, tall, squat, top-heavy. There was a seemingly endless parade of large trees: wild cacaos; jacarandas, which yielded a wood of a fine, dark color; Brazil-nut trees with three-cornered, hard-shelled nuts contained in a large pot-like shell . . . all gave their leaves, their blossoms, their fruits, and their life history to the indefatigable labors of Richard Spruce.

Nor were the smaller things neglected. Ferns grew in bewildering succession, some so minute that they could hardly be discerned, others so tall that they became trees. He found an endless parade of parasites and epiphytes adhering to the trees that his Indians felled, and wherever the soil was turfy from the incessant rains, he found mosses and lichens in cushion-like patches beneath the towering jungle monarchs.

Richard Spruce was a careful botanist. Each tree had a name given to it by the Indians, who had centuries-old acquaintance with it; these names he carefully recorded. If the Indians indicated that a tree was used for medicinal purposes, Spruce gathered the bark, the rind, the leaves, or the fruits, made a concoction, and tried it on himself. If he deemed it important, he sent all the material back to the pharmacists of Kew for examination. Thus, by ferreting out such plants, identifying them with both scientific and native names, and testing their therapeutical efficacy, the explorer-scientists provided the agents of business with a guidebook to the riches of the Amazon.

The dry season ended in January. Rain confined Spruce more and more to his house in Santarem. He got to know most of the 2,000 people, white, black, red, and brown, that filled its three streets and five hundred dwellings. Santarem was, after Pará, the most important trading center on the Amazon, even though jaguars hunted where the town ended. If a wattle-and-daub village of 2,000 souls, with a single two-tower church, was considered a metropolis, one can picture how thinly populated was the rest of the great Amazon territory. In the whole of this immense realm there were scarcely more than 800,000 inhabitants, including all the Indian tribes lost in the depths of the vast mother forest. Trade was desultory and casual. Cacao beans and cattle were the most important products. There was some commerce in nuts and smoked rubber. A gold boom brought in a sudden influx of gold-diggers from California and Australia, but these soon left their grub-stakes in Santarem and their bones, picked white, in the jungle. Trade moved as fast as paddlers could negotiate the river's thousand-mile distances and four-knot current. Flat-bottomed, slow, forty-ton sailing craft were the link between the distant river-towns and Pará. And this was the world's mightiest river!

Nobody at Santarem could recollect the Amazon and Tapajoz rising as rapidly as they did in 1850. Usually the rivers attained their maximum height in June; this year it was in April. Great masses of grass islands filled the river, sure sign the water was rising. Everything became flooded. In two days the Amazon rose forty feet. Water spread itself for four hundred miles on either side of the main channels. Cows were flooded out of their pastures; manioc plantations were inundated; vast fields of food crops were covered by water. And there was a flood of alligators, swept down from their up-river haunts in bewildering thousands. Man and beast alike sought refuge, oft-times in the same house, from the relentless, turgid ocean-river. Then, as the Amazon began to recede, a pestilence struck at the alligators, a sort of murrain that seemed to kill them overnight. Thousands of them died. Night and day there was an endless parade of dead alligators, belly upward, floating downstream. Santarem being a high point, they collected on its banks. The stench of their decomposing carcasses was so overpowering that the whole countryside — *mamelucos,* Indians, Englishmen, Portuguese — was employed for weeks towing them down to a spot far enough away for the town to escape the gagging odors of their putrescence.

No sooner were the alligators disposed of, and Spruce's specimens sent off, than they were besieged with another calamity. Yellow fever broke out in Pará. Half of the population was struck down with it in a single fortnight. Its effects were devastating. The British Consul was its first victim; the brother of Wallace another. All traffic was suspended between the Lower Amazon and Santarem. The alarm of the up-river inhabitants bordered on mass hysteria. "The good people of Santarem," Spruce remembered, "were not ordinarily remarkable for attention to religious observances, except at Christmas, when there is a pious display of rockets, fire-crackers and balloons, and processions of a very dramatic character, but when we were in daily fear of the dreaded fever reaching us, we had vespers every night . . . those families who were happy enough to possess a rude daub of some saint assembled round it on their knees at stated times and recited a number of prayers taken *ad libitum* from the breviary. . . ."

Field pieces were dragged through the streets and fired at intervals to clear the atmosphere of the dreaded *pesta*. Lumps of odoriferous white pitch were fastened on poles, stuck up at street crossings, and set afire at sundown, illuminating the whole town while emitting an agreeable perfume. While the city fathers and native witch-doctors admitted that all this was excellent for exorcizing the *pesta*, the most efficacious preventive of all consisted in "kissing a small wooden figure of São Sebastián, which was nightly exposed at the foot of the altar." Every man, woman, and child paid homage, except Richard Spruce. His omission did not fail to cause remark, "but as I contributed my mite towards the expenses of the feast, my crime was considered venial."

Fortunately the yellow fever did not reach Santarem.

Between floods Spruce was able to collect, for with the inception of the rainy season an entirely new series of flowering plants had come into bloom. While collecting these Spruce met with bands of rubber-gatherers, *seringueros* they called themselves. Working in pairs, the seringueros erected a small rancho (a lean-to of palm leaves) in which their staples of *farinha* in the form of tasteless hardtack, salted fish, and a mosquito net were stored. They then scoured the country for rubber trees. Spruce watched them at their work. He saw them tap the hevea trees with a series of deep chevrons cut into the bark. From these wounds a heavy white viscous milk dripped down into a cup placed to receive it. Smeared over wooden paddles, the rubber was smoked into large, black balls and sent down to Pará.

Santarem was to occupy a singular spot in the sordid, brutal history of rubber; for in this ancient settlement, surrounded with rubber-yielding trees, Spruce's countryman Henry A. Wickham was to make his famous "seed-snatch." Sir William Hooker of Kew Gardens, had approached Richard Spruce, as early as 1850, with the project of obtaining rubber seedlings. Spruce essayed it, but without adequate transportation the task was impossible. He did, however, make a careful study of all rubber-yielding trees, and this invaluable information went back to Kew Gardens, which acted as the official adviser to the government on botanical matters. Brazil, naturally, opposed the taking out of rubber plants. Henry Wickham, however, settled at Santarem twenty years after Spruce, used the data provided by him, gathered hevea rubber seeds, raised them to seedlings, and in 1872 got thousands of them aboard a steamer anchored at Santarem for just that purpose. Down went the rubber seedlings past the Brazilians who had fought by every means they knew to keep rubber an Amazon monopoly, down to the open sea, to Kew, to India, to Singapore, to Malaya. A whole industry, a whole culture, a whole future were taken bodily from Amazonia. The first explorer to open the Americas, La Condamine, called attention to rubber in Europe; and Spruce, a century later, laid the pattern in Santarem for its transference to another sphere. That this had not been his intention is apparent in what he wrote:

". . . How often have I regretted that England did not possess the magnificent Amazon valley instead of India! If that booby King James II, instead of putting Raleigh in prison and finally cutting off his head had persevered in supplying him ships, money and men until he had formed a permanent establishment on one of the great American rivers, I have no doubt but that the whole American continent would have been at this moment in the hands of the English race."

On the 8th of October 1850, in a boat belonging to Frenchmen long settled on the Amazon, Richard Spruce started on his way upward to Manáos.

CHAPTER XXVI
The Land of the Amazons

S PRUCE LAY READING.

The yellow flame of the manatee-oil lamp flickered gently in the breeze while myriads of fireflies, their tiny yellow and blue lights glowing with puzzling inconstancy, helped to light up the water-stained pages of the narrative of Gaspar de Carvajal. Spruce had put off reading this account of the thrilling discovery of the Amazon River by Francisco de Orellana until he had come to this spot. Now his boat lay anchored at the mouth of the Río Trombetas, at the exact place where Orellana had insisted that he was attacked by Amazons, women warriors who fought more fiercely than men.

Spruce raised his head from the book, wiped from his eyes the tears brought on by the strain, and looked out on the vague, ghostly shapes of night. At the moment all was hushed. Then the silence was shattered, the very night trembled in the rhythmic throb of the strumming cicadas. From the river came the throaty, piglike grunts of alligators which floated motionlessly about the boat. A year before, the proximity of alligators would have thrown Spruce into an emotional turmoil; now they meant no more to him than pigs running about the moors of his native Yorkshire. He turned back to the page.

The history of the Amazon's discovery was well remembered. After Cuzco had fallen to the condottieri of Pizarro, the Spaniards had marched on Quito and had added that ancient Indian capital to their list of conquests. It came to them, in 1540, that eastward in the jungles lay a region filled with cinnamon trees. Gonzalo Pizarro, the brother of the conquistador, set out for the "Land of Cinnamon" with an immense concourse of Spaniards, Indians, and live animals driven before them. The Indians melted away in the jungle. They were set upon by head-hunters. Disease and hunger took a dreadful toll. They did find trees that bore a sort of cinnamon bark, but in such trifling quantities as not to seem worthy even of mention. Beyond the little settlement that they carved out of the jungle, to which they gave the name of Canelos (that is, Cinnamon), they came upon a huge serpentining yellow-watered river called the Napo. Where did this river lead? They fell to, these invincible men, and built a fair-sized brigantine on its banks. Francisco de Orellana, second in command to Pizarro, was to sail a short distance in search of food, and to return when it was found. But once that craft shot out into the waters flowing at six knots the hour, there was no turning back. Orellana left Pizarro and his ragged, half-starved followers on the banks of the Río Napo and sailed down the entire length of the monstrous river called the Amazon.

Now Spruce came to the part for which he was searching. The brigantine came down, down, down. At last it anchored at this precise spot on the Río Trombetas. The Indians fought more fiercely than ever. Why? Hear Padre Carvajal, chronicler of the voyage:

"I want it to be known what the reason was why these Indians defended themselves in this manner. It must be explained that they are the subjects of and tributaries to the *Amazons;* and when our coming was known to them, they went to them to ask help, and there came as many as ten or twelve of them, for we ourselves saw these women who were there fighting in front of all the Indians as women captains, and these fought so courageously that the Indian men did not dare to turn their backs and anyone who did turn his back they killed with clubs right there before us. . . . These women are very white and tall and have hair very long and braided and wound about the head . . . they are very robust and go naked save that their privy parts are covered; with their bows and arrows in their hands doing as much fighting as ten Indian men. . . ."

This, then, was the passage in the chronicle that gave the river its name. But were they really Amazons? Spruce knocked a few mouse-size cockroaches off of his provisional table, put his book on it, and thought out the matter. He examined in his own mind all the historical evidence. With his extensive knowledge of Amazonian vegetation, he could identify the areas to which old Carvajal referred. He wrote that two or three days after their fight with the Amazons "he came to a pleasant country where there were Evergreen-oaks and Cork-Trees." Well, as Santarem was the only spot that corresponded to that, and the tree called "cork" grew only in that region, then the Río Trombetas was the region of the Amazons. But who were these Amazons? They were, for one thing, the most sensational of Orellana's discoveries. A historically minded Bishop in the Antilles had been quick to ask: "Did these Amazons cut off their right breasts so as to use the bow more easily?" This was an important point. For in ancient times the Greeks fought against female warriors repeatedly. Achilles slew their Queen, Penthesileia, when they came to the aid of the besieged Trojans. Poor Orellana was bewildered by such learning. He merely reported his discovery of the Amazons at court.

Strangely, he was disbelieved. The Spaniards, who had believed in every conceivable fantasy, doubted Orellana.

Spruce rocked in the waters where the Amazon got its name and mused on the whole episode. "Now Orellana has been much ridiculed and called all sorts of names by people who have never taken the trouble to read his original reports to Emperor Charles V. . . ." It was also true that the Spaniards sailing down the great body of the ocean-river had heard about the mysterious Amazons long before reaching them.

Spruce in his own careful way began to draft the first part of an article, which was never printed until it appeared in his journal.

"The voyagers heard rumors of the Amazons' existence long before reaching them. An Indian chief on the Napo called the Amazons *Coniapuyara*, the masterful women, the old Indian went into some detail about them, but Orellana lacked a good understanding of the language and let the matter go by until their brigantine reached the río Trombetas, about 600 miles from the mouth of the river. . . . There they were attacked by Indians led by the women. The Amazons were tall, fair, robust, naked except for skins about their loins. The bow and arrow in their hands they wielded with deadly accuracy."

This was all that Orellana professed to see with his own eyes. It was not true that Orellana had mistaken men for women because they were long-haired. He had lived for two years among the Indians of the Upper Amazon — Jivaros, Zaparos, Huambizas — where all the males wore their hair waist-long and were attired in knee-length skirts. Then, too, all the fifty persons who followed Orellana on that extraordinary voyage appeared at court in the presence of Carlos V. Although all of them were unfavorably disposed toward Orellana, all affirmed his statement: they were attacked by Indians led by Amazons. "Besides," Spruce said half-aloud, "it is incredible that fifty persons, and amongst them a religious priest, should agree in guaranteeing the truth of a lie, especially when nothing was to be gained by it."

Spruce was surprised to find that all the famous authorities on the Americas — including La Condamine and Humboldt — agreed that the Amazon tradition had been based on fact. Most of the missionaries of the eighteenth century testified to the same tradition. It was no uncommon thing for Indians, in confession, to admit having visited periodically the "women living alone." The tradition could be summed up in the words of an old Indian who lived in the village of Yameos: In respect to the combat of Spaniards with warlike women, no one among the Indians doubted it. For who did not know of the Amazons? This old Indian had heard his forefathers say that, after the coming of white men, the Amazons retired from their villages near the Trombetas and the lower river, to a place on the Río Negro; moreover, that these Amazon villages still existed. Many an Indian, long from home, confessed that he had spent several months among the warrior women. The Amazons would meet the invited Indian at a place previously agreed upon, go through the prescribed love-siege, then dismiss him with presents of gold and green stones. He carried back the male children who had reached the age of three. The female children were retained to be brought up in the Amazonian tradition.

Of course the green stones that the Indians hung about their necks as amulets were famous in history. They were known for a long time as Amazon stones. In Spruce's time they had wholly disappeared, and search as he would, he found no Indians wearing them. La Condamine had said that at Santarem he found them being worn. Those men who possessed them said that they were the gifts of the Amazons, a talisman of restless nights spent among the "women without men." They were thought to possess magical properties. Europeans bought them up as fast as they appeared. Raleigh spoke of Indians on the Orinoco having "chiefly a kinde of greene stones, which the Spaniards called *Piedras Hijadas* which we use for spleene stones, and for the disease of the stone we also esteeme them; of these I saw divers in Guaiana and commonly every king or Casique hath one. . . ." Now the stones had disappeared, but the tradition of the Amazons lingered on. Like the story of El Dorado, the Amazon legend must be based on fact.

Richard Spruce could hear the water of the Amazon lapping against the sides of his *igarité*. Now the night became increasingly vocal. The cicadas shrilled. The frogs croaked with the deafening clangor of an iron-foundry. Now came the thin whine of mosquitoes, and Spruce, finding his hammock occupied by a snoring, pot-gutted Indian, picked up a sheet and wrapped it about himself. Swathed like a mummy, he sought for sleep. And in the morning the boat lifted anchor and continued up the river.

"It took us days to reach Villa Nova from Obidos, although the distance is only 95 miles . . . it was very slow and very hard for a couple of paddles to make headway in our heavy craft against the current of the Amazon. . . ."

Villa Nova, to which they came on Christmas Eve, was a little village of leaf huts. Chocolate-brown babies playing on the white beach, a make-shift church surrounded by the glistening brown bodies of the natives — that was Villa Nova. It had been a thriving community in the time of the Jesuit occupation, although the Indians did not care very much for that spiritual succor. The neophytes revolted against their padres, burnt the houses, razed the church, and buried the church bells. Local tradition had it that these buried bells would be heard ringing on Christmas Eve. This was revealed to Spruce by a half-caste sailor, a *mameluco*, who kept as much to the demijohn of foul-smelling *cachaca* as he did to his paddles. He was a bit of a philosopher in his way and used to amuse Spruce with his cynical views of life.

It was a pleasure to have made the landfall of this village, for one comes upon settlements in the Amazon as a ship at sea onto islands. There Spruce met Padre Torquato, an amiable, good-looking young priest, his cheeks still retaining a Portuguese bloom. He was the very soul of amiability. Under his arm he carried a translation of *Uncle Tom's Cabin* and he spoke with some heat about the "sordid slave problem in the United States." Padre Torquato had acquired great fame as a story-teller; he had been the amiable guide of Prince Adalbert of Prussia, who, acting on Humboldt's suggestion, had made a royal expedition to Brazil, along with Count Bismarck and Count Oriola, in the years 1842-3. The book that resulted, *Voyage to the Xingu*, gave voice to the stories told by this same priest. "We found him," Spruce remembered, "a young man — certainly under forty — exceedingly courteous in his manners, and delightfully wonderful to hear, and therefore not unlikely to be led into the relation of marvelous tales as true, although himself sceptical respecting them." But it was good to talk to one who had seen the outside world and who had been in his time well read. It was over a year since Spruce had arrived on the Amazon, his reading matter had given out, Captain Hislop's papers were months old, and there was only a pitiful handful of literature in Portuguese. The whole white population seemed to be on the very edge of illiteracy, although when they could find something to read, they lapped it up eagerly. Padre Torquato was helpfulness itself. He gave Richard Spruce quantities of information regarding the people, the geography, and the local traditions of the river.

They were now about halfway between Pará and Manáos, and by good luck and with good wind they should be at Manáos in two weeks. Quantities of dried fish and large *farinha* cakes were tumbled aboard the *igarité*. To replace two Indians who had decamped from the boat — along with several articles of the captain's and Spruce's — they secured several black-thatched natives, who took their turns paddling, sleeping, and eating on the narrow, crowded deck of the twenty-five-foot vessel. There was nothing else to do but to fall back on the natives for conversation. Spruce, being an up-country man, was sympathetic. The natives seemed to find him a man of parts, who had, notwithstanding, a charmingly simple approach to life. They often took him into their confidence. Many nights were spent talking of the world outside. The natives had no idea of any country outside of the Amazon, nor, in fact, of any habitable country save a land bordering a navigable river. Often he was asked the same insistent question: "Is the river of your country large?"

Spruce took infinite pains to describe to them the ocean, a raging body of water several times as wide as the Amazon is long. He tried to explain its immense extent, its fathomless depth, how long it took to cross. The Indians gasped in astonishment; there were grunts from every part of the boat. They turned to each other in wonder and awe. "It is the river of his land! What is this little river of ours," said one, pointing to the Amazon, "compared to *that!*" Spruce gave up.

Yet he liked the simple natives, the ones still untouched by the "shirt." For the shirt had become a symbol in Amazonia. The whites seemed to make an absolute distinction between the Indian who wore a shirt and the one who went naked. A native could not be a Christian in his own clothes; no Christian woman would show her breasts. The shirt brought about vast changes in psychology. "God save me from the Indians with shirts," was Spruce's remark, which became a classic on the Amazon.

Fortunately the shirts became less frequent as they ascended. Numerous rivers now poured in their waters; on their right, fifty miles below Manáos, they passed the Río Madeira. Here the trees reach their greatest heights; here the jungles, larger than at any other place on the Amazon, take the name *caa-apóam,* the great woods. The great trunks crowd together until there seems not another foot in which a tree could root.

Then they came upon the Río Negro. The change from the yellow water of the Amazon to the dark water of the Negro was very abrupt. When seen from above, the Negro looks as black as ink; the stones or mud on the bottom appear red. But when Spruce put the water into glass, it was of a pale amber color and quite free from sediment. It was a wild scene as these two rivers came together. Spruce climbed a hill and looked down upon the junction. Nothing was to be seen but jungles, water, and sky, "the two former in equal proportions — lakes, channels, and islands, stretching away. . . . It is impossible to behold such immense masses of water in the center of a vast continent, rolling onwards toward the ocean, without feeling the highest admiration, and, when viewed under the setting sun and afterwards the descending and deepening gloom blends all into an indistinguishable mass, though the tumult of the contending waters is still distinctly audible, I felt it difficult to tear myself from the spot."

Near this wild spot was the little village of Lagos, where the whites and the half-castes, beshirted as Christian custom demanded, were going through all the urban niceties of a European city. In this small wattle-and-daub settlement the Brazilians were the "greatest sticklers of etiquette and customs on the face of the earth." Under the mercury-boiling sun they would make their way to church under the weight of black coats and hats. Spruce was there when the festival of Saint John came upon them. The whole Amazon stops still for this. The whites and the half-castes elaborate great festivals. The Indians, neither knowing nor caring why, buy white man's brew and drink themselves into a stupor from which they do not emerge for a fortnight.

It was dark when the festival began. Ancient custom decreed that a "governer (*Juiz*) and a governess (*Juiza*) be elected as rulers of the feast," upon which Spruce sagely observes "that the Juiz is chosen by the weight of his purse and the Juiza by the amount of her personal attractions." The distance to the shrine was a league. As usual Spruce and his host traveled in the carriage of the Amazon — a canoe. They threaded their way through the inundated forest, where tall buttressed roots stood sentinel. As they approached they could see the sparkling shrine. The reflected lights danced on the waters. The canoe ahead of them arrived in a blaze of light, from lamps of orange-skins filled with turtle oil. The canoe then stopped in the middle of the canal, and one by one the tiny lamps were set afloat, forming a long line of fire. The rapid current bore them swiftly away toward the Amazon.

As soon as they landed they were engulfed in the swarming mass of people. Rockets spluttered into the air; blunderbusses were shot off; coarse-voiced choristers, to the accompaniment of a badly strung guitar, two-holed flutes, tambourines, and an enormous booming drum, churned the idyllic night with ear-splitting cacophony. They were led to the altar, where the good people arranged themselves in a semicircle about the saint. Vespers sung and Saint John sufficiently adored, they repaired to another mud-floored room, where they were given some dulce made from the papaya, and a tapioca biscuit. Rum followed, more freely.

The way was cleared for dancing, and soon, with the concerted noise of the guitar, the drums and the tambourines, began the *contradanças Inglezas*. Richard Spruce had no idea of joining them, but the Juiz came up to him, led him to the Juiza, and suggested that he dance with her. He recalled later that when he saw "it was intended to do me honor and that I should be accounted proud if I refused, I led the lady out, first casting off my shoes in order to be on terms of equality with the rest of the performers. We got through the dance triumphantly, and at its close there was a general *viva* and clapping of hands for the 'good white man who did not despise other people's customs!' Once in for it, I danced all night."

Nothing gives the picture of Spruce so faithfully as his kicking off his shoes and putting himself on equal terms with others. This was the character that made possible the opening of the green world of the Amazon. Able to move in all strata of society, through the heart of the dreaded jungles, into the lairs of head-hunters and serpents, collecting, inquiring, note-taking, without creating enemies anywhere — that was Richard Spruce.

The jungles about Manáos were wonderful collecting regions. Spruce's diary shows how systematically and continuously he explored the country. He adopted a botanical routine — one day he collected, the next was given to preparing, drying, describing, and cataloguing his specimens. Every road, every swamp, every path, clearing, fazenda within walk, ride, or paddle was visited; the plants gathered, collected, labeled, and described in Spruce's neat, well-formed handwriting. The results of this assiduous work were astounding. In the first year and a half he had explored the rivers of the Lower Amazon, mapped them, described their flora, and meanwhile collected 1,100 species of plants. Within six months more he had raised that figure to 2,000. And each one of these 2,000 plants was prepared in sets of twenty. Never had any botanist collected so well and so enormously. His friends in England were more than pleased. The gardens at Kew were being enriched as never before. Museums all over Europe were asking for his collections. The twenty sets were raised to thirty. It meant more work for Spruce, but it meant also more sales and a little more money with which to make this life less hard. With the plants he sent down the river to Pará went a note to his friend George Bentham: ". . . We had a miserable voyage of 63 days from Santarem . . . now I have lost an entire summer. . . . I propose making Manáos my headquarters until the commencement of the dry season, when, if it pleases God, I will penetrate up the Río Orinoco into the Terra Humboldtiana and rifle the spoils of the Cerra Duida. . . ."

The portage of a canoe over the rapids of the Amazon. A contemporary lithograph showing travel in South America during the eighteenth century. Spruce traveled in an open canoe over 18,000 miles of waterways.

Passage up the Amazon as pictured by an artist contemporary with Richard Spruce. Before the introduction of steam this was the typical method of travel. Note the large earthen jug. This contains a fermented drink made from the masticated fibers of manioc roots. Without it no Indian travels.

CHAPTER XXVII
In Humboldt's Country

RICHARD SPRUCE looked upon the ink-black waters of the Río Negro as upon the promised land. No botanist had yet set foot in that green Eden. Alfred Wallace was up there, swallowed in its green immensity, a thousand miles in the interior of the *Alto Orinoco*. Wallace had written glowing reports about the richness of the plants that festooned the dark rivers and spotted the inundated savannas, and this quickened Spruce's interest. During the eleven months that he had made Manáos his headquarters he scarcely could wait for the day when he would complete his arrangements to assault the Upper Orinoco. One could not hurry such an expedition as this. Spruce knew that once he felt the environs of Manáos he would be on his own. He must have his own boat, he must command his own men, he must carry all his provisions, he could count on finding nothing. His own experience suggested it; Wallace confirmed it. In a letter to Bentham that accompanied some 10,000 specimens, he wrote:

"April 1, 1851: I am trying to procure a boat and crew. . . . April 15th: I have now purchased a boat. . . . It is six tons burthen and has a *tolda da popa* — poop cabin — convenient for keeping my goods dry. . . . November 7th: I am hard at work packing up my collections for you and purchasing trade goods for the voyage. It is no use taking money up the Amazon. . . . I am laying out my whole fortune in prints, and other fabrics of cotton, axes, cutlasses, fishhooks, beads . . . the trafficking of these involves a serious loss of time, but there is no alternative. . . ."

The days dragged by. He showed more anxiety about this part of the expedition than any other. Now the dry season was approaching. The annual flood that raised the Río Negro thirty-five feet, deluging everything at Manáos with black water, had dissipated with the July days. The trade winds were blowing, sweeping the treetops; the insects had been momentarily dispersed; Spruce could contain himself no longer.

His Río Negro journal begins: "This day, Friday, November 14, 1851, I left in my batalão with six men for the Río Negro. . . ." Soon he was on the expanse of the river, so wide in parts that the jungles appeared only as indistinct walls of gloom. Whenever the helmsman brought the batalão into a channel that came near the verdure-clad banks, Spruce would bring out a telescope and survey the scene. If he saw trees in blossom, he would command the vessel to swing in, so that he might add to his collection. Time mattered little now. Spruce was delighted with this arrangement. In a letter that he wrote on a packing-box, he gloated:

"The canoe being my own, I am master of my movements. . . . I may premise that the voyage will be on the whole a perfect contrast to that of the Amazon. . . . The cabin, too, is new and commodious. It is long enough to suspend my hammock within it, and I made myself a nice soft bed of thick layers of bark of the Brazil-nut tree, my large boxes ranged along the sides serve for tables and the smaller ones for seats, while from the roof I suspend my gun. The fore-cabin or *tolda da proa* is occupied by baskets of farinha, salt and other things for barter."

When it rained, the crew slept with the *farinha* in the fore-cabin. But in clear weather they preferred to sit on the small deck and watch the night, their savage senses alive and tingling to the world of which they were a part. Spruce kept to his resolve to employ no one with a shirt. His paddlers were pure Indians, Barres, Tarianos, and Manaioas tribesmen, brown-skinned and lynx-eyed, their black hair neatly cropped. He preferred them to half-castes, "for the least streak of white blood in an Indian's veins increases tenfold his insolence and insubordination." They were excellent canoe-men, sensing by instinct the intricate channels of the wandering Río Negro. Since the insects disappeared with the sun, the Indians paddled under the Amazon night. The whole heavens were reflected in the black waters, as if mirrored on a piece of polished obsidian.

One day was like another. The forests appeared as a fine pale green, unbroken by any autumnal tints. Occasionally the solid phalanx of trees would be broken by the finely divided tremulous foliage of a graceful acacia, or the large white starlike leaves of a cecropia, while here and there hung festoons of some brilliant begonia. Red-flowered vines, exhaling a subtle perfume, climbed above lower shrubs that overhung the water, these too bedecked with countless flowers. Spruce suddenly realized that the jungle was not merely trees and shrubs. It was not land at all. It was another element, still unnamed. Every living thing seemed to reach for the sun. Everything in the Amazonian jungles was fashioned for the arboreal life, as fishes were evolved to live in the sea. Everything climbed; if it did not, it perished.

Day after day they passed the same forests, static, rigid, watchful, and enigmatic. Then, after a month's voyage, the country began to change. Rapids became more frequent; large gray boulders cropped up in the center of the river, on the bank. The sound of cataracts increased. Massing ahead were huge granite rocks with

a top dressing of earth, festooned with plants. Great rushes of
water broke about the rocks, fountains of water gushed up,
splashed over the boat, collapsed and pulsed away. Now patches of
lichens, green, yellow and russet, appeared on the white granite.
All hands were kept to manning the vessel. So preoccupied was
Spruce in directing his Indians that he passed the Río Branco with
hardly a glance, and the celebrated *Ilhas de Pedras,* with their
gigantic granite rocks scarred with Indian picture writing. More
rapids; then the *Jurúpari-roka,* the devil's house, a massive forty-
foot boulder, rose before them to block passage. They dared not
pass this vortex of raging water until morning. The *batalão* anchored at its base, and Spruce, with his lichen-hammer, scrambled
up to the summit, scraped off some of the cryptogams, and then
turned his face to the setting sun. The glorious Río Negro spread
out before him empurpled with the rays of the departed sun,
while myriads of shapeless slabs of naked granite studded the
waters. Everywhere the water circled, eddied, and plunged over
partially sunken rocks. The roar of the cataracts even drowned
out the din of the night cicadas.

A week before Christmas, Spruce had reached the *Sitio de Unnauacá.* A small settlement, a cluster of the usual wattle-and-daub
houses, the *sitio* rested on a bluff of land, cleared of vegetation as
well as of industry. Spruce's paddlers asked for a fortnight's respite
to work in their manioc gardens. This gave him the needed interval to pack the 3,000 specimens that he had collected on the voyage
up from Manáos. And as the owner of the *sitio* was himself to
make the descent to Manáos, he obligingly took along the plants
destined for all the famed herbariums of the world.

With every step, with every stroke of the paddle, Spruce was
pushing back the frontiers of South America. His fame in botanical circles grew with every shipment of plants. By this time his
specimens were being eagerly received in London, Edinburgh,
Dublin, St. Petersburg, Vienna, Paris, Budapest, Brussels, Munich,
Göttingen, and Berlin. The fame of these collections was enough
even to bring the venerable Baron von Humboldt out of his map-
cluttered study to inspect them. Spruce indeed was carrying out
long-overdue botanical explorations.

But Spruce was unaware of his fame. He was involved in drying
his plant blotters and preparing for the next phase of his river
voyage. For he had bad news, too. His friend Wallace was ill, very
ill with malaria at São Joaquim at the mouth of the Uaupés. The
fever had reduced him to such a state of weakness that he could
no longer rise from his hammock or even feed himself. Spruce, ending his stay in Unnauacá abruptly, called in his paddlers from

their manioc *rocas* and took to the river again. The rapids increased. It was slow going, even though the trade winds still filled their sails. When the wind failed them in the middle of the day, he chose a favorable spot and spread out his plant blotters to dry while his Indians slept. Late in the afternoon they were on the river, plunging, paddling, bailing with all the care of dynamic death. As Spruce held on to the gunwales of the rearing *batalão,* he mused: "It may be true as Humboldt says that 'perils elevate the poetry of life,' but I can bear witness that they have a woeful tendency to depress its prose. In my own case, so long as the river was smooth and deep, my little vessel went on gallantly and my labors were uninterrupted, but when the river began to be obstructed by rocks and the current to run furiously, anxiety took the place of pleasure, and instead of working among my plants, I had to watch over the safety of the canoe and its contents. . . ."

Spruce had good cause to worry. Ahead of them were the formidable cataracts that separated them from São Gabriel. The roar dimmed out every other noise. Spruce dared not essay them until the whole river was blanketed with sun. At the point of exhaustion, Spruce put the *batalão* into the small backwaters that led to the village of São José. He did not even leave his boat; he took to his hammock and, with the door stopped up with fine linen dropcurtains, he looked eagerly to a long night's rest to give his lean body new strength. He was instantly in deep sleep. Then midnight. The report of a musket. A woman's scream. Spruce jumped up, took his gun from the top of the *toldo,* and readied himself for attack. He thought that the Macús Indians had ambushed the village. He rushed up the embankment. Indians were firing, but not at any foe. They were firing at the moon. "For the love of God," Spruce shouted to his oarsmen, "what is wrong?"

"It is the moon, patrón, the moon."

"Lord save us," thought Spruce, "this is a novel form of lunacy which affects the whole township simultaneously."

He looked at the moon. The sky was clear save for a few fleecy clouds. Then he perceived the reason — the moon was in total eclipse. The Indians were firing and shouting to frighten her back. There was no more sleep that night.

The next day the fight to ascend the river went on. Progress was measured in feet. The five-inch line was taken to a rock and made fast. Those aboard would haul in the line until they made the rock, then the Indians would put the rope about another boulder and the hand-over-hand progress would begin again. At length, São Gabriel came into sight. The sun rose beautifully clear, dispelling the mists from the sierras and tingeing them with gold. To a mind alive to the beauties of nature, such a scene had a soothing and enlivening effect. And thus, aided further by the stimulus of a fragrant cup of coffee, "Richard was himself again."

Spruce could not believe that he was looking at his old friend Alfred Wallace. His body was wasted until each rib and each vein could be counted. But his blue eyes danced and glistened in their yellowed sockets; he held out a long fleshless hand, and managed a smile through his months-old beard. Never had anyone felt so alone, dying of malaria in a country where dying was only a form of life.

Wallace had been up the Uaupés River for a whole year and had traveled far down the Orinoco. His collections in ethnology were excellent, the sketches of plants and people of superb quality. He had made two trips up the Negro. The first time he had crossed over the Pimichin isthmus that separated the Negro from the Orinoco. There his Indians had deserted him. He fought his way down 1,200 miles to Manáos, resting only long enough to prepare another expedition. A few months before Spruce went up in his own boat, Wallace set off again. This time his destination was the Río Uaupés, a large western tributary of the Negro. He had planned to ascend that stream to a point where white men had never set foot. The search for the unknown animated Wallace. The gold-lust that had animated the conquistadores, the enthusiasm with which the soul-collecting padres bridged the inferno of their jungle sufferings to entice natives to God's bosom — all this had been transferred to Wallace, rarefied into energy to push back the frontiers of the unknown. Up Wallace went past the foaming cataracts, into the country of the Jurúparu-worshippers. For weeks he traveled parallel with the equator, battling against malaria and insects. But a body can stand only so much. Even twenty-eight-year-old travel-hardened Alfred Wallace could not stand off forever the protozoa that whipped his body heat to the baking-point. Somewhere on the Río Uaupés he collapsed. He had been brought down by Indians, and Spruce found him at the *sitio* of *São Joaquim*. Yet with care he recovered, and in a few weeks was well enough to travel. Spruce arranged the journey downstream and Wallace, in turn, placed in his hands the commission to ascend the Uaupés.

The days, the months, the years swept by. They were almost wholly unrecorded except when Spruce put the day's date on the notes of his collected specimens. The granite-bound savannas of the Upper Río Negro yielded mountainous piles of plants. Spruce waged unrelenting war against the elements and things of the elements. Vampires sucked his blood, sauba ants carried away his provisions, termites attacked his plants, but still Spruce kept on, his tall frame more lean than ever now with the combined results of travel and foodless days. He had grown a beard, which made him look, with the spectacles that he put on for reading and writing, like some benign friar upon whom the *Weltschmerz* of his time had settled. But the Amazon had not changed his character. Even though he lived in a dilapidated house shared by vampires and sauba ants, his rooms were neatly arranged. Everything had its place. Spruce knew how to be poor without the least hint of squalor or inelegance. Asked once by a native what he would do should he stumble across the treasures of El Dorado, Spruce said that he would continue his life as he had begun — collecting plants.

The fall of 1852 found him on the Río Uaupés; he was fulfilling his promise to Wallace to make this unknown stream one of his collecting stations. Life for the next weeks was a succession of paddle and portage, portage and paddle. The cataracts roared and foamed, seeming almost to defy the ingenuity of man. Yet progress was made. Within two months he had got a hundred miles up the Uaupés. Massive boulders became the dominant motif in the river, standing like jungle gods barring entrance to the raging rivers. The Indians seemed to have sensed this too; on every boulder the ancient people had etched highly stylized figures of the things that were part of their lives: dolphins, fish, people, iguanas, lizards, and even maps showing the course of a river, and a *moloka,* a jungle community house.

Spruce was interested in all phenomena. He began to make drawings of every example of picture writing he found. It gave him an occupation for his unfilled time, and it gave him an insight into the people of the land he was so long to make his home. As he sketched the picture writing, he would ask the Indians: "Who made these figures, and what do they represent?"

To this question he would at first receive the universal reply from the Indian when he does not care to tell or take the trouble to recollect. *"Quién sabe, patrón?"* But Spruce understood enough of the Tariano speech to pick up their jabber-jabber when they explained to one another: "This is so and so." Then Spruce would interrupt and in their own tongue ask: "But don't you think this is so and so?" Thus Spruce got their opinions of most of the rock figures. This information, synthesized with his exact drawings, which numbered in the hundreds, laid the basis for the study of primitive rock writing in Amazonia. The plants did not suffer for these diversions. By means of fish-hooks, jew's-harps, and beads he was able to enlist a troop of dark-brown, stark naked Tarianos, who scrambled up trees to gather blossoms and fruits. By making a game of it — for the Indians would never have done it had they known that they were working — Spruce enriched his collection. Nor was he less interested in the plants that were part of the agricultural economy of the jungle people. He made lists of those which the Indians grew about their *molokas,* carefully entering the native name of the plant with the scientific name. This work helped create ethno-botany. Spruce was an excellent linguist, a patient man with natives, with a facility for recording the will-o'-the-wisp diphthongs of the Arawak language. His diversities helped him to gain much insight into the lives of jungle people.

It was November 1852, and Spruce as usual was collecting in the great mother forest. It was night by the time he reached the *moloka.* Suddenly the *botútos,* the sacred trumpets, began to boom lugubriously, throbbing in the inky blackness. At the sound, every female outside of the giant *moloka* made a rush for the house, before the *botútos* emerged from the jungle. Merely to see a trumpet would be sufficient to sentence her to death. The trumpets were announcing the coming of the *Jurúparu* devils who were to bring their spiritual selves to the great *Dubukarree* — the Feast of Gifts. By the time Spruce gained the flat plaza before the *moloka* he was colliding with hundreds of brown-skinned, geometrically painted Indians. It was a tapestry of primitive life. Men with egret feathers fashioned into towering headdress, anklets of red seeds, bodies painted and bedaubed with red and black, spear points decorated with red-tipped feathers — it was superb jungle pageantry, and Spruce felt part of it. He had been to many feasts. All followed rigid ceremonial patterns, but he was to find something else in this feast.

Dubukarree began outside with a monstrous choral dance, a choreography of graceless, circular, foot-slapping movements by the entire group of a hundred sweating dancers. Then came the manioc beer and then the *caapi.* Spruce had heard of *caapi;* every traveler in the Amazon had — caapi, the-drink-that-makes-one-brave; caapi, the-vine-of-the-souls; caapi, the soul-thread that contacts the drinker with the dead. Spruce watched an old Indian, egret-feather headdress askew, come across the hard mud floor of the *moloka* bearing a calabash of caapi. As he approached one of the caapi-drinkers, he ran over an incantation best described as "Mo-mo-mo-mo-mo-mo." The Indian seized the cup and drained the russet-colored liquid to its dregs; he demanded and got another. In two minutes the caapi took effect. The Indian turned deadly pale and trembled in every limb; then he was seized by a paroxysm. He rose in a fury, seized his spear, and rushed toward the door, where he inflicted violent blows on the ground, on the door. "Thus," he shouted in his delirium, "would I do to mine enemy, were this he." Caapi, the-drink-that-makes-men-brave, had taken its effect. In ten minutes the excitement passed off and the Indian dropped exhausted. Spruce decided to try it himself. He took a cup of caapi and downed it, almost gagging on its bitterness. But before he could take another cup, which made the proper dosage, "the ruler of the feast, desirous apparently that I shall taste all his delicacies at once, came up with a woman bearing a large calabash of manioc-beer, of which I must needs take a copious draught, and as I knew the mode of its preparation, it was gulped down with secret loathing. Scarcely had I accomplished this feat when a large cigar two feet long and as thick as the wrist was put lighted into my hand, and etiquette demanded that I should take a few whiffs of it — I who had never in my life smoked a cigar or pipe of tobacco. Above all this I must drink a large cup of palm-wine. . . ."

Poor Richard. His senses were befogged for some hours as the *Dubukarree* moved on, but one question danced before him. What was this caapi? Hypnotic? Narcotic? Illusion? In the morning he was out beyond the *moloka* with an old Indian, a maker of caapi. The native took him to a palm tree on which grew a thick-stemmed vine — caapi. Fortunately it was in flower, with young fruit, and Richard Spruce saw without surprise that it belonged to the order of the Malpighiaceæ, a family of ornamental climbing vines, and to the genus Banesteria. He named it, on the spot, *Banesteria caapi*.

But his surprise rose "from the fact that there was no other narcotic-malpighiad on record, nor any with strong medicinal properties of any kind." To be certain that the pharmaco-dynamics of caapi be attested, Spruce gathered root specimens from a dozen vines. Unfortunately, the shipment to England was ruined, but Spruce began an epochal series of investigations. His deduction has proved to be correct. Caapi is a narcotic containing phenol alkaloids which produces powerful reactions in the nervous system of mammals, and when it can be controlled, it, like the primitive coca leaf (from which the narcotic cocaine is derived) will take its place in man's materia medica.

The discovery that caapi had real, not imaginary physiological properties, gave Spruce's entire investigation a new direction. He no longer dismissed native traditions about jungle plants and their efficacy. For the first time the green world of the Amazon (the world that had yielded a pharmacopœia to a moiety of Indian tribes since America's beginning) was receiving a positive botanical basis. Spruce collected the plants from which *niopo* snuff was prepared, and although coming from an *acacia,* this, too, proved to be a narcotic. He watched the Indians prepare the niopo seeds by pounding, he observed the manner in which they kept the mull in a jaguar leg-bone, closed at one end with pitch and at the other stopped with a cork. After watching them put an apparatus shaped like the letter "Y" into their nostrils and inhale the snuff, he tried it and found that it produced a narcotic effect. Convinced, he gathered a quantity of niopo seeds and sent them to the Museum of Vegetable Products at Kew. Then he began an investigation into the ways of medicine and magic. Here was no dry-as-dust plant-collector who swooned over finding a new species or who spent his time in putting the obvious in terms of the unintelligible, for Spruce was in this field a ground-breaker, as much as La Condamine or Humboldt or Darwin. Spruce paced the industrial revolution by preparing the botanical path for rubber. He would successfully take out the quinine plants that would make possible man's conquest of the tropics; Spruce, the botanist, spent fifteen years in the Andes and the Amazon laying the botanical basis for almost all the sciences, any one of which is now a whole career for a single scientist, and now the same Spruce was prying into the magic of medicinal plants.

He found that the physician-magicians of the jungles were not animated by illusion or fakery alone. The materia medica that they used had genuine medicinal properties; their methods, of course, merely sprang from their own view of things. Illness was evil. It was brought on by a someone, not a something. Thus, by taking copious draughts of caapi, both physician-shaman and the sick one would be visited by hallucinations. The terror of the unknown makes the mind of man more submissive to mystic influences, and so dreams, brought on by caapi, the vine-of-the-souls, establishes a contact, in their minds, between the dead, who must have the answer to the sickness, and the living who have need of it. But behind all the hocus-pocus of rattles and tobacco smoke, empirical medicine had its rise. The Indians knew the antiblenorrhagic property of pepper, the therapeutic value of yerba maté or guarana; they were acquainted with twilight sleep, which they obtained by using the flowers of the datura, which contain the active principle of scopolamine. The Peruvian Indians had discovered the coca leaf and used it as a soporific. The coca of the Incas was *ipadú* to the Brazilians. Spruce found it cultivated around the *molokas* as well as in a wild state. It was a valued gift to suffering mankind. The coca plants that were sent with Spruce's collection reached Berlin and helped to stimulate the work of Dr. Niemann, who in 1858 isolated the active principle of *Erythroxylon coca,* the alkaloid of which he called *cocaine.* The ipecac which Spruce had often taken to combat dysentery had been known to the Brazilians for centuries. It, like quinine, had been sent to Europe as early as 1672, but only in recent times has the emetic alkaloid of ipecac been prepared in solution for injection against dysentery. Such a list Spruce knew could be extended indefinitely.

July 1853 found Spruce under siege in Venezuela. He had come down the Uaupés and taken his *batalão* up the Río Negro to San Carlos, the Venezuelan village that marked not only the boundary with Brazil, but the region where the Casiquiare joined the Negro to the Orinoco. This was classical ground, for here Humboldt in 1800 had determined the latitude and longitude of the long-known but never proved connection between the Amazon and Orinoco river systems.

"The gratification I naturally feel," Spruce wrote to Sir William Hooker, "at finding myself fairly *in terra Humboldtiana* is considerably lessened by various untoward circumstances." First it was the matter of food, or worse, the lack of it. Much of his time had to be spent looking for it. He was fortunate when he had one solid meal a day. In the time of Humboldt there were missions all along the Negro and the Orinoco, but for the last twenty years no padre dared show his countenance there. "A country without priests, lawyers, doctors and soldiers is not quite as happy as Jean Jacques Rousseau dreamed it ought to be. . . ." No sooner had he arrived in this outpost of water and sky, boulders and jungles, than he ran into difficulties that made him wish for some of those functionaries. He had scarcely set foot in San Carlos when two young Portuguese (the only other white men in this village) disclosed to him, with darting liquid eyes, that the feast of São João would be the signal for the Indians to massacre the whites. The Venezuelan *comisario,* fearing trouble, had decamped. There was no longer any moral or spiritual authority in the village of half-castes and "shirted" Indians — which alone, in Spruce's eyes, augured trouble. He could have taken himself along the river, but he had seen some flowering trees, and he would be damned if an Indian threat would chase him off before all this region had been collected.

The night before the festival of St. John, the Indians began to filter into the two long streets which were San Carlos. Of earth-brown color, and naked save for a cloth sash, they were typical members of the great Arawak family that peopled the Alto Orinoco and the Guianas. Low-browed, with black horsehair cut in a bowl trim, their ears pierced, arms and legs bound with ligatures, they were broad-shouldered and vigorous despite a ridiculous low-hung paunch. Their women brought in endless casks of bureche rum, which they had been weeks in distilling. Their hair was cropped short like the men's; their raiment was a beaded apron that hung down covering front and rear, anklets made of beads, and usually a necklace or two that adorned the small brown bodies.

The village fairly swarmed with natives. At midnight the half-castes began to fire their guns. The Indians, already warmed by the bureche rum, filled the night air with screeching music. Shortly after daylight the two young Portuguese, their knees quaking with fear, came to Spruce, who was bent over his plants, having long given up the thought of sleep in a village filled with brawling Indians. They had heard their Indian servant telling another how on the following night the Indians intended to kill them all. Spruce put his spectacles at the end of his nose, looked down at his papers through them, and then over them at the two Portuguese. Well, there was nothing else for it. He gave his attention to them. "I," he reflected, "had been here a very short time and had no quarrel with anyone . . . but I was accused of having a white skin and of being a foreigner and as with my little stock of merchandise I found myself the richest merchant in San Carlos, pretty pickings were calculated on in the sacking of my house. Such being the case, I declared my readiness to join in any plan of defense. . . ."

There was a quiet resolve about Richard Spruce. His movements were deliberate. His tall figure with the long honey-colored hair and beard, so different from the dark-haired short people who surrounded him, gave everyone pause when he came among them. He put the house in order for a siege: water and provisions were stored where they would not be ruined. He gathered together their arms, cutlasses, machetes; found they were well supplied with ammunition. Doors were barred, slits made for firing. He divided the watch among the three of them in equal shifts, and declared himself ready. Then he went back to plants. That night and the following the drinking, singing, and carousing went on with a din that outnoised the jungle. Spruce gave his opinion that they would not be attacked. The settlers thought they would be. Never had they seen a St. John's Day pass in which there was so little brawling among the Indians; that meant they were saving their energies for something. But somehow the Indians never got up courage. Spruce remained framed in the doorway with two weapons cocked, primed for instant use, and his unhurried figure was just the cool douche all the plans of massacre needed, if the Indians had ever entertained them. Day by day the tension lifted. The Indians, their stomachs swollen with bureche, gradually melted away to their *molokas,* and Spruce was able to go into the forest and collect his plants.

With the passing weeks he was seized with restlessness. There were more things to do. He placed his own vessel in readiness, got his crew, and set off on the Río Casiquiare. He wanted to visit the Cerra Duida and rifle its botanical spoils. He had been captivated by Humboldt's description of this perpendicular mass of rock rising out of the jungles. The Indians said that its top was inaccessible, yet everybody seemed to know perfectly well that it held a round lake inhabited by a large turtle, the genius of the mountain.

He got most of his direction from Don Diego Piña, a small, stooped, gray-haired Venezuelan, the only white man now living in the Cantón del Río Negro, who recollected seeing Humboldt. He was making turtle oil on a playa near the mouth of the Río Apure when Humboldt and Bonpland went down on their way to the cataracts. Spruce passed along the 600-yard-wide canal of Casiquiare, overhung and matted with jungle vegetation, with something akin to awe. He kept Humboldt's *Personal Narrative* opened before him like a Baedeker and identified all the landmarks that Humboldt, fifty years before, had described in his purple prose. There was the little village of Solano carved out of the jungle for a reason no one, not even the inhabitants, could guess. Then appeared Cerro de Cocui, a lofty granite mountain rising a sheer thousand feet above the green jungle, void of verdure almost to its apex. And here on the right side of the canal was the six-house settlement of Pueblo de Ponciano — and more recollections of Humboldt. An elderly Indian woman, who spoke excellent Spanish, recollected that when a very little girl she saw travelers coming down the Casiquiare, one a German, the other a Frenchman, who occupied themselves with gathering flowers by day and gazing at the stars by night. It was a thrilling thing to meet anyone, even an Indian, who had seen the great Humboldt on these rivers.

Spruce saw the black water of the Río Negro give way to the yellow water of the Orinoco; he had reached the point where the color of rivers marked the absolute meeting-place of the Amazon with the Orinoco. He passed great beds of balsa-wood; rubber trees were seen with great frequency; the usual concourse of palms and leathery-leafed melastomes were dominant in the crowded forest. There were many new birds' voices, too; brilliant orange and blue parrots flying in formation opened the day with a raucous, ear-splitting serenade to the sun, and in the evening they brought it to a close with the same procession and the same spine-tingling squawks. The insect plagues were almost impossible to bear. Spruce stuffed his trousers into his socks, he wore gloves, he tied a handkerchief over his ears. Still they came on — biting, stinging, sucking, making life a veritable purgatory.

In the afternoon of the 30th of November he reached the Rock of Guanari, rising out of the forest, an abrupt mass of stone. On that rock Humboldt took his observations to determine the latitude of the canal of the Casiquiare. Then they picked up the massive jagged hulk of Cerro Duida, which rose 8,000 feet out of the valley. He remembered how Humboldt had been driven to ecstasy over this great frowning mass of fantastically piled granite blocks. It was the most magnificent scene Spruce had seen in South America. A wide grassy savanna, undulating, gray, reached to the base of Duida; thence, without a prelude, the rock rose abruptly to its full height. If one can fancy all this seen in the setting sun — the deep ravines that furrow Duida on the east buried in nocturnal gloom, while the sharp, salient edges glittered like silver — one can realize Spruce's emotions. Humboldt had said that the apex was impossible of assault. Spruce had wanted to collect on its summit, but he was greatly discouraged by the natives, none of whom seemed to have the appetite to work, despite the trade goods that Spruce dangled before their dark eyes. At the base of Duida was Esmeralda, a small collection of huts which Spruce visited. It had been a fairly well populated village in Humboldt's time. Now it was almost deserted. About this lugubrious place Spruce had his say:

"You will credit me when I say to the sight Esmeralda is a paradise — in reality it is an Inferno, scarcely habitable by man. When I stood in the middle of the small square, around which are built the houses of Esmeralda — the straw doors all carefully closed and looking as if nothing human ever came forth from them — the warm east wind fanning my face and raising the sand in the plaza, but bringing no sound of life on its wings — no bird or even a butterfly to be seen — amid the luxuriance of vegetable life — animal life is almost extinct — I thought the scene inexpressibly mournful. But the utter absence of living things was only apparent, not real. If I passed my hand across my face I brought it away covered with blood and with the crushed bodies of gorged mosquitoes. In this you have the key to explain the unearthly silence. The apparently tenantless houses had all the inhabitants in them who, bat-like, drowse away the day and only steal forth in the grey of the morn and evening to seek a scanty subsistence. . . ."

At Esmeralda Spruce was visited by a severe depression. The pain in his back, the recurring headaches, meant one thing and one thing only: the dreaded malaria had struck him. Spruce paid no attention to it at first, surrounded as he was with plants to be collected, pressed, and described. There were unknown rivers to ascend and to map. He gave up Duida. And what a pity! It was not climbed until 1928. And when that 8,000-foot-high slab of granite, scaled by American scientists, yielded its secret, there were neither lakes nor tortoises, but 700 different species of plants, of which 200 were completely new to science.

Spruce now branched off from the Duida, went up the little frequented Río Cunacunuma, and there ran into the trail of Richard Schomburgk, who, like Spruce, Wallace, Bates, Darwin, and Humboldt, was an explorer-scientist. Schomburgk had landed in Georgetown in 1841 and begun a systematic exploration of the rivers of British Guiana. He ascended and descended every river of importance, then he struck off to reach Venezuela. No one has explored this part of the world so thoroughly since. It was unfortunate that Schomburgk had not the ability to write well, for his *Reisen in Britisch-Guiana* might have had great influence. Yet Richard Schomburgk, despite the fact that fame passed him by, ranks with his brother Robert among the great explorer-naturalists.

He apparently had left a good impression on the natives. As soon as they saw Richard Spruce collecting plants, taking sights of the sun, studying the trees with a telescope, they grasped that he was one of the same species as Schomburgk, and they helped as much as they could. Spruce kept up his assault on the green world, but the malarial germs were beginning to dissipate his energy. The next months went by as in a trance. He left his boat on the Negro and took passage with a Venezuelan trader down the Orinoco, collecting his plants as in a dream. He vomited frequently, the chills came on more often, the pains in his back increased, the perpetual headache left him in a constant state of ennui. He went down past San Fernando and the rapids of the Río Ventuari, down to the Maipures Mission. Then the good heart of Spruce could sustain him no more. Like Wallace, he was struck down by malaria.

For thirty-eight days Spruce hung on between death and life. He had violent attacks of fever at night, with short respites during the day. His Indians did not desert him, but they sold his equipment to buy rum, with which they kept themselves so besotted that they could not wait on the helpless man. Someone procured a hatchet-faced samba for him — Carmen Reja by name — who looked like an ill-fed buzzard. She reluctantly did what he asked, but "with a scowl almost demoniacal." Spruce dosed himself with quinine and ipecac. The days dragged by. There were violent sweats, then chills, a siege of vomiting. All the while he could hear that buzzard of a woman, sitting on the mud floor of the kitchen, chanting over and over: "Die, you English dog, that we may have a merry watch-night with your dollars."

But Spruce did not die. His health began to return, although he was pitifully weak. A passing Portuguese trader, Senhor Antonio Diaz, who had heard of him, offered him a passage back to Brazil, which Spruce seized as a ray of hope. He was carried to the boat on a stretcher, and back he went to San Carlos, oblivious of everything, even the flowering trees that wafted their perfumes across the fetid Orinoco. Gradually his strength began to return. On uncertain legs, whenever the boat stopped, he would try his hand at collecting. Bit by bit his interests, which were his very life, returned. By November 23, 1854 he was in his own boat again, ready to make the thousand-mile descent to Manáos.

But he had not come to the end of his difficulties. His crew of four Indians began to weave a plot to kill him; only Spruce's knowledge of Indian languages saved him. They had already covered a part of the distance down the now familiar black waters of the Negro. They put up at two shedlike buildings, open on all sides, thatched on top. The boat they left tied up at the edge of the river, some eighty yards away. Spruce, still weak and unsure, had them tie up his hammock at once and threw himself into it. The Indians warmed up a piece of forequarter of an alligator, gave some to Spruce, and assuaged their own hunger from a demi-john of bureche rum. The jabber-jabber of the Indians increased with the hours. Spruce, who dozed fitfully, at first paid little attention to it, until he began to hear constantly recurring the word *"Heinali, heinali."* That word in *Barre* meant "man." Soon Spruce discerned that *he* was the man whom they were discussing. First they plotted to collect their money in advance — as was the custom — and then desert the white *heinali* along the river. Then one of the Indians, mistaking all the piles of wrapped plants for trade goods, asked the others, "Has the *heinali* much merchandise?"

"Hulasikali wala . . . he has plenty."

"Well then, we will kill him."

There was a chorus of approval at that remark, and they passed the bottle around again. *"Doka doka,"* repeated the prime plotter. "Look, it will be easy. They knew that he was a sick man when he left San Carlos; who will be surprised at his death?"

Again a murmur of approval, again the rum bottle was circulated.

Spruce listened to all this with breathless attention. In his mind plans and counterplans raced about a skull still weary with fevers. A plan, however, began to develop out of the most material of considerations. A slight attack of diarrhea forced Spruce to leave his hammock three or four times during the plotting. This established a precedent. The last time he came back it was midnight. The moon was partially obscured. In the far distance an owl screeched through a night dark with its own mystery. The song of the cicadas rose and fell, cutting the air like a saw. The fire had gone out under the palm sheds. Only the dim light of the stars illuminated the interior, as dark as the stain of ink. The air was full of fireflies, and Spruce could smell the dank black earth about him. He walked deliberately to his hammock, got into it, but was careful to keep his feet on the ground, to spring up as soon as they came. A knife that he held in his hand would bring down some of them with him. In a few minutes he could see the shadows of bodies standing to one side. They were whispering:

"*Iduali, iduali.* . . . Now it is good time, now it is good time." The man Yurebe, who was detailed to do the killing, hesitated a moment. Spruce tensed himself; then suddenly, as if he had noticed nothing, he got up and walked again to the forest. As soon as he was out of sight he made for the boat, unlocked the door to the *toldo,* took out the boxes of his beloved plants, and piled them in front of the cabin for breastworks. He then laid out his double-barreled gun, his cutlass, a long knife — and waited. Above the night noises he could hear only the beating of his heart. Then he heard the Indians, cursing him in hoarse whispers.

"Why did he not return to his hammock?" A scouting party was sent out. They spotted Spruce sitting behind his plant bales, ready and alert. A moonbeam glistened on the gun barrel. The game was up. They knew it. Yet Spruce did not relax his watchfulness.

Never had he been so delighted to see the day. Still he would have to handle this diplomatically. He needed these men to take him down the river; he could not afford the luxury of justice. He said nothing. He had the Indians load the boat, but always under the shadow of his cocked shotgun. Daylight had dissipated all their courage. When the time became propitious, he dismissed Yurebe, and the plot, had it ever been seriously maintained, dissolved as they left him on the banks of the Río Negro.

The strain had been too much. All Spruce could do now was to lie back on his boxes and rest. He was exhausted. He was hungry for people, hungry for conversation with Europeans, hungry for food, and hungry for the sight of peaceful Manáos. He had been gone four years. He had covered 4,000 miles of river-travel. His collected plants numbered more than 20,000. He had made maps of unknown rivers, and learned the vocabularies of twenty-one Indian languages. Alone, moving through a country God-forsaken as the moon, Spruce felt that he had at least collected well and thoroughly. Now all he wanted was to see his old friend Senhor Antonio, rest in his easy-going house, walk through the sleepy streets of Manáos, and await the return of his health.

The Negro grew wider — five miles, ten miles, twenty miles, for in flood time the river inundated the *caa-tinga* forests on both sides. They passed familiar islands. Yes, they were nearing Manáos. Spruce noticed an extraordinary amount of traffic on the river. He had counted twenty boats in the last day. They seemed to be hurrying by as if the world would not wait. No one ever hurried in Manáos! Nor did the traffic slacken when they approached the environs of the little settlement. Canoes filled the river; *batalãos* elaborate with giant poop cabins, boats with monstrous piles of trade goods swept by. Then Spruce saw the town. He could not believe his eyes! Not one, but three steamboats were lashed to a well-made new jetty. Their smoke shot up like a rising black cloud in the still air. Steamboats on the Amazon! What a miracle! When he landed he was overwhelmed at the sight of the streets filled with people: whites, browns, blacks, foreigners, dragging trade goods and hurrying by like sauba ants. On the *malecón* huge piles of dark, smoke-stained rubber slabs waited to be loaded on the panting steamboats. The whole city had changed. It was twice its original size; new buildings had sprung up like mushrooms, and at Senhor Antonio's store it was pandemonium. People were buying everything, shouting, pushing, waving money as they fought for trade goods, matches, and guns.

Had someone found the fabled lake of El Dorado? Senhor Antonio looked up from behind the exchange and came to greet his old friend. He threw his arms about Spruce in the traditional *abrazo*.

"Good God," Spruce managed to say, "what has happened, Antonio?"

"Don't you know?" answered the Italian. "Don't you know, Senhor Richardo? We have found the fabled riches. Rubber is king. We are in a rubber boom."

Big business had at last found the Amazon.

CHAPTER XXVIII

"On Her Britannic Majesty's Service"

RICHARD SPRUCE had been isolated too long in the jungle to understand it.

Rubber? Yes, rubber he understood, yet why the hurry? "Sweet Jesus," a bearded, sweating *cauchero* burst out over his drink. Where had Spruce been? Rubber, which a few years ago had been three cents a pound, was now worth one dollar fifty — and going up, up, up. Every day a rubber prospector delayed was so much money lost; naturally they must hurry. "So this is the new theme," muttered Spruce, "hurry, hurry." Yes, the industrial revolution must be a potent weapon to stir the stagnant Amazon.

The demand for rubber goods grew steadily with the expansion of industry. Inventions everywhere called for it. It was going into everything. Why, at the Crystal Palace where the British held the first World's Exposition, rubber products drew the greatest of crowds. War, too, gave it an impetus. The inevitable struggle between the free and slave states in North America was beginning to gobble up tons of this viscous liquid from the tree called *Hevea brasiliensis*. Demand so outstripped supply that the price was upped every week.

No one could resist it. Manáos, fabled in the past as the site of El Dorado, had actually become El Dorado. Gold flowed like water through its streets. The whole city throbbed to the recrudescence of the dream of wealth. Indians who once became fearfully besotted on sense-racking rum now drowned their *Weltschmerz* in champagne. One had *paté de foie gras*, Cross & Blackwell's jams, Huntley & Palmer's biscuits, imported wines. One could sit down to a dinner at which the butter came from Cork, the biscuits from Boston, the ham from Oporto, and the potatoes from Liverpool.

Clerks and barbers, gentlemen, and *mamelucos* who had labored in the past for a handful of milreis now saw visions of unlimited wealth. They plunged into the unknown Amazon country with a confidence that made Spruce wince. Had these fools no idea what they were going into? The beginning of a *cauchero* was simple. You raise money, sell your soul to a *patrão* in rubber, buy a dugout and provisions — *farinha*, dried fish, bottles of wine, salt, expensive imports — then trade goods, and last of all machetes with which to cut and bleed all the rubber trees you find. Many who rushed out to rubber and glory were never heard of again. Many more drifted back, bewildered and fear-shriveled, with tales of being lost, of torture by thirst and hunger and fever, of fighting relentless clouds of stinging, blood-sucking insects, of deluging rainstorms. They told in feverish gasps of staggering through bottomless swamps filled with electric eels, flesh-ripping vines, and underbrush.

Spruce had wanted to see progress come to the Amazon, but never had he believed that this was the way it would be ushered in. The old merchants, who once traded in pitiful quantities of Amazonia's wealth, now found themselves no longer mere merchants; they were tycoons. Heady with success and imported champagne, they painted for Spruce a picture of what Manáos would be in a few years. And no matter how exaggerated their claims, all would fall short of actuality; in twenty-five years Manáos would metamorphose from a village of 3,000 to a teeming, hurrying jungle metropolis of 100,000 inhabitants. Ocean liners would pull up beside its floating docks, marble opera houses would be built, electrically operated trams would careen down paved streets, foreign capital of over $40,000,000 would pour into the city that was built upon the morass of the black gold.

Richard Spruce shuddered to think of what he had so unwittingly help to forge. His plants, his specimens of rubber products, had been on display and had helped to bring on big business. Now there was no stopping its onrush. Rubber-gathering would go on and on with a frenzy unequaled since the discovery of the New World. It would engulf the free denizens of the forest. Whole Indian tribes would be decimated. Rubber would soar to the fantastic price of three dollars a pound. Rubber barons would enslave the whole Amazon, greed and ambition would grow apace with the world's ever increasing clamor for rubber. Barbarities unparalleled since the time of the conquistadores would transform Amazonia into an inferno. Without doubt, as Wolf wrote, "the crimes of this largest of jungle hells constitute an orgy of bestiality without an exact parallel." No resident of the jungle would ever write to a rubber trader the words that had been written to the naturalist-explorer Alfred Wallace by a native resident of the Amazon: "If you ever come to these parts again, you will find that I shall be to you the same as before. . . ."

How long the rubber-frenzy might have gone on no one knows, but the famous "seed-snatch" of Henry Wickham ended it. Black gold became black mud, and by 1900 the morass of the jungle swallowed the dream of a bouncing El Dorado.

Spruce gave himself four months to recover from those four dev-astating years on the Alto Orinoco. Gradually he recovered his strength and set about making plans to go up the Amazon to Peru. He found a British sailor named Charlie Nelson sitting on the quays, hungry and desolate; and thinking it would be good to have a companion, Spruce hired him to carry his plant presses beyond the city. Unhurried, exacting in his work, Spruce continued to col-lect and codify the green world of the Amazon. No one could understand what animated him.

"My friends in Manáos," he wrote, "wonder to see that I still go on working, and tell me that the most industrious European in less than five years generally accommodates himself to the *far niente* to which the climate and example all around him so tempt-ingly invite." But there were new green worlds to conquer; the Amazon flowed from another 2,000 miles of waterways; up there beyond the reach of the rubber boom he might collect in a new realm of plants. His decision made, he put all his impedimenta to-gether, and with Charles Nelson, sometime of the Queen's Navy, put out on the *Monarca,* an iron steamer of thirty-five tons, on March 14, 1855.

What a change this was from his late travels on the Negro! He put up his hammock, stretched his long legs within its inviting folds, and looked out upon the banks of the Amazon. It was called the Solimões now. Beyond the point where the black Negro and the yellow Amazon met, it was monstrously wide; large tree-trunks swept by, small grass islands danced along on the rapidly flowing water; the exposed clay banks were perforated by king-fishers and small white-bellied sand-martins. There was the usual concourse of gaudy-liveried, raucous-voiced parrots who com-manded the dawn, but the whole world for Richard Spruce seemed at peace. His senses were alive to every noise, and he used his gift of creating, through the medium of words, a picture of these jungle sounds in a letter he wrote to his friend Bentham. He explained that in the heat of the day, "from twelve to three o'clock, when birds and beasts hide themselves in the recesses of the forest, there is still the hum of busy-bees and gaily-colored flies, culling sweets from flowering trees . . . innumerable frogs in the shal-lows and among the tall grasses, chant forth their Ave Marias, sometimes simulating the chirping of birds, at others the halloo-ing of crowds of people in a distant wood. About the same hour the carapana-mosquito begins its night-voyage. There are besides, various birds which sing at intervals the night through, and whose names are uniformly framed in imitation of their note: such are the *acurau,* the *murucututu* — a sort of owl — and the *jacurutu,* whose

song is peculiarly lugubrious. A sort of pigeon, which is heard at
five o'clock in the morning, is called, and is supposed to say,
'*Maria já he dia*' (Mary it is already day) — a name which reminded one of the 'Milk the cow clean Katey,' a Yorkshire appel-
lation of the stockdove. Among the birds which most amused me
with their note by day were the '*Bem te vi!*' (I saw thee well!) and
the '*João corta páo!*' (John cut the stick!) "

The sloping banks of the Solimões, clad with long grass, were
a strong contrast to the bankless Negro. Out of the grass would appear the sweeping branches of Humboldt's willow; and tall, white-
barked cecropias like unburnt candelabra would stand out from
the rich verdure, a botanical prelude to the vividly green bamboos
which began as a sort of façade to the matted jungle. It was glorious to sit perched on the upper deck of a steamer and see all this
golden-green world. But it had its bad points too. Spruce could
not command the steamer to put ashore when he saw some interesting flowering plants. Although he had collected 30,000 specimens,
numbering over 7,000 species, Spruce knew he had merely begun.
"Taking the fact that by moving away a degree of latitude and
longitude, I found about half the plants different, as a basis and
considering what very narrow strips have up to this day been explored — and *that* often very inadequately by Humboldt, Martius
and myself — there should remain some 50,000 or 80,000 species
undiscovered!"

As the *Monarca* swept by the high banks of the Solimões, Spruce
saw no end of new plants. From his position on the upper deck,
he surveyed them with disappointed eyes. "There goes a new Dip-
teryx, there goes a new Qualea — there goes a new 'Lord knows
what.' I could no longer bear the sight and, covering my face with
my hands, I resigned myself to the sorrowful reflection that I must
leave all these fine things to waste their sweetness on the jungle
air."

Yet it was, in a way, like a paradise to sit up there on the second
deck and see the world about him. The islands, fixed and floating,
were a constant source of wonder to him; cranes, herons, and
egrets would enliven the air; there was a never-ending parade of
alligators. The fresh-water dolphins chased one another through
the turgid yellow waters, springing through the air as if they were
guiding a sea-borne vessel to its landfall. There were numerous
stops, too, which Spruce put to good advantage. The *Monarca* was
a strongly built steamer, but with low-pressure engines of thirty-
five horsepower, and most of its space was taken up by engines and
wood. A cargo of fuel lasted only thirty-six hours; at the end of
that time they would have to stop, go ashore, and fell trees to

gather enough to carry them another thirty-six hours. This was a botanical windfall for Spruce. The wood most preferred for the boilers was the mulàtto tree, with a shining bark of leaden hue. As it was in flower, Spruce seized upon it and found it to be a species related to the quinine tree. It became — as named by the good Mr. Bentham — *Enkylista Spruceana.* As soon as the wood-gathering was over, all the passengers would pile back on the steamer; then she would resume her chugging up the Solimões. It seemed like the progress of a tortoise; still they covered 1,500 miles to the border of Peru in eighteen days. It had taken Spruce sixty-three days to move 450 miles on the Amazon under sail.

The *Monarca* had now reached Nauta, the limit of steam navigation, fifty miles above Iquitos. Once again one had to use the hated open canoe. They left the puffing steamer and, hiring a broad dugout, went up the Río Huallaga, a large rapid-filled river that came from the highlands of Peru.

The jungle on both sides of the Huallaga rose straight and uninterrupted from the river. Newly cut gashes appeared on the banks, the red earth still raw where the flood waters had gouged out sizable portions of soil. A pitiless sun beat down, and there was no escape from it until they reached Yurimaguas, a village a hundred miles upstream. There, waiting for him as promised, were several horses and mules, sent down by a Don Ignacio Morey, who had invited him to spend some months at Tarapoto.

They had scarcely gone beyond the limits of what we are pleased to call civilization when Spruce found out that he had made a mistake in Charlie Nelson. A false report of gold on the Amazon had brought a sudden influx of derelict English and Americans; Charlie Nelson was one of these. Spruce had found him at first a quiet fellow, strong and eager, "and thinking that a stout companion like him would be invaluable to me in a country where, as report truly said, there was no law but that of the strongest," he engaged him. He did not know that Nelson's path through Peru had been marked with violence, and that he had been in prison there for murder. Now the true Nelson suddenly appeared. He mistreated the Indians, sending them to their canoes with the imprint of his thick boot upon their naked behinds. Knowing neither Spanish nor Portuguese, and being slightly deaf, he fancied everyone was laughing at him. In the plaza of Tarapoto he saw a group of Indians talking and laughing. Straightway he rushed into the crowd like a maddened bull, grabbed hold of a hapless cinnamon-colored fellow, and caved in his mouth with a blow that would have felled an ox. He sought a quarrel with a padre, almost dispatching him with an axe-handle. That was enough for Spruce.

But to get rid of him was not so easy. There were violent scenes between them. Spruce was forced to sleep with a revolver under his pillow after he told Charlie Nelson that he had run the gantlet of Indians, snakes, and rapids for five years without coming to harm and he had no intention of allowing a brawling sailor to cave in the few remaining teeth which malaria and time had left him. If Charlie Nelson ever made a move toward him, he would fill his storm-tossed body with enough lead to provide a harvest for the metal-searching Indians. All this, uttered in the Yorkshire dialect that Spruce used whenever he was aroused, had about it that determination which marks a man of decision. Nelson gave up. Spruce paid him three months' wages and his fare back and sent him down over the jungle trails. But Nelson had no need of his return fare. Somewhere along the Ucayali River violence was met with violence; the Indians turned on him and hacked him to pieces.

The little Peruvian village of Tarapoto, fifteen hundred feet in altitude, was home to Spruce for the next two years. It was set in a large pampa of such dimensions that the whole of old London might have been set down within its boundaries. It was completely surrounded by mountains, the spurs of the Andes forming a vast natural amphitheater. The folkways people, half-Indian, half-Spanish, were as simple as those of Spruce's native Gansthorpe.

Peace had come at last to Richard Spruce. The collecting regions were rich, the people ceremoniously polite, the talk of the padre and Don Ignacio on a high plane. The cool sixty-degree mornings were refreshing enough to bring the bloom again to Spruce's pallid cheeks. Here he met with tribes of plants that he had not seen since he left England — the poppy, the horsetail, a bramble, some shrubs of the bilberry tribe with edible fruits, a species of buttercup, and a hydrocotyle whose round, shining leaves he had once noticed as a boy in the boggy parts of Wellburn Moor. This was now his collecting station. His drawings, which had begun as soft purple lines, took on a character of some promise. His landscapes, his houses, were of increasingly fine draftsmanship. His plant collections, as might be expected, swelled with splendidly prepared notes. The people loved the tall, amiable man who spoke Spanish and Portuguese so softly and with only the slightest touch of accent. His love of anecdote, his love of people, naturally drew him to all walks of life. Spruce would play chess with the padre, or he would walk beside an Indian and discuss with him the merits of native remedies. When ill, the people would call in Don Ricardo; when they were beset with some contractual difficulty, "Don Ricardo would find a way." Once when a poor Indian was set upon by a whole hive of fierce-stinging wasps, Don Ricardo came to the rescue. He took out his flask and began to daub some spirits on the angry knobs and welts. As he bathed the stings with alcohol, the Indian looked up to him, his face horribly disfigured by the swelling, and said through puffed lips: "If it's all the same to you, *patrón*, I'd rather have it inside."

Spruce passed two years at Tarapoto, "the most agreeably placed . . . in my South American wanderings." Then one day, just after he had sent down his largest collection of plants on their 2,500-mile passage to Belém and so to England, the padre gave him a birthday party for his thirty-ninth year. In the midst of the party, a severely simple fiesta, an Indian stumbled in with a packet of mail for Don Ricardo. Mail from home! Spruce opened the sack, which was carefully wrapped in rubber cloth, and out tumbled letters that had been on the way for months. One of the letters was in a long yellow manila envelope. In bold black letters it proclaimed for all the world to see:

"On Her Britannic Majesty's Service."

With nervous fingers Spruce tore open the envelope. What did the government of England want with Richard Spruce, ensconced in the folds of the Andes?

"Her Majesty's Secretary of State for India has entrusted the Hon. Richard Spruce, esq. with the commission to procure seeds and plants of the Red Bark Tree, which contains the chemical ingredient known as quinine and . . ." So that was it. Plants and seedlings of the cinchona tree to be established in India. He was to "proceed" (" 'proceed,' that's a good one") to Ecuador and there, with aid of a Mr. Cross and letters of credit placed at the disposal of Her Britannic Majesty's Consul at Guayaquil, he was to perform these tasks as conditions would best permit. Spruce could see the hand of his friend George Bentham behind his being selected for this important work. British officials doubtless had been shown his immense collection of plants; and Bentham, seconded by Sir William Hooker, had suggested Spruce as just the man. Ever since the Royal Botanical Gardens at Kew had been established in 1730, they had acted as a sort of botanical agent to the government. Kew's representative was on the *Bounty* when bread-fruit trees were distributed in the Pacific. Kew had brought back eucalyptus trees and many other botanical rarities under the directorship of Sir Joseph Banks. Its new friends now were George Bentham and Sir William Hooker, who gave to it the *"editio princeps"* of the Spruce collections, which helped make up its two million plant specimens. The British government had gone to Kew about the question of quinine, and Kew had recommended Spruce. He was ordered to "proceed"; but how?

Formidable, hail-swept mountains lay between Spruce and the high plateau of Peru; after that lay a long trip to the coast; then he would be only in Lima. But no sooner did he think of this route than yellow fever broke out on the Pacific coast, quickly followed by the annual revolution — which came soon enough to remote Tarapoto. One quiet day a native ran into the plaza and shouted: *"Viene el reclutamiento."* Immediately all was panic and confusion. *Reclutamiento* — recruiting in Peru — was like the old press gang of London. The natives rushed about, getting their goods together, and decamped into the jungles. The plaza was filled with people streaking for the plains laden with their household goods, fleeing the recruiting gangs — and the revolution. When the revolutionists arrived they began to sack the houses at once.

Spruce, true to his nature, went quietly home, loaded his six-shooter, took out his double-barrel shotgun, unleashed his dog Sultan, and prepared to defend himself. But before he was set upon, Spruce wanted to know what the revolution was about. The padre was the only one who could give him proper enlightenment. General Castilla, the President, was "in." General Vivanco was "out." Vivanco wanted to replace Castilla. That was the sum of the revolution. One must needs bear with the revolutions as one tolerates the clouds of locusts that periodically devastate the crops. Spruce thought the padre's resignation most Christian, and he regretted that his temperament did not permit him to follow it. He stuck to his guns. The revolution swept in, sufficiently disorganized. Houses were sacked, a bull was shot at by one of the ragged *rotos,* an uprising of the Indians was promptly silenced by the commandant, who ordered his soldiers to charge with fixed bayonets. Spruce was next. He stood by the door of his little house, his revolver in his belt, his shotgun cocked and loaded, ready for use. The commandant advanced and propounded the doctrine: *"En tiempo de revolución todos los bienes son comunes."*

Well, "all the goods would not be common" as far as Spruce was concerned, even if it was in time of revolution. At this effrontery the commandant dropped back and waved his soldiers toward the house. Spruce brought up his shotgun to shoulder level. No word was uttered. That quiet, determined tall figure was enough for them; the revolution swept by Richard Spruce. Unmolested, he and his companions prepared to "proceed," as the document so stuffily ordered, to Ecuador; but not by way of Peru. They selected the back-door route, the route by way of the Río Pastaza.

Spruce wished that he had the Secretary of the State for India with him while he "proceeded" to Ecuador. After all his years in the Amazon, it was the worst, the most horrible trip that he had ever taken, even though it took only three months to complete. The party was separated in two canoes. In the first were Don Ignacio Morey and Don Victoriana Marrieta, two Peruvians on their way to Ecuador for business; five Indians made up their crew. Spruce was alone with seven Indians in his forty-foot mahogany dugout. They descended the Río Huallaga and were caught in its whirlpools. At the very beginning they were almost lost. Sultan, the dog, was so frightened by the roar of the water and the lashing of the canoe against the rocks of the rapids that he went mad. From that hour onward he would drink no water, eat no food. Spruce had reared him since he was a small puppy. Many a time drunken cholos had descended upon the house of Don Ricardo, only to be brought up by the appearance of Sultan, fangs bared, ready for business. Spruce kept Sultan at his side for six days, at great personal risk to himself, hoping to cure him, but then Sultan was reduced almost to a skeleton. When released from the leash he would run straight off into the Indian settlements, uttering the most unearthly sounds, putting Indians, dogs, chickens, and pigs to flight. Spruce got hold of him at last and took him slowly into the lambent green of the jungle. There he tied him to a tree and took aim with his pistol. He could hardly see the blurred outline of Sultan, his eyes were so filled with tears. There was a roar from the gun, the phantoms of sound batted it back and forth across the water, and Spruce walked out to the river. The canoes went on again. They passed through El Pueblo de Laguna, at which mission, a century before, La Condamine and Pedro Maldonado had met to make their way down the Amazon.

A great arm of the Upper Amazon is the Pastaza. Wide, yellow-colored, and swift-flowing, its waters are derived from the melted snows of the volcanoes of Ecuador and the heavy precipitation of the rain-bearing trade winds striking the spurs of the Andes. The canoes made slow progress against its six-knot current. A tenseness began to be felt now. They were coming into the land of the head-shrinking Jivaros. Above the confluence of the Pastaza they had come upon the little village of San Antonio, which had only recently been sacked by the Huambizas. Clothes were scattered about, dishes broken, pots still full of food, suggesting that the attack of the head-hunting Huambizas had been sudden and disastrous. Their Indian paddlers were unnerved. Spruce and his companions had to stand guard at night while their paddlers, wearied by the day's work, slept. Yet for two hundred miles up the river they saw

The Amazon jungle. Through such a green continent of trees Richard Spruce trekked for seventeen years. The trees are draped with epithytes and ropelike lianas.

nothing. No canoes, no habitations, no people. For days it was just paddle and bail, bail and paddle; then, two hundred miles up the straight-flowing Pastaza, they came to the settlement of Andoas.

It was like making a landfall at sea. The tiny cluster of leaf houses, the church made of bamboo stems opened out into boards, topped with an iron crucifix, the sight of even mud-fouled pigs, were enough to make Spruce happy. Twenty palm-plaited houses were all of Andoas, a pitifully small human foothold on the edge of immensity. The church divided the town into two equal *partidos,* one side of which was inhabited by Shimigai Indians, the other by cholos. The Shimigais hung about the church, a pitiful remnant of a tribe which was ceaselessly beset with raids upon their dwindling numbers by the head-hunters. Delicately built, of lowish stature, they had wide mouths, straight noses, the usual jet-black eyes, over which their hair, of horse tail texture, hung in bangs. In back the hair was allowed to flow downward, almost covering the poncho-like *cueshma* which they slipped over their bodies. This and a pair of small cotton drawers constituted their clothes. "Like most Indians," Spruce observed, "who have been brought to 'Christianity,' they have no manufactures of any kind. Their canoes, hammocks, blowguns, etc., are bought from the Infidels!" Yet the Shimigais had not lost their hunting instincts. They were given guns by Spruce and they set out into the forest. They returned a few hours later with two large animals, tapirs with as much flesh as a fatted steer. This Spruce salted down for the next lap of the trip, and quantities of plantains and yucas were procured, as well as pots of fermented *masuto.*

The course of the Pastaza above Andoas changed little. The yellow water seemed to flow just as swiftly, and they painfully set themselves against the current. Seven miles a day was the best they could average. When Spruce was not taking his place paddling among the Indians, he was observing the vegetation and wondering about the word "Andoas." There was a familiarity about it. Where had he heard it before? Andoas! Andoas! Had it ever been mentioned in the annals of exploration? Yes, it had — Mme Godin! Of course, that was it. Andoas was the place to which Mme Godin had been taken after she had been found wandering in the forests on the left bank of the Pastaza. Then the Indians who found her must have been of the Shimigai tribe! The thought that he was now traveling the same river that Mme Godin had traversed a century before made him forget his own discomforts and think back to the horrible experience of this frail woman. It was fortunate for her, he mused, that she was found by these Indians rather than the head-hunters. All during those fourteen days to the next landfall of Sara-yacu his thoughts shifted back again and again to that small, determined Mme Godin. He had picked up the trail of Humboldt in the Orinoco; at Laguna he had come across the meeting place of Maldonado and La Condamine; and now another classic figure, Mme Godin.

The days were a succession of insects and storms. Villages became more frequent now, and the Pastaza shrank to a muddy, shallow, winding river, at places no more than a hundred yards wide. The banks began to be picturesque. Cliffs were clad with ferns and mosses, leathery heliconias with scarlet pendants and yellowish spikes mixed with the giant ferns. Tiny cascades of pure white water fell over them. Then out of the porcelain-blue sky rolled a burst of thunder. At once the sky was mantled with black ugly clouds. In the distance they could see the jungle suddenly convulse, writhing, twisting, turning — then the storm sprang at them. Rain fell in sheets. The jungle turned to shadows in the gray fog. The river rose at once. The Indians, more by instinct than thought, jumped into the canoes and, with a strength given to them only for the emergency, pushed them into a sheltered cove as tons of water rushed by. Everyone held onto the canoes, hoping to prevent them from crashing together. So dense was the gloom that they could see nothing. They were deafened by the pelting rain, numbed by the crash of lightning, shocked by the horrendous rolls of thunder. The river, which nowhere had been more than three feet deep, had risen to over twenty, rushing, tearing, destroying.

At Canelos, the largest of the jungle settlements, Spruce picked up again the trail of Mme Godin. Here it was that she arrived to find the village decimated by smallpox. Here began her odyssey of horrors. All about him was magnificent scenery. The thunder that Spruce thought he heard turned out to be the volcano of Sangay. Out of the green of the jungle, he saw its perfect cone rising seventeen thousand feet into the equatorial heavens. Its top was covered with a mantle of snow, a vivid contrast to the sweating, steaming jungle below. A good way to the right he could see the truncated summit of Los Altares, jagged with eight peaks of nearly equal elevation, glittering in its snow mantle on "altars" at a height no mortal might hope to attain. To the right of Altar was Tunguragua, its bluff, irregular peak rounded with an apex of snow. Farther north, dimly visible, of exactly the same form as Sangay but more distant and lofty, was Cotopaxi, the most formidable volcano on the earth's surface. Far behind Tunguragua, and peeping over its left shoulder, distinctly visible in the far distance, was a paraboloid mass of unbroken snow — the summit of Chimborazo, "forever immortalized," as Spruce suggested, "by its connection in man's memory with such names as Humboldt and La Condamine." Beyond this was the Pacific slope and region of the quinine trees.

Roads were non-existent; paths were transformed to quagmires by a ceaseless downpour. Henceforth they traveled on foot. Through the agency of a padre Spruce obtained eight "shirted" Indians as carriers. On their broad backs boxes were lashed. The carriers were nervously sensitive to every sound; they were treading the realm of the head-hunter. Spruce had seen traces of these tribes everywhere since he had entered the Pastaza, but he had yet to meet a Jivaro. On his second day out from Canelos, where the thin ribbon of path was swallowed up by the immensity of the forest, they ran into the head-hunters. Spruce had his eyes on the ground, trying to find a footing for his next step, when suddenly the Indian ahead stopped abruptly and those behind kept colliding with one another like freight cars coming to a sudden halt. Head-hunters! It was all Spruce could do to keep his Indians from making a dash into the jungle. He cut ahead of them, and came face to face with — two Jivaros.

There was nothing startling in their appearance. They were short, typical Amazonian Indians, their skins light, their features well formed, the nose a bit convex, the eyes dark, sharp, and intelligent. The hair falling down the back was braided with feathers of the toucan. Passing through their ear-lobes were bamboo tubes of pencil thickness. Each wore a bright-threaded cotton skirt that reached below the knees. One held a gun, the other a metal-tipped lance, the end of which he gripped with his toes.

When Spruce came up, tall, bronzed, and rugged, the Indians measured his height with their eyes. They saw the pistol strapped to his waist and the shotgun under his arm. They smiled, Spruce held out his hand, one gripped it, and they were friends. He spoke to them in Quechua, and they answered in Spanish. Spruce suggested food, shelter, and sleep, overriding the alarm of his Indians, and off they went through the jungle to the lair of the head-hunters.

Their *hea* was much like the other jungle dwellings he had seen in Amazonia. It stood in a field which they had hacked out of the jungle. Bananas were planted here, and cotton in the fields. He saw *varvascu,* the roots of which were used in fishing, to poison the waters. There was belladonna too, and he recognized at once the slender vines of the *caapi.* So these grinning head-hunters used the narcotic of the vine-of-the-souls, too? The *hea,*

made from the trunks of the bullet-resisting chonta palm placed
close together, with only enough space between them to admit a
crack of light, was an oval dwelling sixty feet long. The roof was
palm-thatched. There was a single entrance. Spruce took it, and
came into a world of social action as different from his own
as was his from that of cave-dwellers.

The social pattern of the *hea* was similar to that of the *moloka*.
The family was the unit. More than a score of people moved about
in the semi-darkness. Fires were glowing here and there on the
hardened bare earth. The hammock of the *moloka* was missing,
but there were beds of flattened bamboo. Before each, like a hitch-
ing-bar, was another piece of bamboo, with a low-banked fire beneath it. Here the head-hunters warmed their feet as they rested.

Spruce held out mirrors and fish-hooks, and the people hovering
in the shadows surged upon him, held out their hands, took the
offering silently, and retreated again to the shadows. The old Indian who headed the *hea* was given a knife. This he accepted without the least show of gratitude. Spruce was neither disturbed nor
offended by this outward coldness. He had long since learned that
when an Indian receives a present he is never grateful. In this
communistic society where every man could have more than
enough by his own effort, gifts were not gifts, they were mere exchange. Before long the women — dressed in dark cotton tunics
that covered the whole of the body — came forward with bowls of
yuca soup and roasted agouti-flesh. The carriers from Canelos hud-
dled together at one side of the *hea* like a bunch of frightened
guinea pigs; the superiority of the Jivaro Indian to all others was
evident.

In the center of the house was a large signal drum. Blowguns,
long, black, shiny instruments of death, were stacked like billiard
cues against one of the tall uprights. Rifles, greased and ready for
use, hung overhead. There was little doubt that the *hea* was as
much a fortress as a house. Over the fire, tied to the top of a rack
holding dried corn, was a freshly prepared human head, not much
larger than one's fist. Its features, blackened by the shrinking
process, were most human, a lamentable symbol of the Jivaros'
misconception of death. To all primitives, death was brought by a
someone, not a something. While the other Indians contented
themselves with drinking *caapi* and exorcizing demons, the Jivaros
went a step farther. To him who released the demons and sent
death into the *hea,* death must come. He or one of his *hea* must
be killed, his head taken, shrunk (seemingly for convenience'
sake), and subjected to great humiliation during a drunken festival. And the reason? So that the soul of the *tsantsa,* the shrunken

head, which contained limitless power, would be won over to the taker of the head and the members of his *hea;* so that the power of that soul, instead of being used against them, would be used for them. And why? To help the fields produce more crops, the hunt more animals, the women more children.

Spruce would have liked to see more of these head-hunters, but he had to get on. The Jivaros guided them out to the swollen waters that plunged down the Andes. They now followed a road that led along the Río Pastaza. It had turned and was heading due west. Numerous rivers over which they had to cross joined the main stream. At 2,000 feet the drizzle was cold and penetrating. The mud was knee-deep, the forest moss-draped and lofty. At the Puyu, a tributary, they came to a halt. The river was so swollen they could not cross. They must remain on its banks until it subsided. Spruce had the Indians build a lean-to of palm leaves, and took this opportunity to collect. On June 17, he confides to his journal: "My chagrin at this delay was somewhat lessened by the circumstance of finding myself in the most mossy place I had yet seen anywhere. Even the topmost twigs and the very leaves were shaggy with mosses, and from the branches overhanging the river were suspended festoons of several feet in length composed chiefly of *Bryopteris* and *Phyllogonium fulgens* in beautiful fruit. Throughout the journey, whenever rains, swollen streams and grumbling Indians combined to overwhelm me with chagrin, I found reason to thank heaven which had enabled me to forget the moment of my troubles in the contemplation of a simple moss." It was the richest cryptogamic locality on the surface of the globe, and there Spruce laid the foundation for his greatest work, the six-hundred-page *Hepaticæ Amazonicæ et Andinæ.*

The last part of his trip along the side of the gorge of the Pastaza was the worst. Roads were only the merest tracks, such as the tapir makes to his feeding and drinking places. No one ever opened them, no fallen trees had been cleared away, no overhanging branches cut off. At last they passed the roaring, thundering Falls of Agoyan. Baños crept into view, and Spruce, for the first time in three months, could feel that he had "proceeded" as directed.

At Baños he found the cold almost insufferable. At daybreak the thermometer was as low as forty-eight degrees. The cold mist kept Spruce's teeth chattering all day. He was attacked at once by a catarrh, with a cough so violent that blood flowed from his mouth and nose.

Baños was a "poor little place" of about a thousand souls, six thousand feet above sea-level, which took its name from the hot sulphur springs that poured from the base of the volcano Tunguragua. "The patron saint — *Nuestra Señora de las Aguas Santas* — is a very miraculous saint, and *romeros* (i.e. pilgrims) come to adore at her shrine from faraway towns. In large troops they come — bathe nine days in the hot wells, assist at nine masses, rosaries and processions, get drunk every night of the nine — *all* in honour of the virgin — and then after these *actas de devoción,* as they are called, return to their homes rejoicing, having fulfilled some previously-made promise to the saint and feeling secure of her protection for the future."

And these *romeros* Spruce followed over the heaven-high paramo to Ambato. He suffered miserably. It was only the thought that he was on the last lap that made this journey tolerable. He crossed the paramo in a piercingly cold misty rain. Sitting on his mule, wrapped in enough woolen ponchos to be thought a mummy, he was soon unable to tell if he had either feet or hands. He thought of his own Yorkshire moors. Near Teesdale, as far as the Weel, the chilly treeless solitude was something like the paramos of the Andes. The *paramero* swept down, a deadly cold wind charged with frost, whistling among the dead grass-stalks. Along the treeless, undulating, rock-bound paramos, crosses appeared with increasing frequency. A pilgrim from Baños, seeing the look on Spruce's face, reminded him that these were the graves of people who had died during the blast of the *paramero*. He told him that when he was a boy crossing here with his father, they saw a man sitting on an ice-sheathed rock, grinning at them with all his might.

" 'See,' said I, 'how that man is laughing at us.' 'Silence,' roared my father, above the rush of the *paramero*. 'Silence or else say a prayer for the repose of his soul — the man is dead.' "

Spruce came upon the warm, pleasant city of Ambato with all the hopeful ardor of a pilgrim approaching Mecca. At last he would begin the search for the seeds of the quinine. He would . . .

But Ecuador was in the throes of revolution.

CHAPTER XXIX
Cinchona, the Fever Bark

NOVEMBER 2, 1858, ECUADOR. . . . Matters are in a very unsettled state here, and preparations for the war with Peru resound on every hand. Recruiting — forced contributions of money and horses — people hiding in the forest and mountains to avoid being torn from their families — scarcity and dearness of provisions — such are some of the precursors of the contest. And the war, if it actually comes, will be something like what you have read in India, yet nobody knows what it is to be about. These Spanish republics are not unlikely to squabble among one another until — like the Kilkenny cats — there is nothing left of them but their tails, and then Jonathan will step in and make an easy prey of their mangled carcasses, *hibernice loquitur.* . . ."

In Ambato Spruce met Dr. James Taylor, a native of Cumberland, and former medical attendant to General Flores. He had married the daughter of one of Bolívar's generals and was thus well placed. Although it had been fifty years since he had left England and educated society, he still retained enough Greek to read and enjoy Anacreon, "and what is much better," Spruce wrote, "he is a very kind-hearted, honourable man, which can't be said of many Englishmen I have met in South America." There, too, he met Philo White, President Buchanan's Minister to Ecuador, whom he discovered to have "more cosmopolitan sympathies and fewer local prejudices than many of his countrymen." White was a very amiable, sound-hearted man, but "like many diplomatic gentlemen, apt to run into long-winded dissertations not remarkable for either depth or brilliancy." The Minister, too, was in a fog about the war, and unable to explain it satisfactorily.

While Spruce waited, he was able to squeeze in, by running the gantlet of revolution and counter-revolution, an expedition to the region of the *cascarilla roja,* the tree whose red bark produces quinine. The property was owned by General Juan José Flores, lately returned to Ecuador after an absence of fifteen years. He was at first adamant in his refusal: he would neither rent nor sell his property, on which were thousands of trees. Then, under the influence of Dr. Taylor, his one-time physician during the troubled years of his Presidency of Ecuador, he relented and agreed to rent the property — provided that Spruce would not touch the bark of the trees. There now followed weeks of negotiation. Spruce got letters through to Guayaquil and obtained the funds placed in the hands of Her Britannic Majesty's Consul. Then another owner popped up, one Dr. Francisco Neyra, whose lands overlapped those of General Flores. That opened more negotiations. Of Dr. Neyra, Spruce was at once suspicious. He was the grandson of that notorious Neyra who led the attack on Dr. Senièrgues, the physician to La Condamine's expedition. Spruce, however, urged on the British Consul the acceptance of any figure, no matter how unreasonable. The trees were beginning to blossom. He must be on the spot when the seeds began to form. And now at last his letters, years overdue, and periodicals of ancient vintage, poured upon him from a mail-sack that had followed him over much of South America. Some of these urged him to return to England, fearing for his health. To these Spruce replied: "I should be very glad to return to England, as you recommend me — but I have no funds beyond what are in your hands; these would soon be exhausted and poverty is such a positive curse in England. . . . I have often wished I could get some consular appointment here, were it only for £150 a year; but I have no powerful friends, without which a familiarity with the country, the inhabitants and the languages go for little. A person is much wanted to watch over the interests of Europeans on the Upper Amazon. . . ."

Word came now that the time was ripe to work upon the cinchona, the quinine tree. Spruce gathered his gear together, mounted his horse, and with his guides set off in the direction of Riobamba.

They rode two days looking at the great hulk of snow-encrusted Chimborazo, whose glaciers stood out against the blue sky like cut marble. Then they turned west and began to drop down to the thickly matted cinchona forests that lay on the slopes of the giant volcano. All along the line the church bells pealed. Was it peace, or had war broken out again? Spruce asked the first white person he met on the road the meaning of the bells.

"Have you not heard, señor? The bells are tolling in honor of Baron Humboldt. News has just reached us that he has died in Berlin. Ecuador has declared him *benemérito*. . . ."

Once more Spruce was in a jungle.

He had now carried out his instructions, he had "proceeded" to the quinine region. In fact, he was in the very heart of it. He had obtained a small bamboo house mounted on stilts, possessed of one room for cooking, sleeping, and eating, sufficiently open to permit flies and bats to pay frequent visits. The locality he had finally selected was called Limón, a gathering of bamboo huts raised on stilts, on the western flanks of the Andes. Here Spruce began to make his assault on the botanical problem of quinine. Writing his first report to Sir William Hooker, he explained:

"I have succeeded in hiring the forests producing the *Cascarilla roja* after about ten times as much correspondence as would have been necessary in any civilized country. . . . I am also in treaty with the owners of the woods near Loja, which produce the *Cinchona condaminea,* but as this species seems to flower and fruit at the same time as the *Cascarilla roja,* and the localities of the two species are fifteen days apart, under the most favorable circumstances it is plainly impossible that I can see with my own eyes the seeds of both species gathered which is the only way to be sure of having the right sort. . . ."

The plan, as it now stood, was relatively simple in concept. Spruce marked the trees that were in blossom, and these he would visit to see for himself how the fruits were coming along. In the morning, rain, shine, or mist, he would take his guide and his plant press and start off into the jungle. The virgin forests did not tower here as in the Amazon. Although the altitude varied between 3,000 and 5,000 feet, the temperature was very much that of a summer day in London; and although there was a great depth of black soil, the virgin jungle did not climb higher than ninety feet. The *cascarilla roja,* the red-bark, which yielded the quinine, seemed to grow best on stony declivities where there was a good depth of humus. Rain was an essential to cinchona. From January to May it rained without cease; during the dry season the evenings were filled with a cold drizzling mist. These conditions had to be accurately noted and duplicated in India if the tree was to be grown there. Spruce had worked out the procedure. He would wait until the capsules containing the seeds had ripened, and gather them before they fell to the ground. Then he must send for Mr. Cross, who waited with the boxes in Guayaquil, some two hundred miles down the Guayas River. The seeds had to be dried, some cuttings planted; and then the whole collection would go to India under the care of Cross. In essence the plan was simple; the execution was complicated.

The good people of Limón got the notion that Spruce wanted to buy cinchona seeds from them, and he found one morning when he made his customary rounds that two trees had been stripped of every panicle. The seeds were not yet ripe. Fearing that all the rest might be destroyed in like manner, he set off immediately to tell all the inhabitants that the seeds would be of no value unless he gathered them himself. He even paid them to leave the trees alone. This had the desired effect. But then the revolution

was on again. Troops moved through Limón constantly, for Guayaquil, on the coast, was warring with Quito. They seized everyone's
horses; the people of Limón decamped in the face of the armed
hordes, and this was no aid in gathering the cinchona seeds. All
through June and July they ripened. Spruce, whose skin was sensitive after so many years in damp climes, suffered extremely. The
wait for the fruit was long and tedious. The people with whom he
had to associate were gentle cholos, but of the utmost simplicity.
In letters that helped him pass the long nights and enlightened his
friends in England, Spruce explained that "your sanity and social
reformers . . . would be much shocked could they see the promis-
cuous way in which people sleep here . . . the other day I re-
monstrated my landlord . . . one of the best men in the place,
for allowing a number of people of both sexes to sleep together in
the same room — some in beds, some on the floor. 'I assure you,'
replied he, 'we throw open both doors and windows at daybreak.'
He had no idea, poor man, of any possible vitiation of the moral
atmosphere. I thought of the fair Pauline Bonaparte, who, when
an English lady asked her 'How could you sit so naked to that
sculptor?' made answer, 'My dear madam, you forget I had a fire
in the room.' "

Thus did Richard Spruce, with his usual flow of anecdotes, gloss
over an existence in the cinchona forests that was as painful to
him as it was important to the progress of the world. Why had he
been instructed to get out the seeds of the cinchona tree, to be
grown in India? As the quinine-yielding trees grew in South America and the natives gathered the bark, why transport the tree to
India? Did India need a new industry? Yes, that was part of it; but
more than that, quinine had suddenly become immensely important. The Frenchmen Pelletier and Caventou had rediscovered
quinine, the active principle of cinchona bark, in 1820, and it was
now used widely as a specific for malaria. Immense quantities were
needed. South America could no longer supply it all. The careless
exploitation of the quinine-yielding trees had proceeded apace.
Humboldt had observed fifty years before that such devastation
would end in cinchona leaving the South American continent.
That time had come.

It had been only two hundred years since quinine made its dramatic debut into the history of therapeutics. The locale was Loja,
the year 1638. The wife of the Viceroy of Peru, Doña Francisca
Henríquez de Rivera, Countess of Chinchón, was en route to Quito,
accompanied by her physician, Dr. Juan del Vega. In Loja she
was struck down with tertiary malaria. Legend has it that Dr.
Vega, despairing of her life, sought out some ancient Inca practi-

tioners, and they suggested the powdered bark of the quinaquina tree. The cure was almost instantaneous. When the Countess returned to Spain with her husband at the end of his Viceregal term, she carried a supply of the wonderful bark with her, so that, as we have noted earlier, it was long known as the *pulvis comtissæ* — the Countess's powder. Del Vega returned to Spain, too, with a quantity of the quinaquina, which he sold at the high price of a hundred reales the pound. The spread of quinine through Europe was extremely rapid. It was not alone a panacea, but a cause for polemic. Europe was divided into two camps, acrid arguments raged for and against its virtues. Religious factors were involved; since the Jesuits began to export it and the product became known as Jesuit's bark, it became anathema to Protestants. Soon the prejudices melted away, and cinchona took a definite place in the materia medica of the century. In England it was popularized by the great Dr. Sydenham; in France it came into use after the King and the Duke of Anjou were cured by it. Later Linnæus, to honor the memory of the Countess who purportedly had introduced it, named the whole genus of the trees *cinchona* after her. Then came the discovery of the alkaloid quinine; and it became important since it paced the white man's restless conquest of the tropics.

Collecting the bark of the *cascarilla roja* (as the cinchona was called in Ecuador) had been the industry of the people of Limón for centuries. It brought money, they knew, but they had no idea of its use. The prevalent opinion was that a dye was made from it. When Spruce explained how it yielded the precious quinine and its use in medicine, he heard them say to one another: "It is all very fine for him to stuff us with such a tale; of course *he* won't tell us how the dye is made. . . ."

For weeks Spruce waited upon the handsome cinchonas. Then the capsules began to form; the seeds in them were ripening; the time had come for Mr. Cross. In July a report reached Spruce in his bamboo hut, via the bush telegraph, that an Englishman had arrived on the Río Ventanas bringing with him a number of boxes. It was Cross with a supply of Wardian cases. These portable boxes, named after Nathaniel Ward, had a glass top and sides for shipping moisture-loving plants. These were to hold cuttings from the trees, to supplement the seeds. Spruce's instructions were specifically to get seeds, but the cuttings, if they survived, would be better.

Through the months of July and August, Cross and Spruce struggled with the cuttings. As soon as they took root, caterpillars attacked them. Spruce was up for days after that. Then his old enemies the maroon-colored sauba ants appeared, to do their share of destruction. In August the seed capsules began to break. Spruce now employed most of the people of the village. He spread a white sheet under each tree to catch the seeds as they fell. By September he had gathered over 100,000 well-ripened, well-dried cinchona seeds. They had scarcely got everything packed when word came (through the bush telegraph again) that General Flores and his Federal Army had captured Guayaquil, and that communications were opened on the river. So they constructed a huge sixty-foot-square balsa raft, put themselves, the seeds, and the cuttings on it, and with native oarsmen floated down to Guayaquil. Within a month a steamer had arrived up the muddy Río Guayas, and Cross was placed aboard with his cross-section of the wealth of the Americas.

Spruce had finished his work; the rest was in the hands of others. He learned long afterward that the young plants reached India in good condition, the seeds germinated and served as the starting-point of extensive quinine plantations in the Neilgherry Hills of southern India, in Ceylon, and elsewhere. But Spruce was aware of something more as the steamer sent its thick smoke into the flat blue sky and disappeared down the river — of the prophetic words of Humboldt, written among the quinine-yielding trees of Loja: "If the governments in America do not attend to the preservation of the quinaquina either by prohibiting the felling of the trees or obliging the territorial magistrate to enforce the cutters to guard them from destruction, this highly esteemed product of the New World will be swept away from the country. . . ."

Spruce had done the sweeping.

By the year 1860 South America was awakening everywhere to the quickened touch of progress and big business. Machinery poured into the countries, railroads mushroomed, ocean-going vessels began their ascent of the Amazon.

All the careful codifying of the continent's wealth by the explorer-naturalists was eagerly studied by the agents of business. The rubber boom, galvanized by demand from the United States, now caught in the Civil War, zoomed prices astronomically. The wax palms, the lignum vitæ, the hundred and one medicinal remedies which the explorer-naturalists had shown to the world, each was the subject of a business enterprise. Guano, which Humboldt had introduced into Europe, now supported a full-sized industry on the Peruvian coast. The explorer-naturalist, whose directed enthusiasm kept him in the sweating jungles or on the sun-baked pampas long after others would have fled, had provided the world with authentic reports of a continent which had, for a long time, been more dark than darkest Africa. The door to South America was fully opened.

In 1861 Spruce stood on the shores of Guayaquil. It was a long time since La Condamine and his group from the French Academy had set themselves upon South American beaches and forced open the continent. In 1735 South America had been, to the world at large, as little known as the moon. Maps of it were filled with great voids, vast stretches of terra incognita. Now, in a single century and a quarter, explorer-naturalists had woven about it a criss-cross of travel-ways and exploratory roads. The theory of evolution had been virtually conceived in South America by the observations of Charles Darwin and Alfred Wallace. All the "joyefull news out of the newefound worlde" that Europe had expected after the discovery now arrived.

Alas, poor Richard! He was the last link between the colonial and the industrial eras. He had done so much for South America and for science; yet on his return to England there were no parades, no universal celebrations such as were held for Humboldt; no such formal gathering of academies as marked the return of the French Academicians; no burial in Westminster Abbey like that accorded Darwin. He, who had opened the green world of the Amazon, who had spent fifteen years in the jungles and the rock-hard world of the cordilleras, was met by no one other than his old botanical friends. Spruce had returned without funds. In 1861, after he had bid good-by to Cross and seen the cinchona seedlings leave for India, he had deposited all his worldly wealth, £700 to be exact, with the firm of Gutiérrez & Company in Guayaquil. In October of that year the firm failed — and with it went Spruce's money.

Yet he pulled himself together and spent three more years collecting on the Peruvian coast. Then at last, pain-racked and continuously feverish after fifteen years in South America, Richard Spruce took a boat for England. Quietly he debarked at Southampton. There was no committee to meet him. He went straight to Kew Gardens. There, between spasms of pain, he worked over the 30,000 specimens of plants that he had collected, sorted the twenty-one vocabularies of Amazonian Indians, piled up the maps he had made in the course of 10,000 miles of river travel, and looked over the mountain of notes that was to make a consecutive book of his travels. The scientists who knew of his great work were unstinting in their praise of his collections. They tried to find this tall, amiable, soft-spoken, fever-racked man a sinecure of some sort to help him weather the financial storms that would beset him. The most they could secure for the man who brought India a quinine industry, who helped provide the means by which man made his conquest of the tropics, who had collected 30,000 plants and made the gardens at Kew world-renowned, was a pitiful fifty-pound annual pension. By a stroke of irony, the Imperial German Academy — Academia Cæsarea Leopoldiana-Carolina — was the one institution that gave recognition to his work. In 1864 it bestowed upon him the honorary degree of Doctor of Philosophy.

Dr. Richard Spruce lived out the seventeen years remaining to him in a one-room cottage at Wellburn, in his native Yorkshire, working and writing between illnesses. To the very end he kept up his interests. Martius, the old botanist who had preceded him in Brazil, begged in a letter that Spruce take over the handling of some of his plants. Darwin wrote to him, Wallace visited him. The writing went on, but the book, the book which might well have been the greatest since the *Voyage of the Beagle,* never fully materialized. He never quite found the time to put the whole thing together.*

In 1893 the remains of the great explorer-scientist who laid the foundation of botany in South America were buried in the church-yard at Terrington on the Yorkshire moors.

"His name," wrote a local obituary, "is commemorated by the moss *Sprucea.*"

* His book, a collection of botanical papers, letters, and geographical articles, was assembled by his old friend Alfred Russel Wallace and edited by him into a two-volume work: *Notes of a Botanist on the Amazon and Andes: Being Records of Travel on the Amazon and Its Tributaries the Trombetas, Rio Negro, etc. . . . during the years 1849–1864. . . .* Macmillan & Co., 1908.

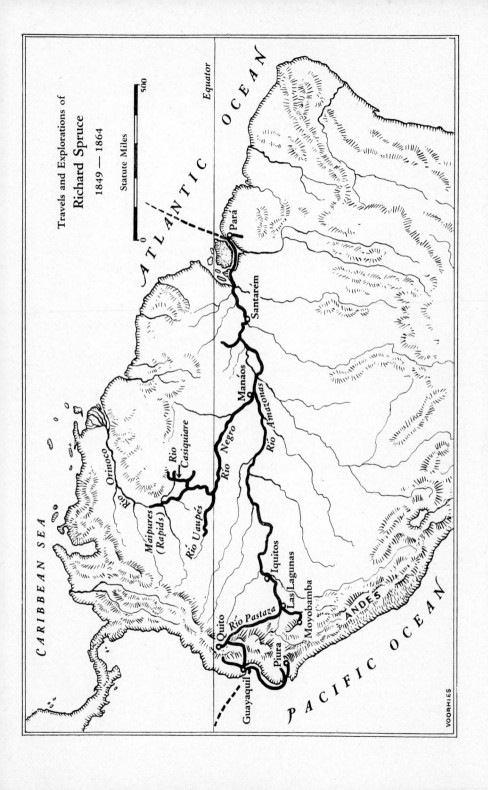

Travels and Explorations of
Richard Spruce
1849 — 1864

Statute Miles

500

ATLANTIC OCEAN

Equator

Pará

Santarém

Manáos

Río Amazonas

Río Negro

Casiquiare

Río Orinoco

Río

Río Uaupés

Máipures
(Rapids)

CARIBBEAN SEA

Iquitos

Las Lagunas

Moyobamba

ANDES

Quito

Río Pastaza

Piura

Guayaquil

PACIFIC OCEAN

VOORHIES

CHAPTER XXX
South America Calling

In the brief interval of the explorers' century, from 1735 until 1859, the massive cornucopia-shaped continent was laid bare to the eyes of the world, effectively opened by the explorer-naturalists. But the work of La Condamine, Humboldt, Darwin, and Spruce was only the beginning. Henceforth there was a veritable parade of savants moving over the verdure-splashed face of South America. The fossils of Patagonia were given more attention; much time was spent on the life histories of South American birds; the Humboldt Current was examined, plumbed, and observed; the Indians, dwellers in lambent green worlds, were subjected to minute observations. Were one today desirous of culling *all* the literature of sciences and of expeditions since the publication of *The Origin of Species,* it would take much of one's life. The list of published studies on South America stretches to the moon. And yet there are great gaps in our knowledge, so that it is easier to record what we do not know than what we know. Of the great civilizations that once studded the soil of South America, only those of the Incas of Peru have been examined. Of Bolivia's past, of the civilizations of Ecuador and Colombia, we know little. For the young archæologists who will brave the *puna* of the Andes there is an inexhaustible intellectual treasure. And of the greater past — the bones of massive animals that lived in the remote geologic eras lie strewn all over the continent waiting to be unearthed. In Patagonia, in southern Chile, in some of the higher Andes, there are veritable ossuaries of extinct monsters. And the inner earth itself is virtually untouched. The nimbus of scientific immortality awaits the young geologist who can spend time exploring the textbook of South America's rock-bound face. No, not everything is known. The neophyte should not be driven off by the sheer mass and ubiquity of literature. It may seem horribly learned, but when one probes deep into it, one sees that much of it is based on pyramiding hypotheses. Animals have been collected, and have been labeled by the taxonomists, but their life histories are little known; the same may be said of the avifauna. The monumental studies of Dr. Frank Chapman on the *Bird Life of the Andes* and the work of Dr. Robert C. Murphy on the *Oceanic Birds of South America* are mere signposts of the direction that the science of ornithology should take. And this holds equally true for the primitive inhabitants of South America. The jungle is filled with tribes, the remote Andes spotted with small isolated Indian groups, that are still as little known as when Columbus set foot on the island of Trinidad in 1498. There is no complete book on the ancient civilizations of South America; there is no complete book on the Indians of South America; neither is there a complete book on the animals or on the birds of South America. South America has a crying need of knowledge of its plants, and of botanists to collect and study them. The green world awaits a man who will carry on the work of Richard Spruce, not a mere "collector," but one who will be deeply stirred by these green mansions to write long and well of the part that plants played in the past and will play in the future. A book on the plant geography of South America — an over-all view of the distribution of plant life — is one of the most needed works. The list of things yet to be done is almost endless. South America has still to reveal the inner core of her riches.

This is the province of the young man. It is a vigorous frontier of science. That is why most of our explorer-naturalists were young men when they took their first scientific steps.

Let the lives of men such as La Condamine, Humboldt, Darwin, and Spruce act as an excitant; with Anatole France, "let us rise on the wings of enthusiasm; so long as we reason we shall never soar." And then, when we believe that all is done, hark to the sonorous sentences of Seneca: *"Multum adhuc restat* — Much remains to be done, much still will remain, nor shall any man born after the revolution of a thousand ages be denied the opportunity to contribute something."

South America is calling.

BIBLIOGRAPHICAL REFERENCES
PART I
Charles-Marie de La Condamine

To set the scene of America's discovery and its effect on Europe, I have used Samuel Eliot Morison's *Admiral of the Ocean Sea* (Boston, 1942), *Amerigo,* by Stefan Zweig (New York, 1942), as well as his *Magellan* (1938). The account of the explorations that followed is based on reprints of the reports of the Spanish explorers, published by the Hakluyt Society, as well as an excellent book on the *History of Geographical Discovery and Exploration,* by J. N. L. Baker (Boston, 1931), and *A History of Geographical Discovery in the 17th and 18th Centuries,* by Edward Heawood (Cambridge, 1912). The background for the science of the seventeenth century that led to the controversies on the shape of the earth was found in an excellent encyclopedic work, *A History of Science . . . in the 16th and 17th Centuries,* by A. Wolf (London, 1935). *The Making of Geography,* by R. E. Dickinson and O. J. R. Howarth (Oxford, 1933) outlines the problem of finding universal formulæ for degrees and latitudes, all of which is put forward very vividly in *Men of Mathematics,* by E. T. Bell (New York, 1937) and in the *Life of Isaac Newton,* by L. T. More (New York, 1934).

The background of the earth controversy in France and the part that the French Academy played in it was found in *L'Ancienne Académie des Sciences,* by L. F. Alfred Maury (Paris, 1864). A general critique of French society of that period can be found in R. B. Mowat's *Age of Reason* (Boston, 1934), and a corresponding exposition in Louis Kronenberger's *Kings and Desperate Men* (New York, 1942), showing the state of English society at the time. For Voltaire's part, I used *Voltaire,* by Georg Brandes (New York, 1930), and Guizot's *History of France.* For a survey of names, dates, and places in relation to eighteenth-century science I am indebted to two books: *History of Biology* by Erik Nordenskiöld (New York, 1929) and *A Short History of Science* by Charles Singer (New York, 1941).

The material for La Condamine has come from La Condamine's writings, which are:

1. The Distance of the Tropicks (1738).
2. *Relation abrégée d'un voyage fait dans l'intérieur de l'Amérique méridionale* (Paris, 1745).
3. *Lettre sur l'émeute populaire de Cuenca* (Paris, 1746).
4. *Mesure des trois premiers degrés du méridien* (Paris, 1751).
5. *Histoire des pyramides de Quito* (Paris, 1751).
6. *Journal du voyage fait par ordre du roi a l'équateur* (Paris, 1751).

Also: Condorcet: *Éloge de La Condamine,* read in the Académie des Sciences; Delille: *Discours de reception à l'Académie Française;* Buffon: *Réponse au discours de reception de La Condamine à l'Académie Française;* Revue encyclopédique, t. XII, p. 483; Voltaire: *Dictionnaire philosophique,* "Curiosité" (article); and Chaudon et Delandine, *Dictionnaire universelle historique, critique et bibliographique,* as well as the reports of Pierre Bouguer: *La Figure de la terre* (Paris, 1749), and the reports of Maupertuis's expedition to Lapland that appeared in Pinkerton's *Voyages.*

Much use has been made of Jorge Juan y Santacilla and Antonio de Ulloa's work: *Relación histórica del viaje a la América meridional* (Madrid, 1747, 4 vols.), since these Spaniards paid close attention to all the minutiæ of Spanish colonial life and were with the French explorers much of the time. Good material was found in their *Noticias secretas de América* (London, 1807), as well as the life of Juan, under the title of *Jorge Juan y la colonizacion española en América,* by Cervera y Alfaro (Madrid, 1927) and Heyes's *Vida de Ulloa* (Madrid, 1847). These all possess details that explain much left unsaid in the works of the French Academicians. *Cartagena* by R. B. Cunninghame-Graham (New York, 1926) was used for a description of the colonial city, as well as the instructive and accurate work of Philip Ainsworth Means: *The Spanish Main* (New York, 1935).

Rarities, such as *Relación histórica política y moral de la Ciudad de Cuenca* (Madrid, 1894) have been used; and classics, such as Means's *Ancient Civilizations of the Andes* (1931) and his *Fall of the Inca Empire* (1933) set the archæological and historical scene. For La Condamine's researches on rubber I have used Howard and Ralph Wolf's *Rubber, A Story of Glory and Greed* (New York, 1936). For Pedro Maldonado, Stevenson's *A Historical and Descriptive Narrative of Twenty Years' Residence in South America* (London, 1825, 3 vols.). Intimate knowledge of the whole country of Ecuador, as well as Quito, gave me the background for describing that city, helped greatly by such scholarly books as Bernard Moses's *South America on the Eve of Emancipation* (New

York, 1908), and *Academic Culture in the Spanish Colonies,* by John Tate Lanning (New York, 1940).

The story of Isabela Godin des Odonais appears in La Condamine's *Relations* (Paris, 1751), a translation of which appears in Pinkerton's *Voyages* (London, 1813), Vol. XIV, pp. 259 et seq. There is further critical material in E. Frio de Daux: *Documents inédits sur Godin des Odonais, Société des Américainistes.* All the background material came from my own experience in the same regions where Mme Godin was lost, most of which is contained in von Hagen's *Off with Their Heads* (New York, 1937).

PART II

Alexander von Humboldt

THE BIOGRAPHICAL material on Humboldt is quite extensive, but in the main uncritical, and written mostly too soon after his death to have the "pathos of distance" so necessary in correct evaluation of a man and his times. That used mostly in the preparation of this book were: *Life of Humboldt,* by Karl Bruhns (2 vols., Boston, 1873); *Alejandro de Humboldt,* by Herbert Rau (6 vols., Mexico, 1873–4); *Humboldt,* by Arnold Krumm-Heller (Mexico, 1910); *Alexander von Humboldt: Bibliographische Übersicht seiner Werke,* etc., by Julius Loewenberg, *Lettres américaines d'Alexandre d' Humboldt (1798–1807)* (Paris, 1904); *Humboldt en America,* by Carlos Pereyra (Madrid, 1917); *Alejandro de Humboldt: Su Vida y Su Obra,* by Vito Alessio Robles (Mexico, 1940); and the bibliographical material contained in the first edition of *Viaje a las regiones equinocciales del Nuevo Continente,* by Eduardo Roehl (Caracas, 1941).

When we begin on Humboldt's travels, we encounter immediate difficulties, for with the exception of his explorations in Venezuela, he never wrote a continuous narrative of his American travels. Humboldt lavished the greater part of his American odyssey on the work first published in French as: *Voyage aux régions équinoxiales du Nouveau Continent (1799–1804)*, which took some years to publish in its entirety. The first English edition, under the title of *Personal Narratives,* was published between the years 1814 and 1829. But in re-creating Humboldt's America I have used the later English edition published in three thick octavo volumes in Bohn's Library, London, 1850.

For the state of the Capitanía of Venezuela in Humboldt's time, I have used *Travels in South America during 1801–4*, by F. Depons (3 vols., London, 1807) , *Spain's Declining Power in South America (1730–1806)* , by Bernard Moses (Berkeley, 1919) , *Colonial Hispanic America*, by C. E. Chapman (New York, 1933) , *Bolívar and the Political Thought of the South American Revolution*, by Andrés Belaunde (Baltimore, 1938) .

When Humboldt enters the Orinoco country, his own work is used extensively, with the background filled in with writings known and little known, such as: *Up the Orinoco*, etc. by J. J. Mozans (London, 1910) ; *Reise nach der spanischen Ländern in Europe und America in den jahren 1751–1756*, by Peter Loefling (Berlin, 1766) ; Padre José Gumilla's fantastic work, *El Orinoco illustrado y defendido* (Madrid, 1745) ; and in modern times, Arthur O. Friel's *The River of the Seven Stars* (New York, 1924) and Earl P. Hanson's *Journey to Manáos* (New York, 1938) .

In Nueva Granada, now known as Colombia, we again enter familiar ground. Here I have used Humboldt's *Researches Concerning the Institutions of America*, which is in the main archæological. Parts of his *Personal Narratives* deal with his stay at the Río Sinu, but for atmosphere, I made full use of R. B. Cunninghame-Graham's *Cartagena and the Río Sinu* (New York, 1925) , which dealt impressionistically with that in which Humboldt was less profuse. For Cartagena, I am indebted very much to the most excellent book *Colombia — Gateway to South America* (New York, 1940) by Kathleen Romoli. The account of the trip up the Magdalena is supplied not by Humboldt, but by a contemporary, Captain Charles Cochrane's *Journal of a Residence and Travels in Colombia* (2 vols., London, 1825) . Hamilton's *Travels through the Interior Provinces of Colombia* (London, 1827) , Sir Clements Markham's *Conquest of New Granada* (New York, 1912) , and A. F. Bandelier's remarkable study, *The Gilded Man* (New York, 1893) complete the material for Colombia. Much of the original material on Colombia by Humboldt appears in his *Ansichten der Natur*, published as *View of Nature* (London, 1850) , and the untranslated *Kleine Schriften* (1845) .

When we enter Ecuador with Humboldt, the picture is very clear. Here I am on well-known ground, and my *Ecuador the Unknown* (New York, 1939) and my detailed knowledge of the terrain are the best source. Much of the Ecuadorian material is found in Humboldt's *Views of Nature*, and for the narrative part of his stay in Quito I am indebted to the two-volume *Life of Humboldt* by Karl Bruhns (Boston, 1873) and the other two *Lives, Humboldt's Travels and Researches* (Edinborough, 1836), which gives some material not obtained from Bruhn's *Life,* and *Lives of the Brothers Humboldt,* by Klencke and Schlesier (London, 1852). For conditions in Quito during this time, W. B. Stevenson's *A Historical Descriptive Narrative of Twenty Years' Residence in South America* (3 vols., London, 1825) gives much detail not found elsewhere. And finally *America Hispaña,* by Waldo Frank.

The climbing of Chimborazo Humboldt himself has narrated in a letter that appears in Bruhn's *Life of Humboldt,* but for details on this I have used that singularly amusing and instructive book, *Travels among the Great Andes of Ecuador,* by the celebrated alpinist Edward Whymper (London, 1892). In addition to being a writer of parts, Whymper checked altitudes at the points at which Humboldt scaled Chimborazo. Dr. Teodoro Wolf's *Geografía y Geología del Ecuador* (Leipzig, 1892) is invaluable to the student and biographer, as well as Frank M. Chapman's *The Distribution of Bird Life in Ecuador* (New York, 1926) for its confirmation of Humboldt's work on physical geography.

The part of this work that deals with Peru is based on some of Humboldt's own writings that appear scattered through *Kosmos* (1859), *Anischten der Natur* (1850), and his *Kleine Schriften* (1845). The most valuable and detailed account of travels in Peru come not from Humboldt, whose writings on this part are scattered, but from the remarkable book of travel, research, and observation, *Travels in Peru,* by J. J. von Tschudi (New York, 1847). Von Tschudi traveled over much of the ground covered by Humboldt. In that part of the book which deals with the Humboldt Current and guano, I have relied fully and completely on my own travels and Dr. Robert C. Murphy's *Bird Islands of Peru* (New York, 1925), as well as *The Andes of Southern Peru,* by Dr. Isaiah Bowman (1916), and Dr. Murphy's *Oceanic Birds of South America* (2 vols., New York, 1936).

Finally, for the place of Humboldt in the field of science, I am indebted to the short summaries given in Erik Nordenskiöld's *History of Biology,* (New York, 1929); Julian M. Drachman's *Studies in the Literature of Natural Science* (New York, 1930); Charles Singer's excellent summary, *A Short History of Science* (New York, 1941), and *A History of Geographical Discovery and Exploration,* by J. N. L. Baker (New York, 1931).

On Humboldt's relation to Darwin and the literature from which this is drawn, the reader is referred to the bibliography to Part III.

PART III
Charles Robert Darwin

THE LIVES OF Charles Darwin are many, yet almost all of them deal with the mature Darwin rather than the Darwin in the making. For his early life I have consulted and sometimes used the material contained in: *Charles Darwin,* by Leonard Huxley (1921); *Charles Darwin,* by Karl Pearson (1923) ; *Darwin,* by Gamaliel Bradford (1926) ; *The Evolution of Charles Darwin,* by G. A. Dorsey (1927) ; and the recent and the best piece of Darwiniana, *Charles Darwin, a Portrait,* by Geoffrey West (1938).

Once the voyage begins, I have relied entirely on Darwin's *Diary of the Voyage of the Beagle* (edited from the manuscript by his granddaughter, Nora Barlow), and the various editions of *Journal of the Voyage of the Beagle.* For the history of Brazil, I have used *Good Neighbors,* by Hubert Herring (1941), *Brazil,* by Stefan Zweig (1942), and *South American Excursion,* by Ernest Young (New York, 1940).

On Argentina, *24 Years in the Argentina Republic,* by Col. J. A. King (London, 1824) ; *Travels in South America during the Years 1819–20–21,* by Alexander Caldcleugh (2 vols., London, 1825) ; and *Gleanings and Remarks — At Buenos Aires,* by Major Alexander Gillespie (London, 1819) about complete the picture of the end of the colonial period and the beginning of the Republic.

Once Charles Darwin is on the savannas of Patagonia, his journal has been used, as well as the works of W. H. Hudson: *El Ombu, The Purple Land That England Lost, Idle Days in Patagonia, The Birds of La Plata,* for some details of the country and the people. G. C. Musters's *At Home with the Patagonians* (London, 1871) has been consulted, as well as some of the more modern explorers' travels, such as G. G. Simpson's *Attending Marvels* (New York, 1934).

The literature about Cape Horn and Tierra del Fuego is abundant. The finest and most complete work is *Cape Horn,* by Captain Felix Riesenberg (New York, 1939), whose brilliant pages suggested many avenues of reading and research to make Darwin's stay in Tierra del Fuego profitable for the reader. *Magellan, Conqueror of the Seas,* by Stefan Zweig (New York, 1938), succeeds in capturing the mood of the ice-bound cape, while other books, *By Way of Cape Horn,* by Alan J. Villiers (New York,

1930), *Fifty South to Fifty South,* by W. M. Tompkins (New York, 1938), and Rockwell Kent's *Voyaging* (New York, 1934), add numerous personal impressions of the land and water that are Tierra del Fuego. Finally, the culture of the Fuegians was thoroughly learned through the reading of the truly monumental volume by Dr. Martin Gusinde, *Die Feuerland Indianer* (Vienna, 1937).

Chile and Peru I know at first hand. For Darwin's period I have consulted: *Travels into Chile over the Andes in the Years 1820 and 1821,* by Peter Schmidtmeyer (London, 1824); the authentic and excellent work of S. B. Stevenson, *A Historical and Descriptive Narrative of 20 Years' Residence in South America* (3 vols., London, 1825), and Basil Hall's *Extracts from a Journal Written on the Coasts of Chile, Peru and Mexico* (2 vols., Edinburgh, 1824). The books of Philip Ainsworth Means: *Ancient Civilization of the Andes* (New York, 1931), *Fall of the Inca Empire* (New York, 1932), and *The Spanish Main* (New York, 1935), give some idea of the pre-Columbian and the colonial background of Chile; and on recent times the excellent *Good Neighbors* of Hubert Herring (New Haven, 1941), Earl Hanson's *Chile* (1942), *South American Excursion,* by Ernest Young (New York, 1940), and the most recent *Chile,* by Erna Fergusson (New York, 1943). All these give historical backgrounds and personal impressions of people and politics which, with Darwin's own acute impressions in his *Diary* and his *Journal,* provide the material on the coast and interior of Chile.

In the Galápagos section, personal knowledge of the terrain of the Enchanted Islands has helped greatly in interpreting young Darwin's impressions of these islands that stimulated the theory of evolution. I have written many, altogether too many, articles on these islands, but most of the material has been published in von Hagen's *Ecuador the Unknown* (New York, 1939) and *Herman Melville's Las Encantadas* (Burlingame, Cal., 1939). Other works that touch on the Galápagos are *World's End,* by William Beebe, no more than it purports to be — some eight thousand minutes on the Galápagos — and the chapter on the Galápagos contained in Donald C. Peattie's *Green Laurels.*

The material for Darwin's later life was gathered from his letters, *The Life and Letters of Charles Darwin,* edited by Francis Darwin (3 vols., London, 1907); from correspondence with his son, the late Major Leonard Darwin of Sussex; from the prefatory remarks of his granddaughter, Mrs. Nora Barlow, in the edition of his *Diary* (New York, 1934); and from *Charles Darwin, a Portrait,* by Geoffrey West (New Haven, 1938).

PART IV
Richard Spruce

RICHARD SPRUCE left no biographical material of note other than what appears in the first twenty pages of his *Notes of a Botanist on the Amazon and the Andes . . . (1849–1864)*, as edited and con‑ densed by Alfred Russel Wallace. At his death there were short obituaries in botanical journals, but for the most part Spruce tells us in his journal more about himself than we can learn elsewhere.

In re-creating the life of Richard Spruce and his years on the Amazon, I use his own words as generously as a biographer can without reprinting the whole of his work. All this came from the two-volume work: *Notes of a Botanist on the Amazon and the Andes* (2 vols., London, 1908). For other botanical explorations in the Amazon that augmented Spruce's there are R. R. Gates's *A Botanist in the Amazon Valley* (London, 1927); H. H. Rusby's *Jungle Memories* (New York, 1933); and *Pioneers of Plant Study*, by Ellison Hawks (London, 1928), which gives the lives and achievements of the early botanists.

As for the Amazon itself, the works are many. The following were used or consulted: *The Discovery of the Amazon*, by José Toribio Medina (New York, 1934); *The Land of the Amazons*, by Baron de Santa Ana Nery (New York, 1901); *Reise in Brasi‑ lien*, by Spix and Martius (Munich, 1823–31); *A Narrative of Travels on the Amazon and Río Negro*, by Alfred R. Wallace (London, 1853); *Reisen in Britisch-Guiana*, by Richard Schom‑ burgk (Berlin, 1847–8); *Narrative of a Journey from Lima to Pará*, by Smyth and Lowe (London, 1836); *Naturalist on the River Amazon*, by Henry Walter Bates (2 vols., London, 1863); *A Voy‑ age up the Amazon*, by W. M. Edwards (London, 1847). And then, in these modern times, the excellent impressionistic work-journey of a tramp steamer up the Amazon: *The Sea and the Jungle*, by H. M. Tomlinson (New York, 1920). Also *Meine Reise durch Nord-Brasilien zum Orinoco*, by the late great W. Thomas Koch‑ Grunberg (Berlin, 1913), and Dr. A. Hamilton Rice's *El Río Negro (Amazonas) y sus Grandes Afluentes de la Guayana Bra‑ sileña* (Cambridge, 1934). And then those books which live over again Spruce's Río Negro journey: Dr. William McGovern's *Jun‑ gle Paths and Inca Ruins* (New York, 1927); the seriocomic *White*

Waters and Black, by Gordon McCreagh (New York, 1926) ; and the recent *Back of Beyond,* by Harold Noice (New York, 1939) .

Other books that assisted in one phase or another of Spruce's investigations were: *A History of Medicine* by Arturo Castiglioni (New York, 1941) , and *A Naturalist in Brazil,* by Konrad Guenther (New York, 1931) .

Of much aid was the work of Professor Paul Russell Cutright, *The Great Naturalists Explore South America* and this with other books and articles on localized explorations in the Upper Amazon helped to plot Spruce's Upper Amazon journey. Much of this ground had been traveled over by me, and because of this I was able to dip generously into my own thread of memory. *Off with Their Heads* by von Hagen (New York, 1937) contains material for the areas through which Spruce passed, and for the period in Ecuador Spruce's work is used generously, as well as my own research for *Ecuador the Unknown* (New York, 1939) .

The botanical material is all too slight, but it must be remembered that the field in which Richard Spruce was a pioneer still remains fertile ground for study. There is yet to appear a single good broad work on the whole of Amazonian botany. Had it existed, Spruce's work would have been made the more clear.

CHRONOLOGY 1498–1859

1498 *Columbus discovers South America*

1504 *Amerigo Vespucci declares it a "terra nova"*

1507 *Waldseemüller names it "America-terra-nova" in his* COSMOGRAPHIA

1513 *Vasco Nuñez de Balboa discovers the Pacific*

1531 *Pizarro conquers the Incas*

1541 *Francisco de Orellana discovers the Río Amazonas*

1595 *Sir Walter Raleigh explores the lower Orinoco*

1638 *Pedro Texeira makes first ascent of the Amazon, reaching Quito by way of the Napo*

1651 *Thesaurus of Mexican Plants by Francisco Hernández published*

1672 *Jean Richer experiments with pendulum in Cayenne, French Guiana*

1686 PRINCIPIA MATHEMATICA *of Isaac Newton published*

1691 *Father Fritz publishes first detailed map of the Amazon River*

1707 *Louis Fueillée explores coast of Chile and Peru*

1712 *Amédée François Frézier explores coast of Peru*

1735 *Carl von Linné (Linnæus) publishes* SYSTEMA NATURÆ

1735–44 *Expedition to the equator by Academie des Sciences by C. M. de La Condamine, Pierre Bouguer, and Louis Godin. This begins the scientific history of South America.*

1742   *Celsius perfects 100-degree scale thermometer*

1750   *Expedition of Iturriaga and Solano to Río Orinoco*

1749   *Löfling, pupil of Linnæus, collects on Orinoco*

1749   *Buffon publishes* Histoire naturelle . . . *discusses evolution*

1780   *Expedición botánica: José Celestino Mutis in Santa Fé de Bogotá*

1781   *Ornithological investigations in Peru of Ruiz, Pavon, and Dombey*

1783   *Coastal surveys of South America by Captain Alessandro Malaspina*

1783   *Félix de Azara makes geographical survey in Paraguay-Paraná basin; works for thirteen years*

1789   *A. L. de Jussieu publishes* Genera Plantarum

1799–   *Expedition and travels of Alexander von Humboldt and*
1804   *Aimé Bonpland to Venezuela, Ecuador, Colombia, and Peru, Upper Amazon*

1809   *Lamarck publishes* Philosophie zoölogique

1810   *Revolution breaks out in South America*

1811   *W. L. von Eschwege explores Brazil*

1814   *Prince Maximilian von Wied-Neuwied explores central Brazil*

1816   *Auguste de Saint-Hilaire, ornithologist and botanist, collects in Brazil*

1817   *Explorations of von Martius and von Spix in Upper Amazon and Brazil*

1822   *Independence of South American states — Venezuela, Colombia, Ecuador, Peru, and Bolivia freed from Spain*

1826   *Boussingault lays basis of meteorological science in Ecuadorian Andes*

1827   *A. D. d'Orbigny carries on extensive research in Argentina and Bolivia*

1831–5   *Charles Darwin explores South America on H.M.S. BEAGLE. Argentina Patagonia, Tierra del Fuego, southern Chile, Peru, and Galápagos Islands. MODERN PHASE OF ZOOLOGY BEGINS.*

1835–44 *The brothers Schomburgk explore the Guianas: Robert, 1835–59; Richard, 1840–4*

1838   *Travels of J. J. von Tschudi in Peru*

1839   *Charles Darwin publishes JOURNAL OF THE VOYAGE OF THE BEAGLE; inspires scientific activity in South America*

1843   *Expedition of Count François de Castelnau in Peru and Upper Amazon*

1848   *Henry Bates and Alfred Wallace explore the Amazon River*

1849–66 *Richard Spruce works in Amazon Valley and the Río Negro for seventeen years. Lays the botanical history of South America. Takes out cinchona plants for India.*

1854   *Herndon and Gibbon publish EXPLORATIONS IN THE VALLEY OF THE AMAZON*

1859   *Alexander von Humboldt dies in Berlin*

1859   *Charles Darwin publishes ORIGIN OF SPECIES*

Index

Index

Index

Index

Index

Index

Index

Index

Index

A NOTE ON THE TYPE USED IN THIS BOOK

The text of this book has been set on the Linotype in a type-face called "Baskerville." The face is a facsimile reproduction of types cast from molds made for John Baskerville (1706–1775) from his designs. The punches for the revived Linotype Baskerville were cut under the supervision of the English printer George W. Jones.

John Baskerville's original face was one of the forerunners of the type-style known as "modern face" to printers: a "modern" of the period A.D. 1800.

The typographic scheme and the binding design are by W. A. Dwiggins. The book was set up in type, printed, and bound by The Plimpton Press, Norwood, Massachusetts.